Tennessee All-in-One Student Workbook

Grade 3

Includes:

- Review of key concepts/skills
- Practice for each lesson
- Reteaching for each lesson

Scott Foresman·Addison Wesley

enVisionMATH™

Tennessee

Learning Solutions

New York Boston San Francisco
London Toronto Sydney Tokyo Singapore Madrid
Mexico City Munich Paris Cape Town Hong Kong Montreal

Cover Art: Luciana Navarro Powell

This special edition published in cooperation with Pearson Learning Solutions.

Pearson Learning Solutions, 501 Boylston Street, Suite 900, Boston, MA 02116
A Pearson Education Company
www.pearsoned.com

Printed in the United States of America

1 2 3 4 5 6 7 8 9 10 V312 15 14 13 12 11 10

000200010270645920

CP

ISBN-10: 0-328-62593-0
ISBN-13: 978-0-328-62593-2

Table of Contents

Review From Last Year

Name ____________________________________

Number Patterns

Continue the pattern.

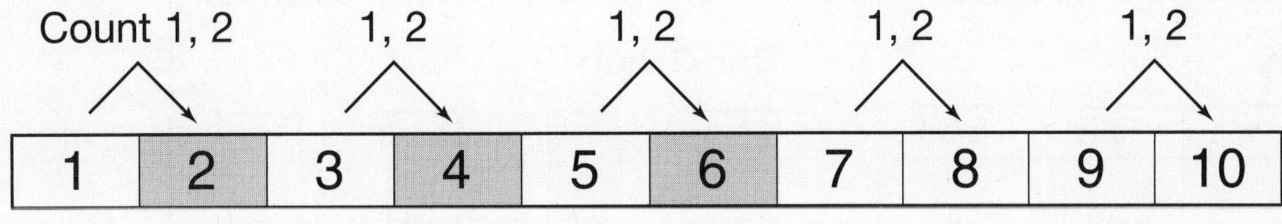

Next is **8,** then **10.**

Continue the patterns. Color the numbers.

1.

1	2	3	4	5	6	7	8	9	10
11	12	13	14	15	16	17	18	19	20
21	22	23	24	25	26	27	28	29	30
31	32	33	34	35	36	37	38	39	40

2.

1	2	3	4	5	6	7	8	9	10
11	12	13	14	15	16	17	18	19	20
21	22	23	24	25	26	27	28	29	30
31	32	33	34	35	36	37	38	39	40

3.

1	2	3	4	5	6	7	8	9	10
11	12	13	14	15	16	17	18	19	20
21	22	23	24	25	26	27	28	29	30
31	32	33	34	35	36	37	38	39	40

Name ____________________

Problem Solving: Graphing

Each **table** or **graph** shows data on how students get to school.

Tally

How	Tally	Total
Bike	I	1
Bus	~~IIII~~ I	6
Car	III	3
Walk	IIII	4

Pictograph

Bike	🯅
Bus	🯅🯅🯅🯅🯅🯅
Car	🯅🯅🯅
Walk	🯅🯅🯅🯅

Each 🯅 means 1 child.

Bar Graph

Use the tally data to complete each table or graph.

My Favorite Season

Tally

Season	Tally	Total
Summer	~~IIII~~ I	
Fall	II	2
Winter	IIII	
Spring	III	

Pictograph

Summer	
Fall	
Winter	
Spring	

Each ☺ means 1 child.

Bar Graph

Name ______________________________

Explore Addition and Subtraction

Brad's team had 4 . They bought 5 more 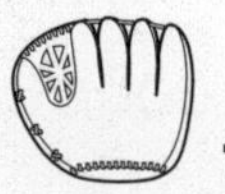. How many did they have? Use counters.  **4** + **5** = **9**	A pond had 8 . 3 went away. How many were left? Use counters. 12345678 **8** − **3** = **5**

Solve each problem. Use counters.

1. 7 were turned on.

Meg turned 5 off.

How many were left on?

7 − **5** = __________

2. 2 were in the lost and found box.

4 more were put in the box.

How many in all?

2 + **4** = __________

3. A worker had 6 .

He lost 2 .

How many were left?

6 − **2** = __________

4. Jan used 3 to paint her room. She used 6 more to paint the garage. How many did she use in all?

3 + **6** = __________

5. There were 9 on a tree.

4 fell off.

How many were left? ______________________

Name ______________________________

Review 4

Addition to 18

Find 6 + 7.

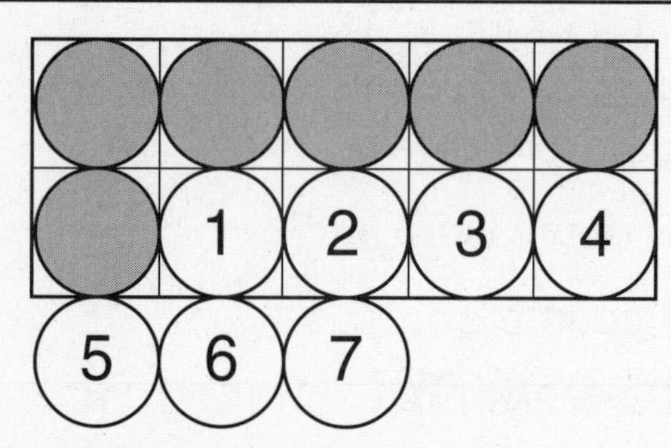

6 counters are on the ten frame.

4 more counters make a 10.

3 extra counters make 13.

6 + 7 = 13

Find each sum.

1. 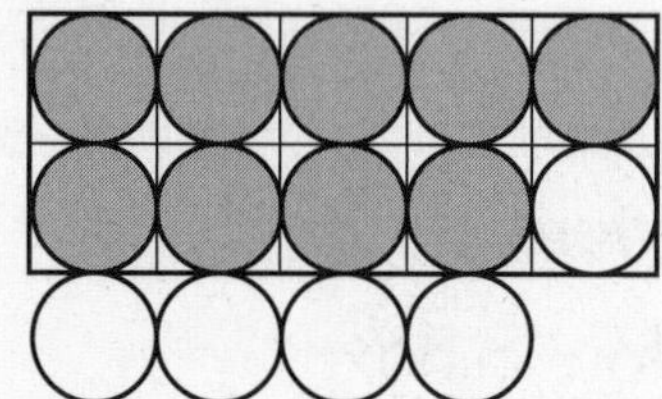

9 + 5 = ______

2. 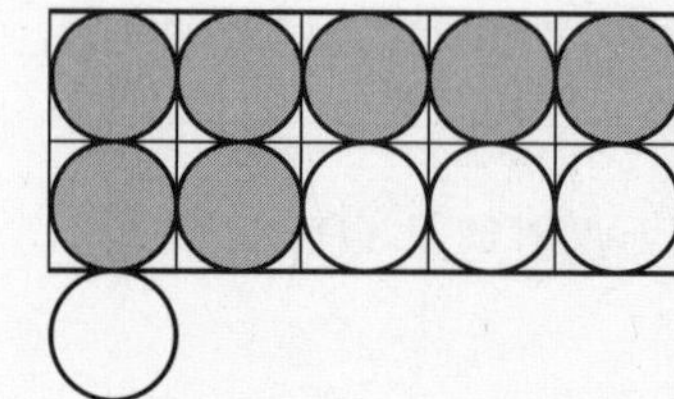

7 + 4 = ______

3. 8 + 6 = ______ 7 + 8 = ______ 9 + 6 = ______

4. 6 + 10 = ______ 9 + 8 = ______ 8 + 8 = ______

5. 7 + 5 = ______ 8 + 9 = ______ 9 + 9 = ______

6. 10 + 7 = ______ 7 + 7 = ______ 8 + 4 = ______

7. Mark made 5 phone calls during the week. He made 10 calls on the weekend. How many calls did he make in all? ______________

Name ______________________________

Review 5

Subtraction to 18

Find 14 − 7.

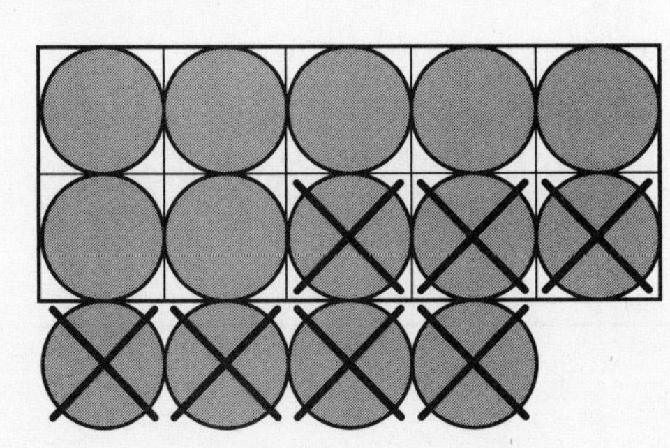

14 counters are shaded.

7 are crossed out.

7 counters are left.

14 − 7 = 7

Find each difference.

1. 

12 − 5 = ______

2. 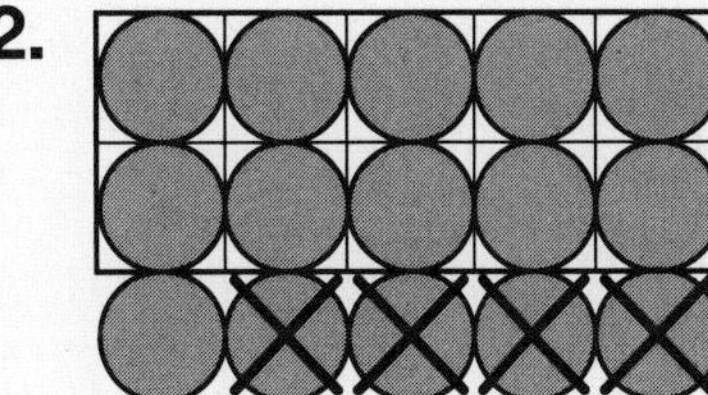

15 − 4 = ______

Subtract.

3. 18 − 9 = ______ 14 − 9 = ______ 7 − 5 = ______

4. 11 − 9 = ______ 9 − 6 = ______ 17 − 6 = ______

5. 13 − 6 = ______ 11 − 4 = ______ 8 − 3 = ______

6. 12 − 8 = ______ 16 − 5 = ______ 16 − 9 = ______

7. Tania saved $15. She spent $8 on a gift for her brother. How much did she have left? ______

Name ____________________________________

Review 6

Fact Families

Complete the fact family. Add or subtract.

All the facts in a fact family use the same numbers. This fact family uses 6, 9, and 15.

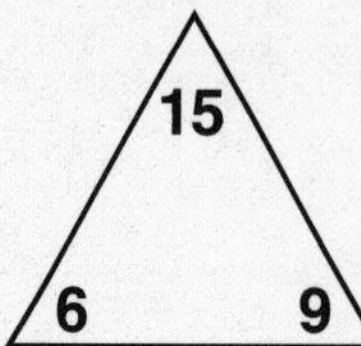

6 + 9 = 15 15 − 9 = 6

9 + 6 = 15 15 − 6 = 9

Complete each fact family. Add or subtract.

1. 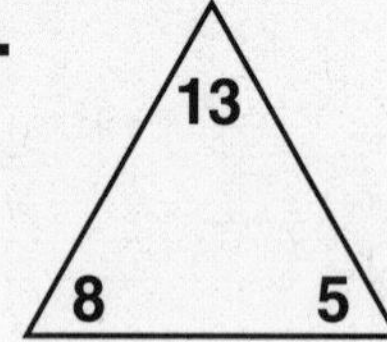

8 + 5 = ________

5 + 8 = ________

13 − 5 = ________

13 − 8 = ________

2. 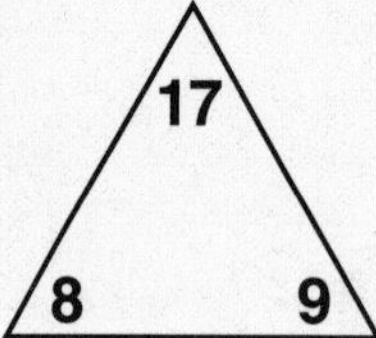

8 + 9 = ________

9 + 8 = ________

17 − 9 = ________

17 − 8 = ________

3. 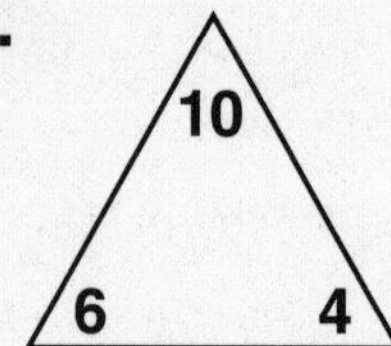

6 + 4 = ________

4 + 6 = ________

10 − 4 = ________

10 − 6 = ________

4. 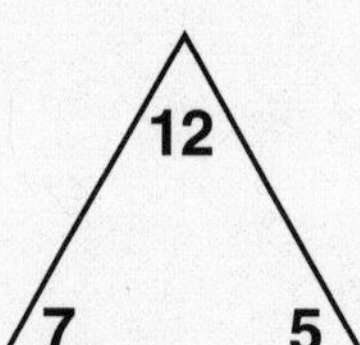

7 + 5 = ________

5 + 7 = ________

12 − 5 = ________

12 − 7 = ________

5. 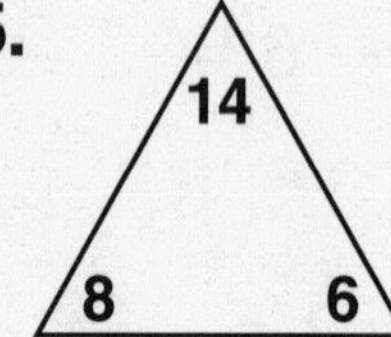

8 + 6 = ________

6 + 8 = ________

14 − 6 = ________

14 − 8 = ________

6. 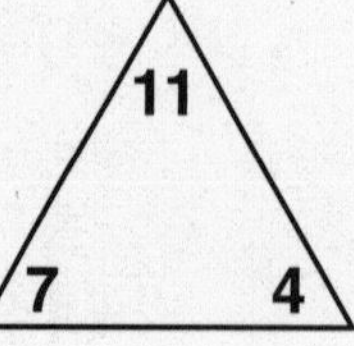

7 + 4 = ________

4 + 7 = ________

11 − 4 = ________

11 − 7 = ________

7. One fact in a fact family is 16 − 7 = 9. ____________________

What are the other facts? ____________________

____

Name ______________________________

Numbers to 100

The number 75 comes after 74 and before 76.

70	71	72	73	74	75	76	77	78	79

Write the missing numbers.

1	2	3						9	
				15			18		20
21					26				
			34			37			
	42								50
		53			56				
			64			67			
	72							79	
81									90
				95			98		

Write the missing numbers.

1. 80, 81, 82, ______, ______, ______, ______, ______, ______

2. ______, ______, 95, 96, ______, ______, ______, ______

Name ______________________________

Money

Count on to find how much money.

25, 35, 45, 55, 60, 61, 62, 63, 64 | 64¢

Start. Count by 10s, by 5s, and by 1s.

Count on to find how much. Write the total.

1.        

25, 35, ____, ____, ____, ____, ____, ____ ☐ ¢

2.        

____, ____, ____, ____, ____, ____, ____, ____ ☐ ¢

3.        

____, ____, ____, ____, ____, ____, ____, ____ ☐ ¢

4. Draw 6 coins to make 38¢.

Name ______________________________

Review 9

Time

Write the time.

Write the time.

1.

_____:_____

2.

_____:_____

3.

_____:_____

4.

_____:_____

5.

_____:_____

6.

_____:_____

7.

_____:_____

8.

_____:_____

9.

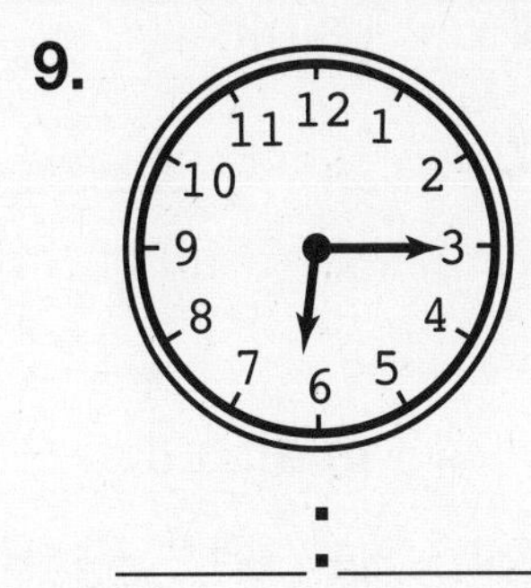

_____:_____

Name ______________________________

Review 10

Estimating Sums and Differences

Estimate the sum of 26 + 43. Use nearest tens.

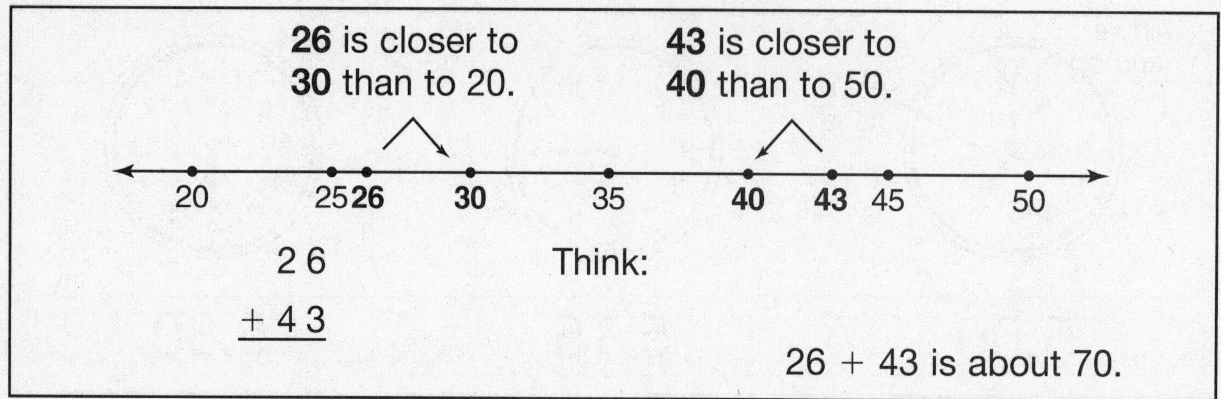

2 6
+ 4 3

Think:

26 + 43 is about 70.

Estimate the sum or difference. Use nearest tens.

1. 19 + 72 Think: 20 + 70 = ☐

19 + 72 is about ______.

2. 57 − 38 Think: ☐ − ☐ = ☐

57 − 38 is about ______.

3. 82 − 29 Think: ☐ − ☐ = ☐

82 − 29 is about ______.

4. 37 + 47 Think: ☐ + ☐ = ☐

37 + 47 is about ______.

5. 46 + 43 Think: ☐ + ☐ = ☐

46 + 43 is about ______.

6. 74 − 51 Think: ☐ − ☐ = ☐

74 − 51 is about ______.

7. Marcus has 51 Space Race toys. Reynaldo has 28 Space Race toys. About how many more does Marcus have than Reynaldo has? ______

Name ______________________

Two-Digit Addition

Find 24 + 63. Find 37 + 59.

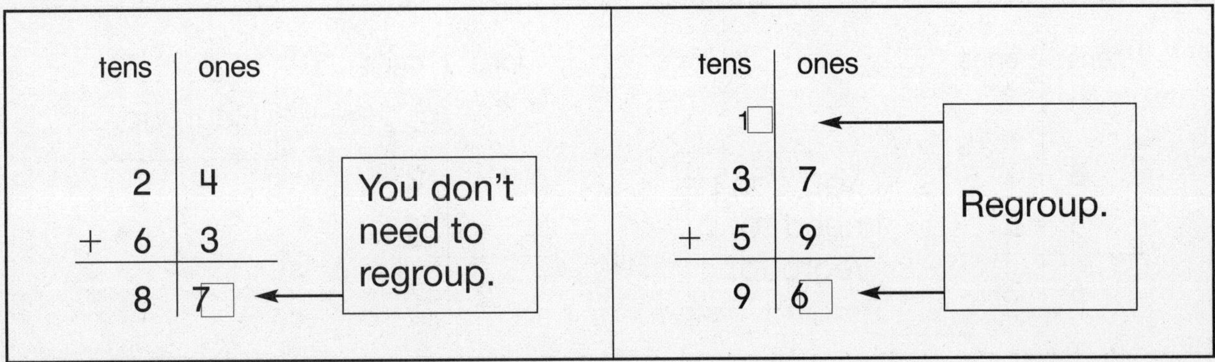

Add. Regroup if needed.

1. 24 + 49 (tens: 1; ones: 3)

2. 27 + 62

3. 45 + 35

4. 10 + 84

5. 66 + 21

6. 37 + 58

7. 29 + 61

8. 44 + 45

9. 81 + 9

10. Tom had three suitcases weighing 35 lb, 27 lb, and 23 lb. How much did they weigh altogether?

____

Name ______________________________

Two-Digit Subtraction

Find 87 − 24. Find 42 − 15.

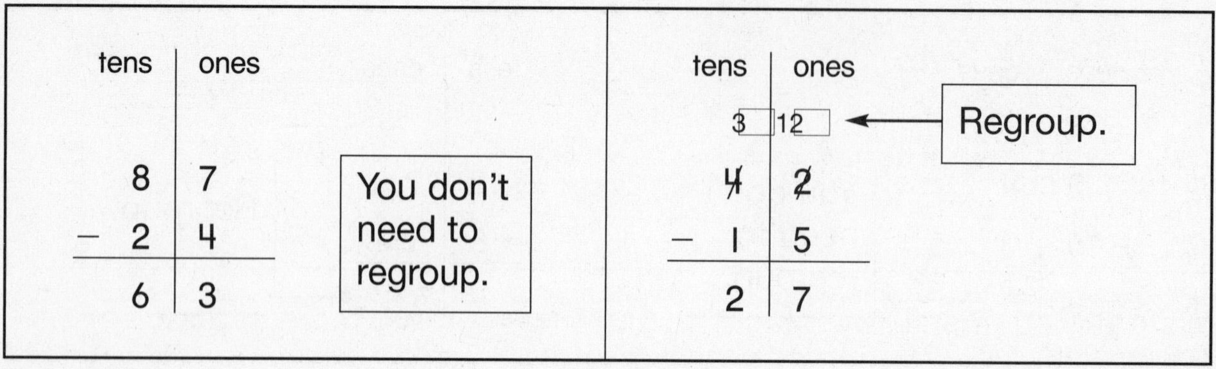

Subtract. Regroup if needed.

	tens	ones
1.	4	11
	5	1
−	2	3
		8

	tens	ones
2.	7	8
−	2	4

	tens	ones
3.	3	7
−	1	5

	tens	ones
4.	6	4
−	2	9

	tens	ones
5.	8	2
−	3	5

	tens	ones
6.	4	0
−	2	7

	tens	ones
7.	9	3
−	4	3

	tens	ones
8.	2	8
−	1	9

	tens	ones
9.	5	7
−	4	2

10. Mary had 44 books. She sold 27 of them at a garage sale. How many did she have left? ______________

Name ______________________________

Numbers to 1,000

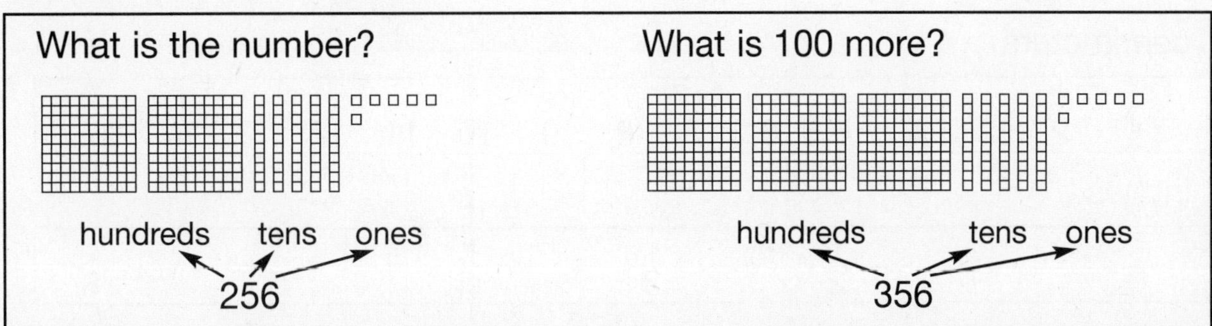

Write the number. Draw blocks to show the number more or less.

1. What is the number? What is 100 more?

_____ _____ _____ _____ _____ _____

2. What is the number? What is 100 less?

_____ _____ _____ _____ _____ _____

3. What is the number? What is 300 more?

_____ _____ _____ _____ _____ _____

4. What is the number? What is 300 less?

_____ _____ _____ _____ _____ _____

Name ______________________________

Review 14

Length

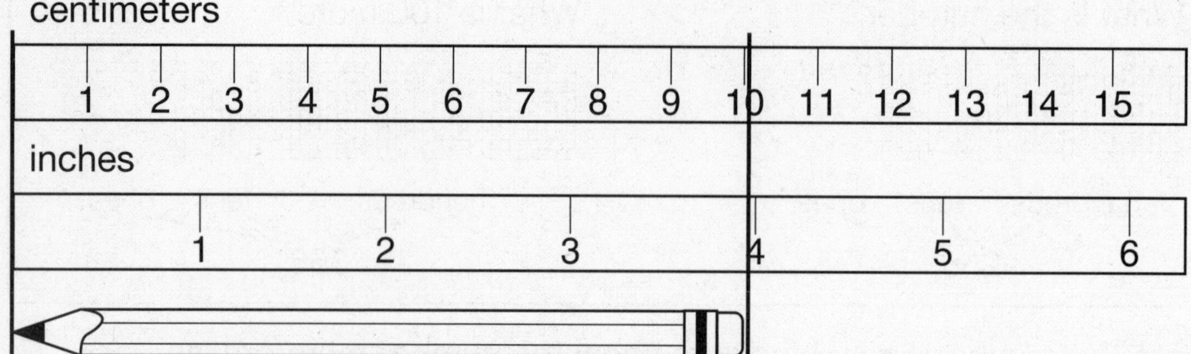

This pencil is about 10 centimeters. It is about 4 inches long.

Estimate. Then measure using inches.

1. 

Estimate. ________ inches

Measure. ________ inches

2. 

Estimate. ________ inches

Measure. ________ inches

Estimate. Then measure using centimeters.

3. 

Estimate. ________ centimeters

Measure. ________ centimeters

4. 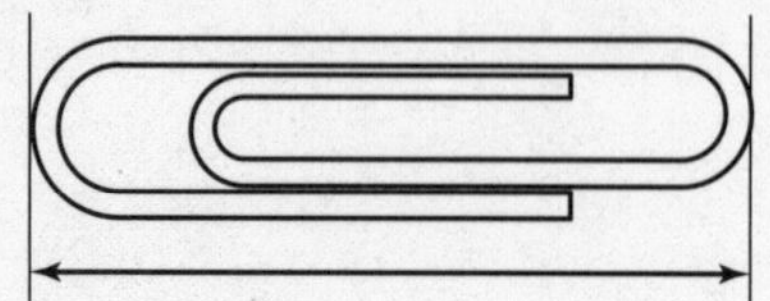

Estimate. ________ centimeters

Measure. ________ centimeters

5. Start at the dot. Draw a line about 5 inches long.

●

6. Start at the dot. Draw a line about 11 centimeters long.

●

Name ____________________

Solids

flat surface

vertex

The cube **cannot** roll.

It has **8** vertices and **6** flat surfaces.

flat surface

The cylinder **can** roll.

It has **0** vertices and **2** flat surfaces.

Complete the table.

Solid	Roll?	Shape of Flat Surfaces	Number of Vertices	Number of Flat Surfaces
1.	No			
2.				
3.				
4.				
5.				

Name ______________________________

Review 16

Shapes

Flat surfaces of solids are shapes. Some shapes have names.

Rectangle   Square   Triangle   Circle

Draw the shape on the **bottom** of the solid. Name the shape.

1.  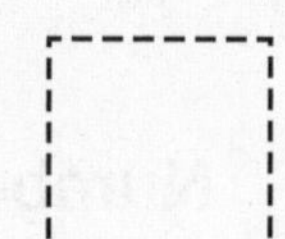

shape ____________

2. 

shape ____________

3. 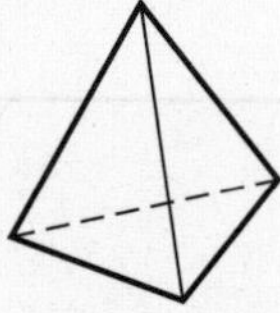

shape ____________

4. 

shape ____________

5. 

shape ____________

Name ______________________________

Fractions

Write the fraction for parts that are shaded.

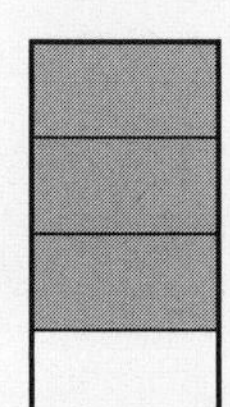

3 parts shaded
4 parts in all
$\frac{3}{4}$ is shaded.

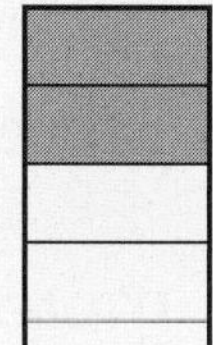

2 parts shaded
5 parts in all
$\frac{2}{5}$ is shaded.

Write the fraction for parts that are shaded.

1. 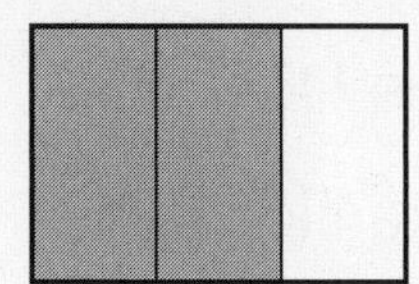

_____ parts shaded.
_____ parts in all.
_____ is shaded.

2. 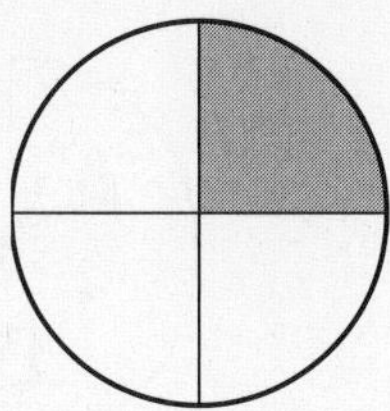

____

3. 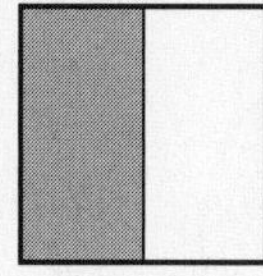

____

4. 

____

5. 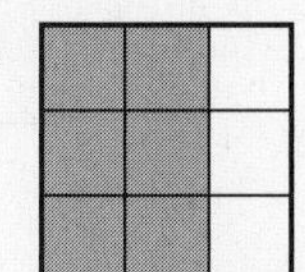

____

6. 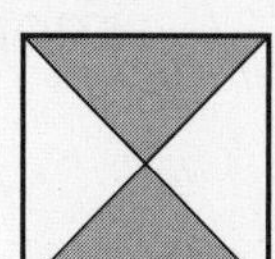

____

Shade each fraction.

7. Shade $\frac{3}{4}$.

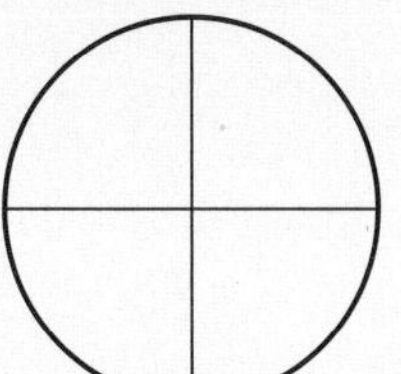

8. Shade $\frac{1}{3}$.

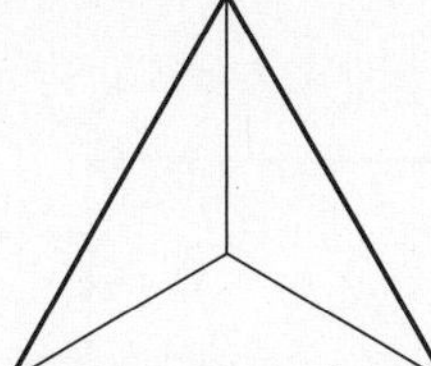

9. Shade $\frac{4}{6}$.

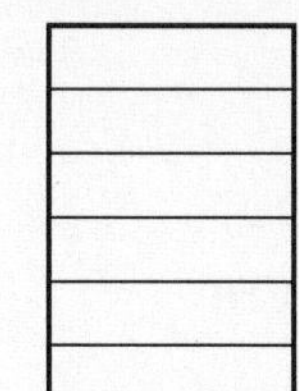

10. Shade $\frac{5}{8}$.

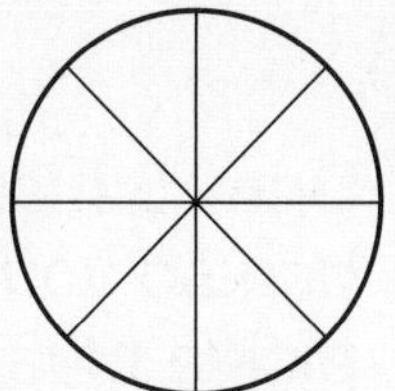

Name ______________________________

Review 18

Probability

Would you more likely spin stars or spin stripes?

more likely stars

more likely stripes

Circle the more likely spin.

1. 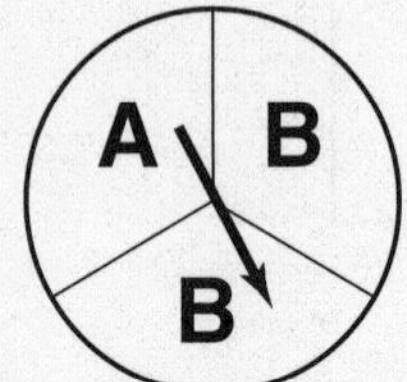

more likely A

more likely B

2. 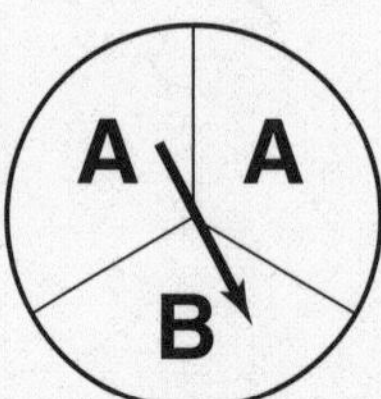

more likely A

more likely B

3. 

more likely 1

more likely 2

more likely 3

4. 

more likely 1

more likely 2

more likely 3

Circle whether you will always, sometimes, or never pick an object.

5. Pick a marble.

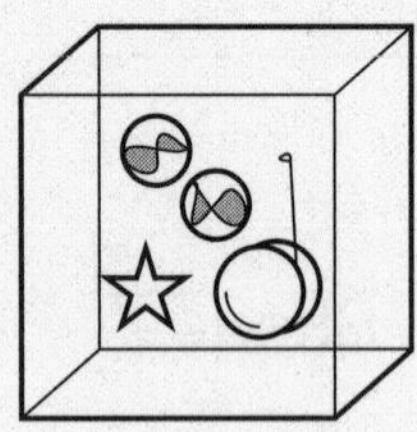

always

sometimes

never

6. Pick a star.

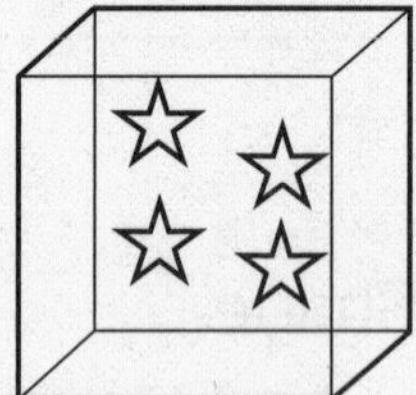

always

sometimes

never

7. Draw 5 marbles in your bag so you could never pick a blue marble.

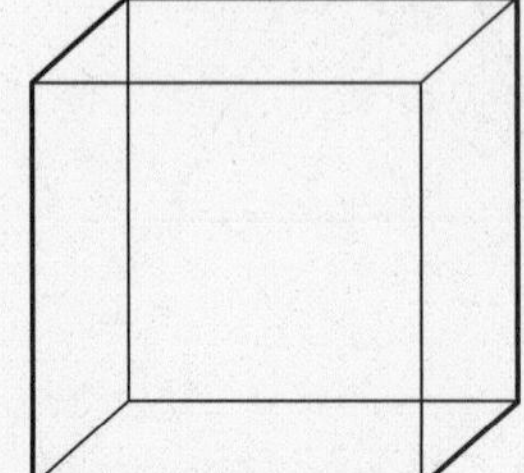

Name ______________________________

Multiplication Concepts

Show 3×2. | Show 2×3.

You can add or multiply to find how many in all.	*You can multiply numbers in any order and get the same product.*
○ ○ ○ ○ ○ ○ $2 + 2 + 2 = 6$ $3 \times 2 = 6$	○ ○ ○ ○ ○ ○ ○ ○ ○ ○ ○ ○ $3 \times 2 = 6$ $2 \times 3 = 6$

Draw groups. Find the product.

1. Draw groups to show 4×2.

○ ○ ○ ○
○ ○ ○ ○

How many in all? _______

2. Draw groups to show 2×4.

How many in all? _______

3. Draw groups to show 4×3.

How many in all? _______

4. Draw groups to show 5×1.

How many in all? _______

5. Draw groups to show 5×3.

How many in all? _______

6. Draw groups to show 2×2.

How many in all? _______

7. Does 5 rows of 2 counters have more counters than 2 rows of 5 counters? Explain.

____

Name ______________________________

Division Concepts

Show 6 ÷ 3.	Show 6 ÷ 2.
Divide 6 counters into 3 equal groups to find the answer. 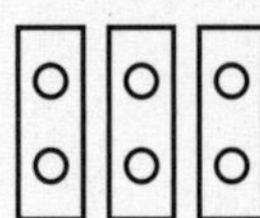 There are 2 counters in each group. So, 6 ÷ 3 = 2.	*Divide 6 counters into 2 equal groups to find the answer.* There are 3 counters in each group. So, 6 ÷ 2 = 3.

Draw groups. Complete the number sentence.

1. Draw groups to show 4 ÷ 2.

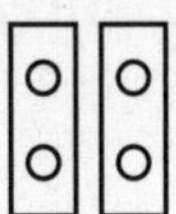

4 ÷ 2 = ______

2. Draw groups to show 8 ÷ 2.

8 ÷ 2 = ______

3. Draw groups to show 5 ÷ 1.

5 ÷ 1 = ______

4. Draw groups to show 10 ÷ 5.

10 ÷ 5 = ______

5. Draw groups to show 7 ÷ 7.

7 ÷ 7 = ______

6. Draw groups to show 20 ÷ 4.

20 ÷ 4 = ______

7. Tanisha has 15 books. She gives 5 books to each friend. How many friends get books from Tanisha?

____

Reteaching and Practice

Name ______________________________

Hundreds

Here are different ways to show 612.

place-value blocks: 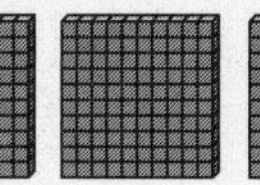 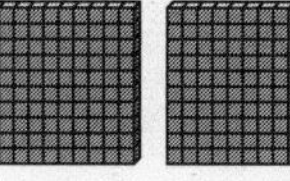 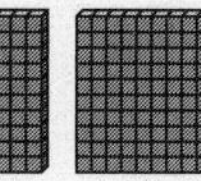 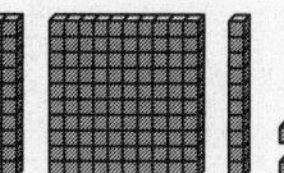

expanded form: 600 + 10 + 2
standard form: 612
word form: six hundred twelve

Write each number in standard form.

1. 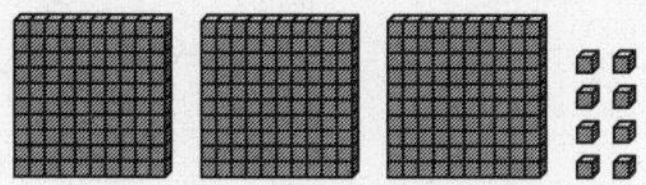

____

2. 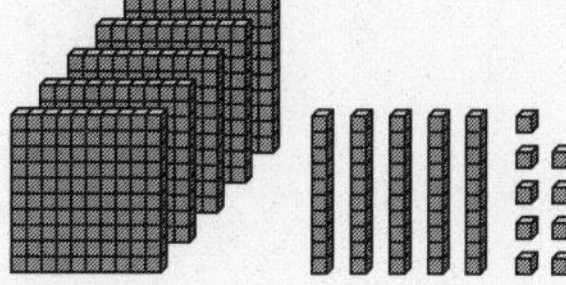

____

3. 400 + 30 + 7 ______________

4. six hundred twenty ______________

5. 200 + 50 + 1 ______________

6. three hundred forty-five ______________

Write the word form for each number.

7. 285 ______________________________

8. 892 ______________________________

9. 146 ______________________________

10. 378 ______________________________

11. Number Sense Write a 3-digit number with a 2 in the hundreds place and a 4 in the tens place. ______________

Name ______________________

Practice
1-1

Hundreds

Write each number in standard form.

1. ______

2. 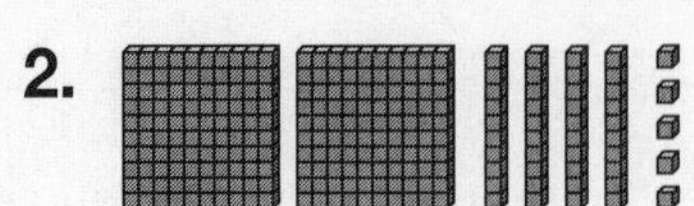 ______

3. ______

4. 600 + 70 + 9 ______

5. 800 + 3 ______

6. four hundred thirty-one ______

Practice 1-1

Write each number in expanded form.

7. 392 ______

8. 710 ______

Write each number in word form.

9. 539 ______

10. 904 ______

11. Algebra Find the value of the missing number.

462 = 400 + ☐ + 2

12. Explain It Why are five hundreds and three ones written as 503?

______

______

______

13. Number Sense Which is the standard form of six hundred forty?

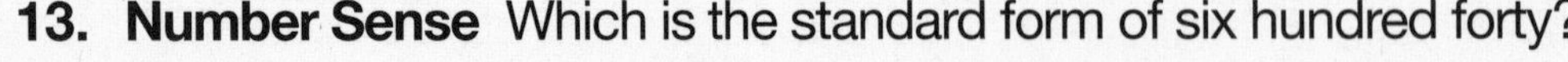

A 64 **B** 604 **C** 614 **D** 640

Name ______________________________

Thousands

Here are different ways to show 2,263.

place-value blocks:

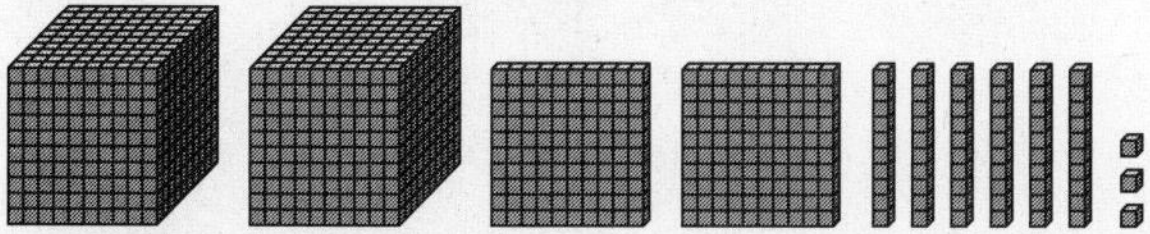

expanded form: 2,000 + 200 + 60 + 3

standard form: 2,263

word form: two thousand, two hundred sixty-three

Write each number in standard form.

1. 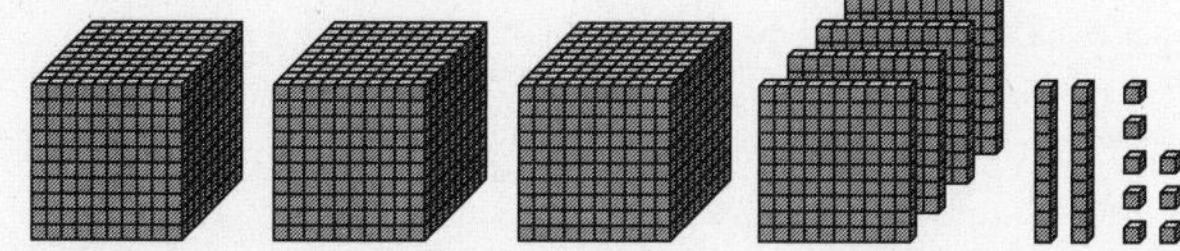 ______________

2. 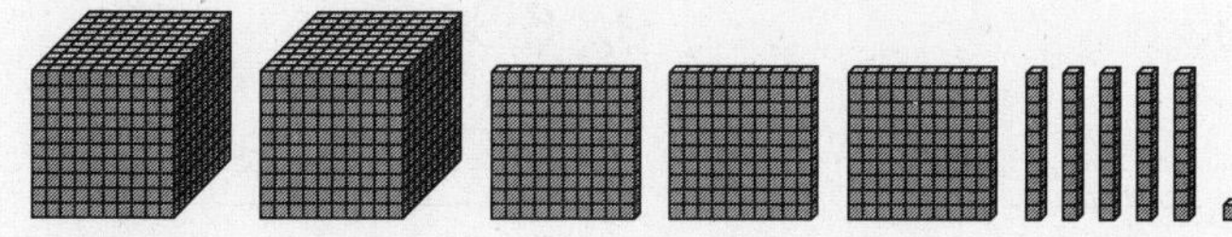 ______________

3. 7,000 + 400 + 40 + 8 ______________

4. five thousand, seven hundred fifty-five ______________

Write each number in expanded form.

5. 1,240 ______________________________

6. 6,381 ______________________________

7. **Number Sense** Write a 4-digit number with a 7 in the thousands place and a 6 in the ones place. ______________

8. **Reasoning** Jason will build a number with the digits 4, 7, 2, and 6. In what order should he put the digits if he wants to make the greatest number possible? ______________

Name ______________________________

Thousands

Write each number in standard form.

1. 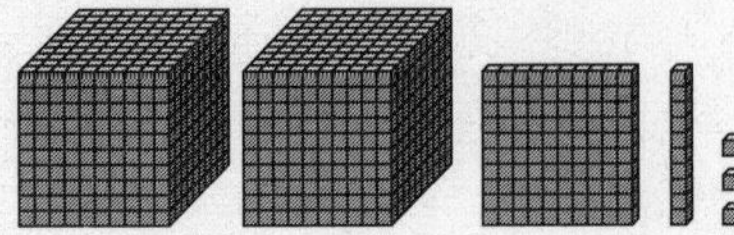

____

2. 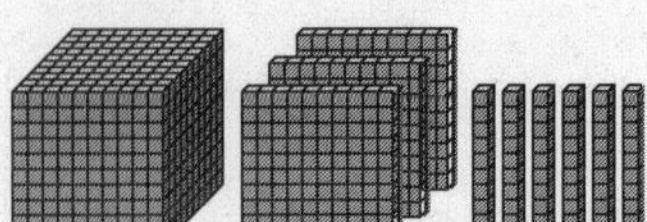

____

3. 3,000 + 900 + 40 + 7

____

4. 6,000 + 70 + 1

____

Write each number in expanded form.

5. 5,193

____

6. 4,308

____

Write the place of the underlined digit. Then write its value.

7. 5,<u>3</u>42

____

8. <u>7</u>,095

____

9. 6,3<u>9</u>8

____

10. **Explain It** An arena can seat nine thousand, forty-eight people. How is that number written in standard form? Explain.

____

____

11. **Number Sense** Which is the word form of 8,040?

A eight hundred forty

B eight thousand, forty

C eight thousand, four

D eight thousand, four hundred

Name ______________________________

Greater Numbers

A period is a group of three digits in a number, starting from the right. A comma is used to separate two periods.

Thousands Period			Ones Period		
hundred thousands	ten thousands	thousands	hundreds	tens	ones
2	4	7,	0	6	2

Here are different ways to show 247,062.

expanded form: 200,000 + 40,000 + 7,000 + 60 + 2

standard form: 247,062

word form: two hundred forty-seven thousand, sixty-two

Write each number in standard form.

1. 60,000 + 8,000 + 200 + 50 + 1 ______________

2. 30,000 + 600 + 30 + 2 ______________

3. four hundred one thousand, four hundred fifty-four ______________

4. five hundred twenty-nine thousand, three hundred seventy-eight ______________

5. Write 522,438 in expanded form.

____

6. Write 349,281 in expanded form.

____

7. **Number Sense** What is the value of the 7 in 86,752? ______________

8. The area of Lake Ontario is 18,960 square kilometers. Write the area of Lake Ontario in expanded form.

____

Name ______________________

Practice 1-3

Greater Numbers

Write each number in standard form.

1. seventy-five thousand, three hundred twelve ________
2. one hundred fourteen thousand, seven ________
3. 100,000 + 40,000 + 2,000 + 500 + 30 + 2 ________
4. 600,000 + 70,000 + 8,000 + 30 + 9 ________

Practice 1-3

Write each number in expanded form.

5. 73,581 ________________________
6. 390,062 ________________________

Write the place of the underlined digit. Then write its value.

7. 6<u>3</u>,219 ________
8. 3<u>8</u>2,407 ________
9. <u>9</u>72,362 ________

10. **Algebra** Find the missing number.

    57,026 = 50,000 + ■ + 20 + 6 ________

11. **Explain It** Which is greater, the greatest whole number with 5 digits or the least whole number with 6 digits?

    ____

    ____

    ____

12. **Number Sense** Which is the word form for 280,309?

    A two hundred eight thousand, three hundred ninety
    B two hundred eighty thousand, thirty-nine
    C two hundred eighty thousand, three hundred nine
    D two hundred eighty thousand, three hundred ninety

Name ______________________

Reteaching 1-4

Ways to Name Numbers

An ordinal number is used to show order.

The ordinal numbers from 1–13 are shown below.

1	2	3	4	5	6
1st first	2nd second	3rd third	4th fourth	5th fifth	6th sixth

7	8	9	10	11	12	13
7th seventh	8th eighth	9th ninth	10th tenth	11th eleventh	12th twelfth	13th thirteenth

For numbers greater than 13:

Use *-th* for numbers that end in 0, 4, 5, 6, 7, 8, and 9.

Use *-nd* for numbers that end in 2 with the exception of those that end in 12.

Use *-rd* for numbers that end in 3 with the exception of those that end in 13.

Write the ordinal number and the ordinal word form of the number.

1. 8 ______________________

2. 36 ______________________

3. 40 ______________________

4. 91 ______________________

Name the number in two ways.

5. 1,700 ______________________ ______________________

6. 5,200 ______________________ ______________________

7. **Number Sense** In the movie-ticket line, there are sixteen people ahead of Kim. In which place in line is she?

____

Reteaching **1-4**

Name ______________________

Practice 1-4

Ways to Name Numbers

Write the ordinal number and the ordinal word form of that number.

1. 26 ______________________

2. 43 ______________________

3. 51 ______________________

4. 60 ______________________

Name the number in two ways.

5. 3,600 ______________________

6. 4,700 ______________________

7. 6,900 ______________________

8. 9,400 ______________________

9. **Number Sense** The population of St. Louis, MO, is 344,362 and the population of Newark, NJ, is 280,666. Which city has the greater population?

____

10. The Coopers live at one thousand, seven hundred six South Central Avenue. How do you write the number of the Cooper's home?

____

11. Albert is running in a race. There are 21 people ahead of him. Write the ordinal number and the ordinal word form for Albert's place in line.

____

12. What is another way to write 7,600?

A seven thousand, six

B seventy-six hundred

C seven thousand, sixty

D seventy-six thousand

Practice 1-4

Name ______________________________

Comparing Numbers

Use these symbols to compare numbers.

< is less than **> is greater than** **= is equal to**

Compare 375 and 353.

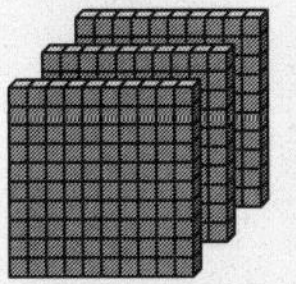
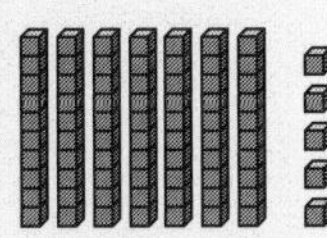

375

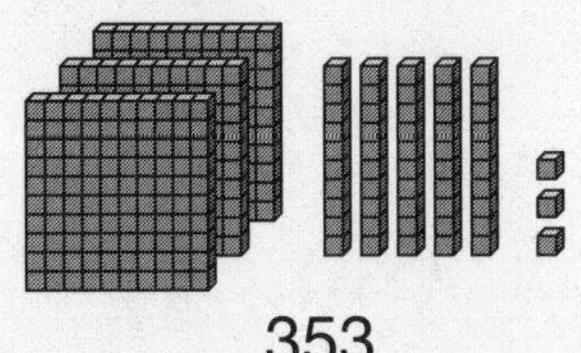

353

Both have the same number of hundreds.
Compare the tens. 375 has more tens.

375 is greater than 353. 375 > 353

Compare the numbers. Use <, >, or =.

1. 36 ◯ 27 **2.** 278 ◯ 285 **3.** 692 ◯ 690

4. 842 ◯ 824 **5.** 4,669 ◯ 4,705 **6.** 7,305 ◯ 7,305

7. 1,100 ◯ 998 **8.** 5,436 ◯ 5,436 **9.** 323 ◯ 333

10. Number Sense Write a 3-digit number greater than 699.

____

11. Write a 2-digit number less than 40.

____

12. Explain It Every digit in 798 is greater than any digit in 4,325. Explain why 4,325 is greater than 798.

____

____

____

Name ____________________

Comparing Numbers

Compare the numbers. Use <, >, or =.

1. 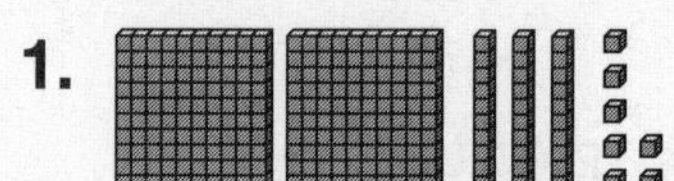 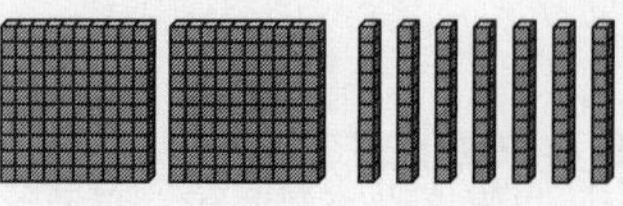

237 _____ 273

2. 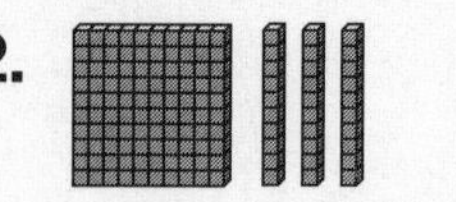 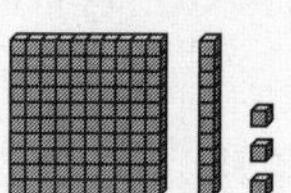

130 _____ 113

3. 725 ◯ 739 **4.** 831 ◯ 813 **5.** 926 ◯ 926

6. 2,734 ◯ 2,347 **7.** 4,827 ◯ 583 **8.** 5,327 ◯ 5,372

Use the table for **9** and **10**.

9. Between which pair of cities is the distance the greatest? See table.

____

____

Distance in Miles

New York, NY, to Rapid City, SD	1,701
Rapid City, SD, to Miami, FL	2,167
Miami, FL, to Seattle, WA	3,334
Portland, OR, to Little Rock, AR	2,217

10. Explain It Which has a greater distance, Rapid City to Miami or Portland to Little Rock? Which digits did you use to compare? See table.

____

____

Number Sense Write the missing digits to make each number sentence true.

11. 7□7 < 713 **12.** 8□5 > 889 **13.** 3,□64 = 3,2□4

14. Which sentence is true?

A 4,375 > 4,722 **C** 5,106 = 5,160

B 6,372 > 6,327 **D** 7,095 < 795

15. Which number is greater than 8,264?

A 8,246 **B** 8,275 **C** 6,842 **D** 8,195

Name ______________________

Ordering Numbers

You can use place value to order numbers.
Order these from least to greatest.

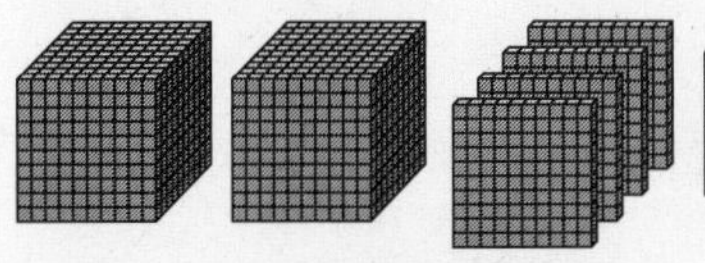
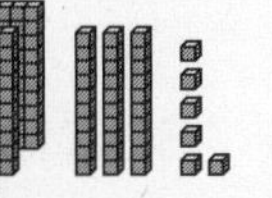
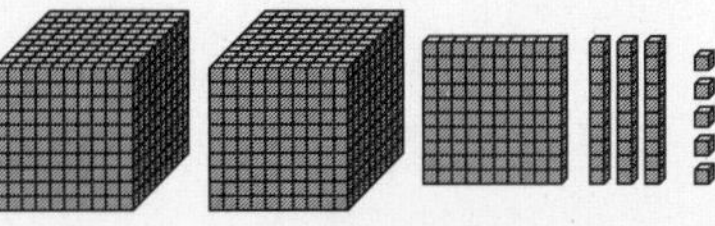
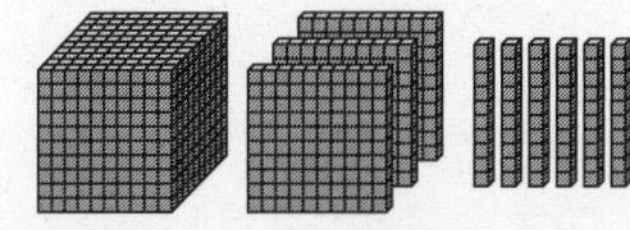

2,436 **2,135** **1,362**

Compare the thousands.
1 thousand < 2 thousands, so 1,362 is the least number.

Compare the hundreds in the remaining two numbers.
4 hundreds > 1 hundred, so 2,436 is the greatest number.

From least to greatest, the order is: **1,362** (least) **2,135** **2,436** (greatest)

Order the numbers from least to greatest.

1. 560 583 552 ______
2. 583 575 590 ______
3. 576 580 557 ______

Order the numbers from greatest to least.

4. 973 1,007 996 ______
5. 5,626 5,636 5,716 ______

6. **Number Sense** Use the table. Put the roller coasters in order from shortest to longest.

______

______

______

Roller Coaster	Length
Boss Eureka, Missouri	5,051 feet
Chang Louisville, Kentucky	4,155 feet
Titan Arlington, Texas	5,312 feet

Name ______________________________

Ordering Numbers

Order the numbers from least to greatest.

1. 216 208 222

____

2. 3,795 3,659 3,747

____

Order the numbers from greatest to least.

3. 633 336 363

____

4. 5,017 5,352 5,193

____

Use the table for **5** through **7**.

5. Number Sense New Hampshire has a land area of 8,968 square miles. Which states in the table have a greater land area than New Hampshire?

____

____

Land Areas (in square miles)

State	Land Area
Maryland	9,774
Massachusetts	7,840
New Jersey	7,417
Vermont	9,250

6. Order the states in the table from greatest to least land area.

____

7. Explain It The Amazon River is 4,000 miles long. The Yangtze River is 3,964 miles long and the Nile River is 4,145 miles long. Write the steps you would use to order the lengths of the rivers from greatest to least.

____

____

8. Which number is between 6,532 and 6,600?

A 6,570 **B** 6,523 **C** 6,325 **D** 5,623

9. Which number makes this sentence true?
4,735 < ______ < 4,820

A 4,396 **B** 4,758 **C** 4,832 **D** 4,915

Name ___________________________

Reteaching
1-7

Counting Money

To count the money, start with the bills.
Count on from the greatest to the least value.

Count on: $5.00 **$6.00** **$7.00**

$7.25 **$7.35** **$7.45** **$7.50** **$7.51**

Write the total value in dollars and cents.

1. 

____

2. 

____

3. Draw a Picture Show two ways to make $0.75 without using a half dollar or pennies.

Name ______________________

Practice
1-7

Counting Money

Write the total value in dollars and cents.

1.    ________

2. 1 one-dollar bill, 2 quarters, 2 dimes, 1 nickel, 3 pennies

____

3. 2 one-dollar bills, 3 quarters, 2 dimes, 2 pennies

____

4. 1 five-dollar bill, one half dollar, 3 quarters, 1 nickel

____

5. 1 five-dollar bill, 2 one-dollar bills, 3 dimes, 3 nickels

____

Compare the amounts. Write <, >, or =.

6. $1.55 ◯ 1 one-dollar bill, 2 quarters

7. $1.90 ◯ 8 quarters

8. **Reasoning** Claire has 5 coins worth $0.61. What coins does she have?

____

9. Mark has 6 bills worth $14.00. What bills does he have?

____

10. What is the least number of coins you can use to show $0.37?

____

11. Which is equal to exactly $1.00?

A 3 quarters and 2 dimes

B 2 quarters, 2 dimes, and 2 nickels

C 1 half dollar, 1 quarter, and 1 dime

D 1 half dollar and 5 dimes

12. **Explain It** How can $0.60 be shown two different ways using only 3 coins each time?

____

Name ______________________________

Making Change

Jill bought a sandwich that costs $3.65. She paid with a $5 bill. How much change should Jill receive?

Start with the amount Jill spent, which is $3.65. What coins do you need to get to the next dollar, which is $4.00? What bill do you need to use to get to $5.00?

Count up from the amount spent using the coin with the least value to the bill with the greatest value.

$3.65	$3.75	$4.00	$5.00
	$0.10	$0.35	$1.35

Jill should receive $1.35 in change.

List the coins and bills to make the change. Write the amount of the change.

1. Cost: $0.78
Amount paid: $1.00

____

____

2. Cost: $2.40
Amount paid: $5.00

____

____

3. Cost: $1.29
Amount paid: $2.00

____

____

4. Cost: $3.81
Amount paid: $5.00

____

____

5. Reasoning Joey and Ross each bought yo-yos for $4.25 and paid with $5 bills. Joey received only one type of coin for change. Ross did not receive the type of coin that Joey got. What coins did each receive?

____

____

Name ______________________________

Making Change

List the coins and bills to make the change. Write the amount of change.

1. Cost: $0.64
   Amount paid: $1.00

   ____

   ____

2. Cost: $1.18
   Amount paid: $2.00

   ____

   ____

3. Cost: $2.89
   Amount paid: $5.00

   ____

   ____

4. Cost: $4.04
   Amount paid: $5.00

   ____

   ____

5. **Algebra** Alice paid for a newspaper with a $1 bill. She received $0.35 in change. How much money did the newspaper cost?

   ____

6. **Reasonableness** A new hair clip costs $1.60. Janice paid with 2 one-dollar bills. She received 3 coins back in change. What were they?

   ____

7. **Explain It** If pencils cost $0.26 each, could you buy four pencils with $1.00? Explain.

   ____

   ____

8. Lizzie is going to buy a ruler for $0.55 with a one-dollar bill. Marcy said Lizzie should get 1 quarter and 2 dimes for change. Patti said Lizzie should get 4 dimes and a nickel for change. Who is correct: Marcy, Patti, both, or neither?

   ____

9. Johnny bought a magazine for $3.24. He paid with a $5 bill. Which should be his change?

   A $1.76 **C** $2.76

   B $1.86 **D** $2.86

Name ______________________

Reteaching
1-9

Problem Solving: Make an Organized List

Todd has given Maclan these clues to guess the identities of one or more 3-digit numbers.

- The ones digit is odd.
- The tens digit is greater than 8.
- The hundreds digit is less than 2.

Use the clues for each digit to make an organized list.

The ones digit is odd.	The tens digit is greater than 8.	The hundreds digit is less than 2.
The odd numbers are 1, 3, 5, 7, and 9.	The only digit greater than 8 is 9. The tens digit is 9.	The digit in the greatest place of a whole number cannot be 0. The hundreds digit is 1.

So, the list would have 191, 193, 195, 197, or 199.

Make an organized list to solve.

1. Barbara, Lisa, and Maria are having their picture taken for the yearbook. List the ways that they can line up in a straight line for the picture. You can use their initials.

____

____

2. List all the 3-digit numbers that fit these clues.

- The hundreds digit is greater than 7.
- The tens digit is less than 2.
- The ones digit is the same as the hundreds digit.

____

____

3. **Reasoning** In how many ways can you make 10 cents using dimes, nickels, and pennies? List them.

____

____

Reteaching 1-9

Name ___________________________

Practice
1-9

Problem Solving: Make an Organized List

Make an organized list to solve.

1. List all the 3-digit numbers that fit these clues.

- The hundreds digit is less than 3.
- The tens digit is less than 2.
- The ones digit is greater than 7.

____

____

2. List all the 4-digit numbers that fit these clues.

- The thousands digit is greater than 8.
- The hundreds digit is less than 4.
- The tens and ones digits are the same as the thousands digit.

____

____

3. Jim and Sarah are running for class president. Cayla and Daniel are running for vice president. What combinations of president and vice president could there be?

____

____

____

4. List the ways that you can arrange the letters A, B, and C.

____

____

5. **Reasoning** What is this 3-digit number?

- The hundreds digit is 4 greater than 3.
- The tens digit is 1 more than the hundreds digit.
- The ones digit is 3 less than the tens digit.

____

6. In how many ways can you make 30 cents using quarters, dimes, or nickels?

A 4

B 5

C 6

D 8

Practice 1-9

Name ______________________________

Addition Meaning and Properties

The Commutative (Order) Property

You can add numbers in any order, and the sum will be the same.

6 + 2 = 8

2 + 6 = 8

The Associative (Grouping) Property

You can group addends in any way, and the sum will be the same.

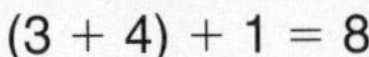

(3 + 4) + 1 = 8

3 + (4 + 1) = 8

The Identity (Zero) Property

The sum of any number and zero equals that same number.

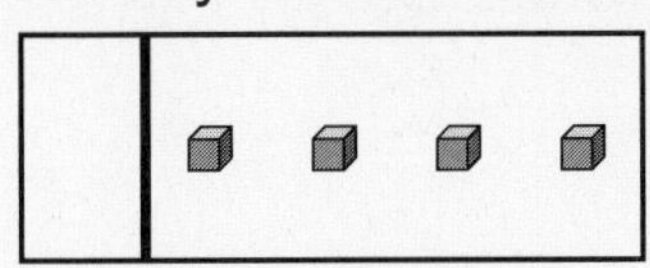

0 + 4 = 4

Find each sum.

1. 3 + (2 + 4) = ______
2. (0 + 5) + 2 = ______
3. (8 + 3) + 4 = ______
4. 9 + 2 + 6 = ______

Write each missing number.

5. 3 + 4 = 4 + ______
6. ______ + 7 = 7
7. (2 + 3) + 4 = ______ + (2 + 4)
8. 9 + (2 + 7) = (9 + 2) + ______
9. **Reasoning** Does (4 + 5) + 2 = 9 + 2? Explain.

____

____

Name ______________________________

Practice **2-1**

Addition Meaning and Properties

Write each missing number.

1. $7 + 2 = 2 + ■$ ______
2. $3 + ■ = 3$ ______
3. $(2 + 4) + 5 = 2 + (■ + 5)$ ______
4. $3 + ■ = 5 + 3$ ______
5. $■ + 0 = 6$ ______
6. $(5 + 3) + 9 = 8 + ■$ ______

Practice 2-1

7. **Reasoning** What property of addition is shown in the following number sentence? Explain.

   $7 + (3 + 5) = (7 + 3) + 5$

   ____

   ____

8. **Number Sense** Minnie has 6 country CDs and 5 rock CDs. Amanda has 5 rock CDs and 6 country CDs. Who has more CDs? Explain.

   ____

   ____

9. Show how the Commutative Property of Addition works using the numbers 2, 3, and 5.

   ____

10. **Explain It** Jake says that adding 0 does not change a sum. Is he correct? Explain.

    ____

    ____

11. Which property of addition is shown by $5 + 2 = 2 + 5$?

    A Associative Property
    B Distributive Property
    C Commutative Property
    D Identity Property

Name ___________________________

Reteaching
2-2

Adding on a Hundred Chart

You can use a hundred chart to add.
To add 37 + 26, follow these steps:

- Start at 37.
- Go down 2 rows to add 20.
- Go right 3 spaces to add 3 more.
  So far you have added 20 + 3, or 23.
- To add 3 more, go down to the next row and go right 3 spaces.
- You end at 63.

So, 37 + 26 = 63.

1	2	3	4	5	6	7	8	9	10
11	12	13	14	15	16	17	18	19	20
21	22	23	24	25	26	27	28	29	30
31	32	33	34	35	36	37	38	39	40
41	42	43	44	45	46	47	48	49	50
51	52	53	54	55	56	57	58	59	60
61	62	63	64	65	66	67	68	69	70
71	72	73	74	75	76	77	78	79	80
81	82	83	84	85	86	87	88	89	90
91	92	93	94	95	96	97	98	99	100

You could also do it this way:

- Start at 37.
- Go down 3 rows to add 30.
- Go left 4 spaces to subtract 4.
- You end at 63.

So, 37 + 26 = 63

1	2	3	4	5	6	7	8	9	10
11	12	13	14	15	16	17	18	19	20
21	22	23	24	25	26	27	28	29	30
31	32	33	34	35	36	37	38	39	40
41	42	43	44	45	46	47	48	49	50
51	52	53	54	55	56	57	58	59	60
61	62	63	64	65	66	67	68	69	70
71	72	73	74	75	76	77	78	79	80
81	82	83	84	85	86	87	88	89	90
91	92	93	94	95	96	97	98	99	100

Use a hundred chart to add.

1. 30 + 45 ________ **2.** 52 + 40 ________ **3.** 26 + 43 ________ **4.** 37 + 23 ________

5. 28 + 45 ________ **6.** 47 + 18 ________ **7.** 39 + 35 ________ **8.** 26 + 54 ________

9. **Reasoning** To find 38 + 45, you could first find 38 + 50 = 88.
Then what should you do?

____

Name ______________________

Practice
2-2

Adding on a Hundred Chart

Use a hundred chart to add.

1	2	3	4	5	6	7	8	9	10
11	12	13	14	15	16	17	18	19	20
21	22	23	24	25	26	27	28	29	30
31	32	33	34	35	36	37	38	39	40
41	42	43	44	45	46	47	48	49	50
51	52	53	54	55	56	57	58	59	60
61	62	63	64	65	66	67	68	69	70
71	72	73	74	75	76	77	78	79	80
81	82	83	84	85	86	87	88	89	90
91	92	93	94	95	96	97	98	99	100

1. 45 + 30 ________

2. 36 + 33 ________

3. 52 + 46 ________

4. 27 + 23 ________

5. 36 + 45 ________

6. 49 + 24 ________

Practice 2-2

Number Sense Compare. Use <, >, or =.

7. 32 + 40 ◯ 42 + 38

8. 27 + 52 ◯ 52 + 27

9. 46 + 34 ◯ 33 + 45

10. 22 + 54 ◯ 28 + 48

11. 37 + 44 ◯ 32 + 50

12. 51 + 25 ◯ 41 + 25

13. **Number Sense** Mickey lives 35 miles away from his grandparents' home. His Aunt Roz lives 24 miles farther than his grandparents. How far does Mickey live from his Aunt Roz?

____

14. Kirsten spent 45 minutes doing her math homework and 35 minutes studying for science class. How much time did Kirsten spend studying all together? ________________

15. Which addition problem has a sum of 65?

A 37 + 28 **B** 46 + 29 **C** 34 + 32 **D** 27 + 39

Name ______________________________

Using Mental Math to Add

You can break apart numbers to make them easier to add mentally.

Add 31 + 45 by breaking apart numbers.

Break the numbers into tens and ones.

	tens		ones
31 =	30	+	1
45 =	40	+	5

Add the tens: 30 + 40 = 70.

Add the ones: 1 + 5 = 6.

Add the sums: 70 + 6 = 76.

So, 31 + 45 = 76.

Add 26 + 17 by breaking apart numbers to make a ten.

Use a number that adds with the 6 in 26 to make a 10. Since 6 + 4 = 10, use 4.

Think: 17 = 4 + 13.

Add 26 + 4 = 30.

Add 30 + 13 = 43.

So, 26 + 17 = 43.

Find each sum using mental math.

1. 24 + 71 = ________ **2.** 36 + 43 = ________ **3.** 54 + 23 = ________

4. 25 + 49 = ________ **5.** 37 + 56 = ________ **6.** 77 + 13 = ________

7. Number Sense To add 32 + 56, Juanita first added 30 + 50. What two steps does she still need to do to find the sum? What is Juanita's sum?

____

____

8. Reasoning How can Steve add 48 + 34 by making a ten? What is the sum?

____

____

____

Name ______________________

Using Mental Math to Add

Use breaking apart to add mentally.

1. 53 + 34

34 = 30 + ☐

53 + ☐ = 83

83 + ☐ = 87

So, 53 + 34 = ☐

2. 42 + 29

29 = 20 + ☐

42 + ☐ = 62

☐ + 9 = 71

So, 42 + 29 = ☐

3. 47 + 41

41 = ☐ + 1

47 + ☐ = 87

☐ + 1 = 88

So, 47 + 41 = ☐

Make a ten to add mentally.

4. 27 + 24

24 = 3 + ☐

27 + ☐ = 30

☐ + 21 = 51

So, 27 + 24 = ☐

5. 54 + 19

19 = ☐ + 6

☐ + 6 = 60

60 + ☐ = 73

So, 54 + 19 = ☐

6. 38 + 27

27 = ☐ + 25

38 + ☐ = 40

40 + ☐ = 65

So, 38 + 27 = ☐

Find each sum using mental math.

7. 52 + 26 ______

8. 47 + 8 ______

9. 32 + 17 ______

10. 28 + 31 ______

11. 43 + 38 ______

12. 72 + 7 ______

13. 42 + 33 ______

14. 36 + 14 ______

15. Number Sense Ashton broke apart a number into 30 + 7. What number did he start with? ______

16. What is the sum of 27 + 42 using mental math?

A 68 **B** 69 **C** 78 **D** 79

Name ______________________________

Rounding

You can use place value to round to the nearest ten or hundred.

Find the rounding place. If the digit in the ones or the tens place is 5, 6, 7, 8, or 9, then round to the next greater number. If the digit is less than 5, do not change the digit in the rounding place.

Round 17 to the nearest ten: 20

Explain. 7 is in the ones place. Round to the next greater ten.

Round 153 to the nearest ten. 150

Explain. Because 3 is in the ones place and 3 is less than 5, the digit in the tens place doesn't change.

Round 575 to the nearest hundred. 600

Explain. Because the 7 in the tens place is 5 or greater, round to the next greater hundred.

1. Round 63 to the nearest ten: __________

Explain. ______________________________

Round each number to the nearest ten.

2. 58 __________

3. 71 __________

4. 927 __________

5. 3,121 __________

Round each number to the nearest hundred.

6. 577 __________

7. 820 __________

8. 2,345 __________

9. 8,750 __________

10. Reasoning If you live 71 mi from a river, does it make sense to say you live about 80 mi from the river? Explain.

____

Name ______________________

Practice
2-4

Rounding

Round to the nearest ten.

1. 37 ______ **2.** 93 ______ **3.** 78 ______ **4.** 82 ______ **5.** 24 ______

6. 426 ______ **7.** 329 ______ **8.** 815 ______ **9.** 163 ______ **10.** 896 ______

Round to the nearest hundred.

11. 395 ______ **12.** 638 ______ **13.** 782 ______ **14.** 246 ______ **15.** 453 ______

16. 529 ______ **17.** 877 ______ **18.** 634 ______ **19.** 329 ______ **20.** 587 ______

21. **Number Sense** Tyrell says 753 rounds to 800. Sara says 753 rounds to 750. Who is correct? Explain.

____

____

22. **Explain It** How would you use a number line to round 148 to the nearest ten.

____

____

23. There are 254 counties in Texas. What is that number rounded to the nearest ten? What is that number rounded to the nearest hundred?

____

24. Which number does not round to 400?

A 347 **B** 369 **C** 413 **D** 448

Name ____________________

Reteaching **2-5**

Estimating Sums

Suppose your class has a goal of saving 275 cereal box tops.

136

152

Does your class have enough box tops to reach the goal?

Since you only need to know if you have enough, you can estimate.

You can estimate by rounding. You can round each addend to the nearest ten or hundred. Then add the rounded numbers.

Round to the nearest ten.

$$\begin{array}{rcr} 136 & \rightarrow & 140 \\ +\ 152 & \rightarrow & 150 \\ \hline & & 290 \end{array}$$

Since 290 > 275, you have enough.

Round to the nearest hundred.

$$\begin{array}{rcr} 136 & \rightarrow & 100 \\ +\ 152 & \rightarrow & 200 \\ \hline & & 300 \end{array}$$

Since 300 > 275, you have enough.

Round to the nearest ten to estimate each sum.

1. 42 + 98 = ________ **2.** 36 + 59 = ________ **3.** 288 + 475 = ________

Round to the nearest hundred to estimate each sum.

4. 378 + 136 = ________ **5.** 436 + 309 = ________ **6.** 76 + 487 = ________

7. Reasonableness Sun-Yi estimated 270 + 14 and got 300. Is her estimate reasonable? Explain.

____

____

Reteaching **2-5**

Name ______________________

Practice
2-5

Estimating Sums

Round to the nearest ten to estimate.

1. 58 + 43 ______ **2.** 87 + 69 ______ **3.** 37 + 141 ______ **4.** 422 + 296 ______

Round to the nearest hundred to estimate.

5. 536 + 393 ______ **6.** 242 + 359 ______ **7.** 713 + 82 ______ **8.** 313 + 405 ______

Practice **2-5**

Use compatible numbers to estimate. Sample answers are given. Accept reasonable answers.

9. 83 + 34 ______ **10.** 329 + 64 ______ **11.** 212 + 347 ______ **12.** 537 + 244 ______

13. Reasonableness Miguel has 325 baseball cards and 272 football cards. He said that he has 597 cards in all. Is his answer reasonable? Explain using estimation.

____

____

____

14. Write a Problem Natalie has 138 DVDs and 419 CDs. If you were to estimate the sum of the DVDs and CDs, what sentence could you write? Then find your estimated sum.

____

15. Which of the following shows estimating 287 + 491 by using compatible numbers?

A 100 + 500 **B** 300 + 400 **C** 280 + 400 **D** 280 + 500

Name ______________________________

Adding 2-Digit Numbers

To find 27 + 57, first estimate by rounding. Since 7 > 5, round 27 to 30 and 57 to 60. Then add: 30 + 60 = 90.

Add the ones. Then add the tens. • Add the ones. 7 + 7 = 14 ones • Add the tens. 5 tens + 2 tens = 7 tens 7 tens = 70 • Find the sum. 14 + 70 = 84	Tens Ones + 70 + 14 = 84	27 +57 14 70 84
Add the ones, then regroup the sum into tens and ones. • Add the ones. 7 + 7 = 14 ones • Regroup 14 ones into 1 ten, 4 ones. • Add the tens. 1 ten + 2 tens + 5 tens = 8 tens 8 tens = 80 • Find the sum.	Tens Ones + = 70 14 ones = 1 ten, 4 ones 70 + 10 + 4 = 84	1 27 +57 84

Estimate. Then find each sum.

1. 28 + 34

2. 56 + 22

3. 84 + 17

4. 49 + 72

5. 26 + 19

6. 65 + 23

7. 22 + 79

8. 38 + 85

9. **Reasonableness** Hannah added 65 and 26 and got 81. Is this answer reasonable? Explain.

____

Name ______________________________

Practice **2-6**

Adding 2-Digit Numbers

Estimate. Then find each sum.

1. $73 + 19$ **2.** $16 + 48$ **3.** $52 + 79$ **4.** $28 + 25$ **5.** $47 + 34$

6. $53 + 45$ **7.** $37 + 21$ **8.** $63 + 24$ **9.** $59 + 76$ **10.** $29 + 44$

11. 58 + 28 ______ **12.** 53 + 72 ______ **13.** 66 + 23 ______ **14.** 42 + 31 ______ **15.** 36 + 52 ______

Practice **2-6**

16. Critical Thinking Mr. McWilliams drove 76 miles Monday and 43 miles Tuesday. Follow the steps to find how many miles Mr. McWilliams drove all together.

a. Write a number sentence to show how to solve the problem.

____

b. Estimate the total distance Mr. McWilliams drove.

____

c. Find the actual total distance.

____

17. Reasoning Using four different digits, what is the least sum you can get when you add two 2-digit numbers? Write your problem.

____

18. There are 72 people on a train when 25 more people enter. How many people are on the train now?

A 79 **B** 87 **C** 97 **D** 98

Name ______________________________

Reteaching
2-7

Models for Adding 3-Digit Numbers

Find 152 + 329.

Step 1: Show each number with place-value blocks.

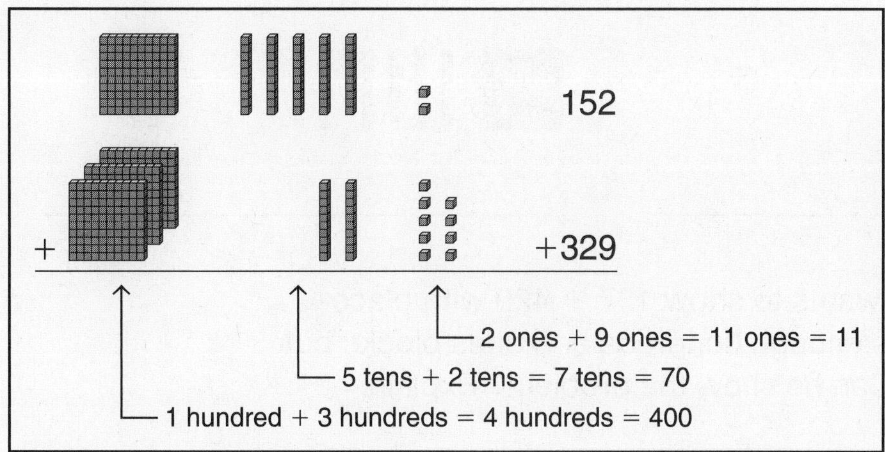

Step 2: Combine the ones. $2 + 9 = 11$

Step 3: Combine the tens. $50 + 20 = 70$

Step 4: Combine the hundreds. $100 + 300 = 400$

Step 5: Add. $400 + 70 + 11 = 481$

Write each problem and find the sum.

1. 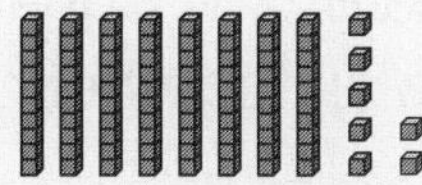 ______________________

2. 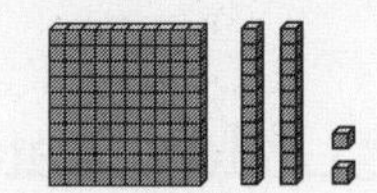 ______________________

3. 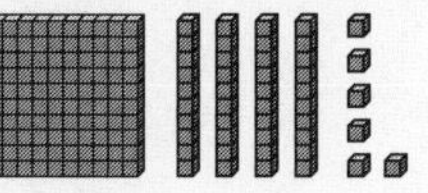 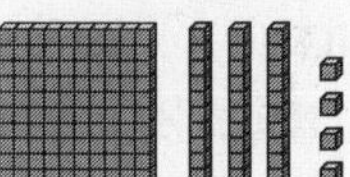 ______________________

4. 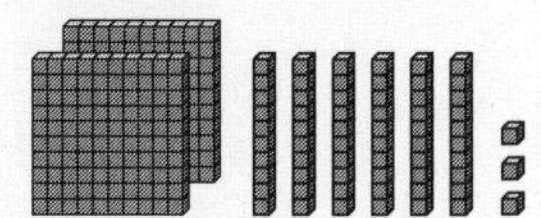 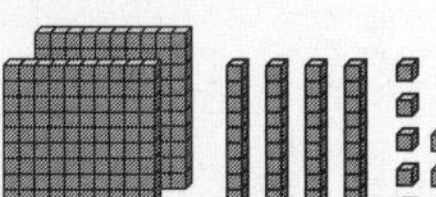 ______________________

Reteaching **2-7**

Name ______________________________

Practice
2-7

Models for Adding 3-Digit Numbers

Write each problem and find the sum.

1.

____

2.

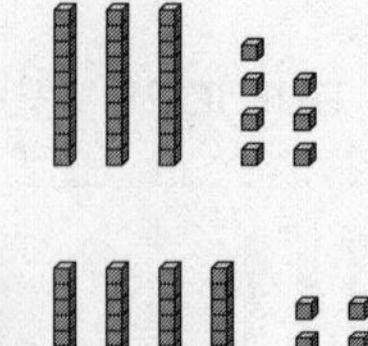

____

3. **Number Sense** Ed wants to show 137 + 429 with place-value blocks. He has enough hundreds and ones blocks but only 4 tens blocks. Can he show the problem? Explain.

____

____

4. Museum A has 127 steps. Museum B has 194 steps. How many steps do the museums have all together? Place-value blocks may help. __________

5. The country of Malta has an area of 316 square miles. The country of Saint Kitts and Nevis has an area of 261 square miles. What is the area of the two countries all together?

__________ square miles

6. The longest vertical lift drawbridge in the United States is the Arthur Kill Bridge at 558 feet. The longest steel truss bridge in the United States is the Glade Creek Bridge. The Glade Creek Bridge is 226 feet longer than the Arthur Kill Bridge. How many feet long is the Glade Creek Bridge? __________ feet

7. Larry was playing a board game. Larry scored 273 points on the first game and 248 points on the second game. How many points did Larry score in all?

A 411 **B** 421 **C** 511 **D** 521

Name ___________________________

Reteaching
2-8

Adding 3-Digit Numbers

Find 237 + 186.

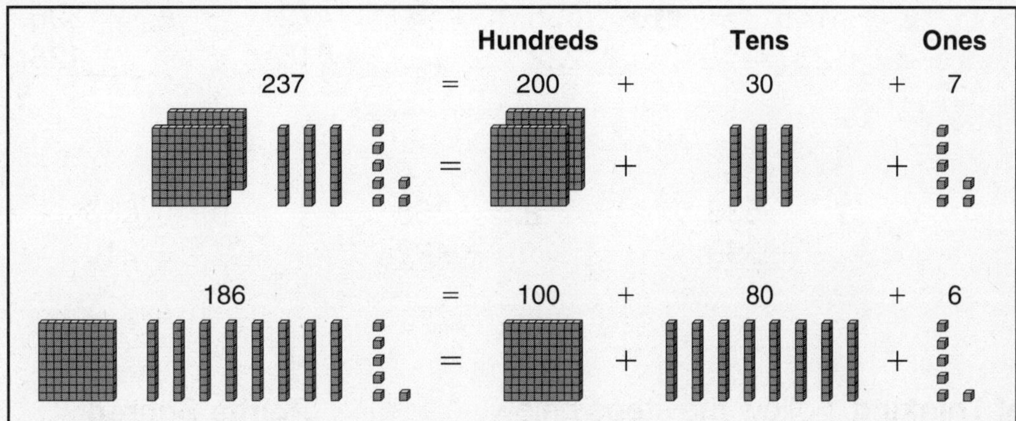

Step 1: Add the ones. 7 ones + 6 ones = 13 ones

Regroup. 13 ones = 1 ten, 3 ones

Step 2: Add the tens. 1 ten + 3 tens + 8 tens = 12 tens

Regroup. 12 tens = 1 hundred, 2 tens

Step 3: Add the hundreds.

1 hundred + 2 hundreds + 1 hundred = 4 hundreds

Add together the hundreds, tens, and ones.

400 + 20 + 3 = 423

Estimate. Then find each sum.

1. 118 + 146

2. 283 + 147

3. 542 + 109

4. 220 + 479

5. Find the sum of 456 and 238. ____________

6. Add 109 and 656. ____________

7. **Estimation** Estimate to decide which sum is less than 600: 356 + 292 or 214 + 356. ____________

Reteaching 2-8

Name ____________________

Practice **2-7**

Adding 3-Digit Numbers

Estimate. Then find each sum.

1. $329 + 468$

2. $148 + 231$

3. $555 + 222$

4. $472 + 515$

5. $396 + 428$

6. $645 + 79$

7. $536 + 399$

8. $268 + 422$

9. $633 + 210$

Practice **2-8**

10. Critical Thinking Follow the steps below to find how many combined points were scored by Howie and Theo.

Points Scored

Player	Points
Howie	272
Theo	325
Isabel	288

a. Write a number sentence to show how to solve the problem.

____

b. Estimate the total points scored by Howie and Theo.

____

c. Find the actual total. ____________________

11. Explain It Write an addition story for two 3-digit numbers. Write the answer to your story.

____

12. Sharon can run 278 yards in one minute. Pete can run 145 more yards than Sharon in one minute. How many yards can Pete run in one minute?

____

13. There were 752 people at a town meeting last week. There were 163 more people this week. How many people attended this week's meeting?

A 815 **B** 825 **C** 915 **D** 925

Name ______________________

Adding 3 or More Numbers

Find 137 + 201 + 109.

To add three numbers, you can add two numbers first. Then add the sum of the first two numbers and the third number.

Step 1	Step 2
Add 137 + 201.	Add 338 + 109.
137 + 201 338	1 338 + 109 447

So, 137 + 201 + 109 = 447.

Find each sum.

1. 32 + 64 + 71

2. 127 + 39 + 87

3. 293 + 312 + 78

4. 358 + 427 + 127

5. 382 + 45 + 181 = ______

6. 52 + 238 + 76 = ______

7. **Number Sense** Ranier has 37 baseball cards, 65 football cards, and 151 hockey cards. How many sports cards does he have in all? Explain how you found your answer.

____

____

Name ____________________

Adding 3 or More Numbers

Find each sum.

1. 75 + 36 + 58

2. 142 + 297 + 116

3. 524 + 97 + 176

4. 273 + 187 + 64 + 249

5. 319 + 48 + 136 + 347

6. 237 + 75 + 49 ________

7. 49 + 7 + 63 + 8 ________

8. 143 + 47 + 219 + 136 ________

9. **Estimation** Estimate the sum of 327 + 419 + 173.

____

10. **Number Sense** Justine has 162 red buttons, 98 blue buttons, and 284 green buttons. She says she knows she has more than 500 buttons without adding. Do you agree? Explain.

____

____

11. Carlos ate or drank everything that is listed in the table. How many calories did Carlos consume?

Food	Amount	Calories
Bran flakes	1 ounce	90
Banana	1	105
Orange juice	1 cup	110
Milk	1 cup	150

____

12. In winning the 1884 U.S. presidential election, Grover Cleveland received 219 electoral votes. He received 168 electoral votes in 1888, and lost. Then he received 277 electoral votes and won in 1892. How many electoral votes did Cleveland receive in all?

____

13. Kyle has 378 pennies, 192 nickels, and 117 dimes. How many coins does he have all together?

A 495 **B** 570 **C** 677 **D** 687

Name ______________________________

Problem Solving: Draw a Picture

Don sold 18 watermelons in the morning and 14 in the afternoon. How many watermelons did he sell in all?

You can draw a rectangle to show addition.

32 watermelons in all

18	14
Morning	Afternoon

Each part of the rectangle represents one of the addends. Add the parts to show how many in all.

Don sold 32 watermelons in all.

1. Two buses are carrying students to a field trip. There are 36 students on one bus and 30 students on the other. How many students are on the buses in all?

   ________ students in all

36	30
Bus #1	Bus #2

2. **Estimation** Vanessa bought a sweater for \$27 and a skirt for \$22. About how much money did Vanessa spend in all?

   ________ in all

\$30	\$20
Sweater	Skirt

3. A pet store sold 26 puppies and 14 kittens last month. How many animals were sold in all?

   ________ animals in all

26	14

4. Ken has 15 rap CDs, 20 country CDs, and 30 rock CDs. How many CDs does Ken have in all?

   ________ CDs in all

15	20	30

Name ______________________

Practice
2-10

Problem Solving: Draw a Picture

1. Kelly bought a CD for $15 and a book for $13. How much money did Kelly spend in all?

_______ in all

$15	$13
Cost of CD	Cost of book

2. **Estimation** There are 28 students in the chorus and 31 students in the band. All will be performing tonight. About how many students will be performing in all?

_______ students in all

30	30
Chorus	Band

Practice 2-10

3. Jane sold 25 raffle tickets Monday, 30 raffle tickets Tuesday, and 40 raffle tickets Wednesday. How many raffle tickets did Jane sell all together?

_______ tickets in all

25	30	40

4. Dan cycled 12 miles Saturday and 18 miles Sunday. How many miles did he cycle all together?

_______ miles in all

12	18

The table shows the number of students who belong to clubs. Use the table for **5** through **7**.

5. How many students belong to the Spanish and Science clubs?

_______ members in all

Club Membership

Club	Members
Math	24
Spanish	18
Running	15
Science	6

6. About how many students belong to the Math and Spanish clubs?

_______ members in all

7. How many students belong to the Math, Running, and Science clubs?

_______ members in all

Name ______________________________

Subtraction Meanings

Dawn received a total of 12 stars on Monday and Tuesday. She received 7 of the stars on Monday. How many stars did she receive on Tuesday?

You can draw a picture to find how many stars Dawn received on Tuesday.

First, draw 12 stars.

Next, put a line through the 7 stars that Dawn received Monday.

Count the number of stars that are not crossed off.
There are 5.
So, $12 - 7 = 5$.

You can add to check subtraction: $7 + 5 = 12$, so $12 - 7 = 5$.

Dawn received 5 stars on Tuesday.

Find each difference. Make a drawing to help you.

1. $13 - 4 =$ ______ **2.** $16 - 9 =$ ______ **3.** $15 - 7 =$ ______

4. $11 - 6 =$ ______ **5.** $12 - 8 =$ ______ **6.** $14 - 5 =$ ______

7. There are 15 players on the Titans baseball team. Only 9 players can play at any one time. How many players are not playing? ______

8. **Geometry** An octagon has 8 sides. A pentagon has 5 sides. How many more sides does an octagon have than a pentagon? ______

Name ______________________

Subtraction Meanings

Write a number sentence for each situation. Solve.

1. Terrance has 14 CDs. Robyn has 9 CDs. How many more CDs does Terrance have than Robyn?

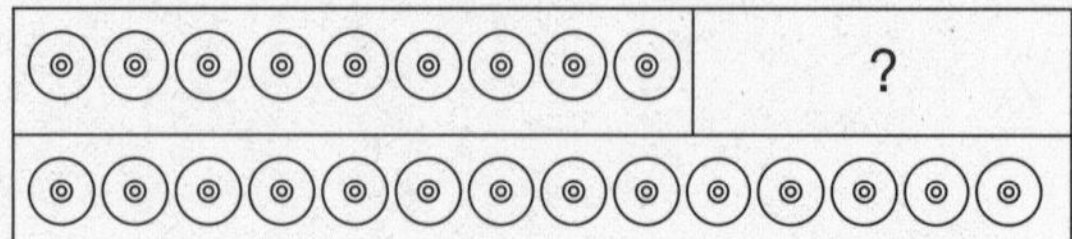

____

2. How many more black stars are there than white stars?

☆☆☆☆☆☆☆	?
★★★★★★★★★★★	

____

3. Arizona has 15 counties. Connecticut has 8 counties. How many more counties does Arizona have than Connecticut?

____

4. A baseball hat costs $12. Nancy has a coupon for $4 off. How much money will Nancy spend on the baseball hat?

____

5. **Draw a Picture** Carrie invited 13 girls to a party. Five of the girls have already arrived. How many girls have yet to arrive? Draw a picture to show the problem.

____

6. **Number Sense** Write the fact family for 3, 9, and 12.

____

____

____

____

7. LaToya has 12 postcards and 4 photographs on a bulletin board. How many more postcards does LaToya have than photographs?

A 7 **B** 8 **C** 9 **D** 16

Name ______________________

Reteaching
3-2

Subtracting on a Hundred Chart

You can use a hundred chart to subtract.
To subtract 72 − 37, follow these steps:

- Start at 72.
- Go up 3 rows to subtract 30.
- Go left 1 space to subtract 1.
- Move up to the row above and go left 6 spaces.
- End at 35.

1	2	3	4	5	6	7	8	9	10
11	12	13	14	15	16	17	18	19	20
21	22	23	24	25	26	27	28	29	30
31	32	33	34	35	36	37	38	39	40
41	42	43	44	45	46	47	48	49	50
51	52	53	54	55	56	57	58	59	60
61	62	63	64	65	66	67	68	69	70
71	72	73	74	75	76	77	78	79	80
81	82	83	84	85	86	87	88	89	90
91	92	93	94	95	96	97	98	99	100

So, 72 − 37 = 35.

You could also do it this way.

- Start at 72.
- Go up 4 rows to subtract 40.
- Go right 3 spaces to add 3.
- You end up at 35.

1	2	3	4	5	6	7	8	9	10
11	12	13	14	15	16	17	18	19	20
21	22	23	24	25	26	27	28	29	30
31	32	33	34	35	36	37	38	39	40
41	42	43	44	45	46	47	48	49	50
51	52	53	54	55	56	57	58	59	60
61	62	63	64	65	66	67	68	69	70
71	72	73	74	75	76	77	78	79	80
81	82	83	84	85	86	87	88	89	90
91	92	93	94	95	96	97	98	99	100

So, 72 − 37 = 35.

Use a hundred chart to subtract.

1. 57 − 30 ______

2. 63 − 20 ______

3. 77 − 52 ______

4. 54 − 33 ______

5. 51 − 18 ______

6. 74 − 27 ______

7. 93 − 36 ______

8. 84 − 25 ______

9. **Reasoning** To find 62 − 24, you could first find 64 − 24 = 40. Then what should you do? Explain.

____

____

____

Name ________________________

Subtracting on a Hundred Chart

Use a hundred chart to subtract.

1	2	3	4	5	6	7	8	9	10
11	12	13	14	15	16	17	18	19	20
21	22	23	24	25	26	27	28	29	30
31	32	33	34	35	36	37	38	39	40
41	42	43	44	45	46	47	48	49	50
51	52	53	54	55	56	57	58	59	60
61	62	63	64	65	66	67	68	69	70
71	72	73	74	75	76	77	78	79	80
81	82	83	84	85	86	87	88	89	90
91	92	93	94	95	96	97	98	99	100

1. 53 − 20 ______

2. 76 − 40 ______

3. 73 − 30 ______

4. 67 − 50 ______

5. 94 − 26 ______

6. 34 − 18 ______

7. 56 − 24 ______

8. 84 − 39 ______

9. 63 − 49 ______

10. 77 − 40 ______

11. 93 − 55 ______

12. 64 − 36 ______

13. At full speed, a lion can run 50 miles per hour. A grizzly bear can run 30 miles per hour. How much faster can a lion run than a grizzly bear? ______ miles per hour

14. **Reasonableness** Bobby subtracted 75 − 45 and said the difference is 30. Is his answer reasonable? Why or why not?

____

____

15. By how many points did the Terriers win?

______

16. Which subtraction sentence has a difference of 34?

A 57 − 33 = ■

B 61 − 17 = ■

C 72 − 37 ■

D 63 − 29 = ■

Name ______________________________

Using Mental Math to Subtract

You can change numbers to make subtraction problems easier.

There are two ways to subtract 42 − 28.

One way is to add 2 to 28.

$$\begin{array}{rl} 42 & \rightarrow 42 \\ -\ 28 + 2 & \rightarrow 30 \\ \hline & 12 \end{array}$$

Because you added 2 to 28, add 2 to the difference.

12 + 2 = 14

So, 42 − 28 = 14.

Another way is to add 2 to both 42 and 28.

$$\begin{array}{rl} 42 + 2 & \rightarrow 44 \\ -\ 28 + 2 & \rightarrow 30 \\ \hline & 14 \end{array}$$

What you do to the bottom number, also do to the top number.

So, 42 − 28 = 14.

Find each difference using mental math.

1. 32 − 17 = ________ **2.** 51 − 46 = ________ **3.** 42 − 18 = ________

4. 36 − 19 = ________ **5.** 63 − 56 = ________ **6.** 78 − 16 = ________

7. 94 − 18 = ________ **8.** 55 − 33 = ________ **9.** 81 − 13 = ________

10. Number Sense Rob had $60 when he went to the mall. He bought a DVD for $15. How much money does he have left? Write the number sentence you used to solve the problem.

____

Name ______________________

Practice
3-3

Using Mental Math to Subtract

Find each difference using mental math.

1. 38 − 14 ______ **2.** 42 − 13 ______ **3.** 55 − 12 ______ **4.** 62 − 17 ______

5. 72 − 19 ______ **6.** 94 − 11 ______ **7.** 32 − 15 ______ **8.** 85 − 18 ______

9. 43 − 16 ______ **10.** 66 − 15 ______ **11.** 53 − 19 ______ **12.** 72 − 16 ______

13. Number Sense Gillian started solving 88 − 29. This is what she did.

88 − 29 = ?
88 − 30 = 58

What should Gillian do next? ______________________

14. Explain It Tell how to find 81 − 16 using mental math.

____

____

____

15. Tiffany will use a total of 63 tiles for her art project. She only needs 17 more tiles. Use mental math to find how many tiles she has already.

____

16. To solve 35 − 19, Jack used 35 − 20 and then

A added 1.
B subtracted 9.
C subtracted 1.
D added 9.

Name ______________________________

Estimating Differences

Members of the Biology Club caught 288 butterflies and 136 grasshoppers in their nets. About how many more butterflies than grasshoppers did the club catch?

You can estimate by rounding. To round to a certain place, look at the digit to the right of that place. If the digit is 5 or greater, round up. If the digit is less than 5, round down.

Round to the nearest hundred.
Look at the digits in the tens place.

2**8**8	→	300
− 1**3**6	→	100
		200

There were about 200 more butterflies than grasshoppers caught.

Round to the nearest ten.
Look at the digits in the ones place.

28**8**	→	290
− 13**6**	→	140
		150

There were about 150 more butterflies than grasshoppers caught.

Estimate by rounding to the nearest hundred.

1. 442 − 112

2. 725 − 278

3. 363 − 187

Estimate by rounding to the nearest ten.

4. 68 − 42 = ______ **5.** 88 − 17 = ______ **6.** 231 − 109 = ______

7. Explain It Charlie estimated 293 − 44 and got a difference of about 250. Is this a reasonable estimate? Explain.

____

____

____

Name ______________________

Practice **3-4**

Estimating Differences

Round to the nearest hundred to estimate each difference.

1. 478 − 267 ______ **2.** 236 − 119 ______ **3.** 588 − 321 ______

Round to the nearest ten to estimate each difference.

4. 677 − 421 ______ **5.** 296 − 97 ______ **6.** 312 − 157 ______

Use compatible numbers to estimate each difference.

7. 84 − 36 ______ **8.** 427 − 163 ______ **9.** 609 − 243 ______

10. Number Sense Fern rounded to the nearest ten to estimate 548 − 132. She subtracted 540 − 130 and got 410. Is Fern's estimate correct? Explain.

____

____

11. Waco, TX, has an elevation of 405 feet. Dallas, TX, has an elevation of 463 feet. About how many feet greater is Dallas's elevation than Waco's elevation? ______

12. On Friday, 537 people attended a play. For Saturday's matinee, there were 812 people. About how many more people attended the play on Saturday than on Friday? ______

13. A football team scored 529 points one season and then 376 points the next. About how many points less did the team score in the second season? Round to the nearest ten. ______

14. George got a 94 on his spelling test and a 68 on his math test. Which number sentence best shows about how many more points George got on his spelling test than on his math test?

A 90 − 60 = 30

B 90 + 70 = 160

C 100 + 60 = 160

D 90 − 70 = 20

Name ______________________________

Reteaching
3-5

Problem Solving: Reasonableness

The island of Elba has an area of 86 square miles. The island of St. Helena has an area of 47 square miles. How many square miles larger is Elba than St. Helena?

You can subtract to find how many square miles larger Elba is than St. Helena. Use mental math or a hundred chart to subtract.

86 − 47 = 39

Make sure you answered the correct question.

The question asked how many square miles larger Elba is than St. Helena. The correct question was answered.

86 square miles in all

47	?

Elba is 39 square miles larger than St. Helena.

Make sure that your answer is reasonable.

Since 47 + 39 = 86, the answer is reasonable.

1. The JP Morgan Chase Tower in Houston has 75 stories. The Renaissance Tower in Dallas has 56 stories. How many more stories does the JP Morgan Chase Tower have than the Renaissance Tower?

75 stories in all

56	

2. The Bulldogs scored 49 points in last week's game. This week, they scored 62 points. How many points did the Bulldogs score in all in the two games?

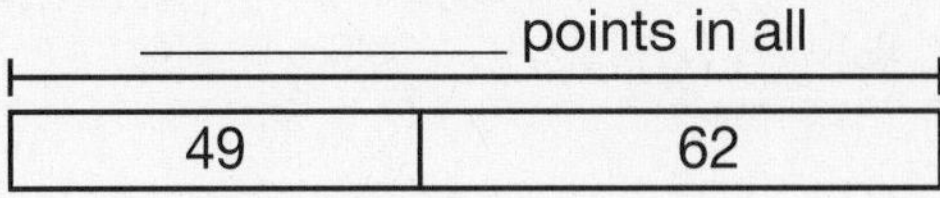

3. **Write a Problem** Write a problem about something you did that can be solved using addition or subtraction. Then solve the problem and check that your answer is reasonable.

____

____

____

Reteaching **3-5**

Name ______________________

Problem Solving: Reasonableness

Solve. Then check that your answer is reasonable.

1. The Aggies scored 59 points in the first half and 56 points in the second half. How many points did the Aggies score altogether?

_______ points in all

59	56

2. Ms. Rice is driving 92 miles to a meeting. After driving 54 miles, she stops to buy gasoline. How many more miles does she have left?

92 miles in all

54	

3. There are 45 students going on a field trip. Of those students, 27 are from Mrs. Unser's class. The rest are from Mr. King's class. How many students are from Mr. King's class?

45 students in all

27	

4. **Estimation** In the 2004 Summer Olympics, the United States won 36 gold, 39 silver, and 27 bronze medals. About how many medals did the United States win?

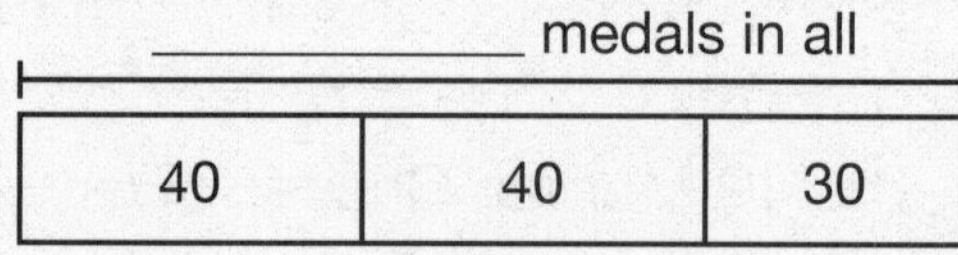

5. Christine is reading a short story that is 76 pages long. She just finished reading page 47. How many more pages does she have left to read?

76 pages in all

47	

6. Wyoming has 23 counties. Wisconsin has 49 more counties than Wyoming. How many counties does Wisconsin have?

A 26 **B** 62 **C** 72 **D** 82

Name ______________________________

Models for Subtracting 2-Digit Numbers

Here is how to subtract 2-digit numbers.

Find 55 − 36.

Estimate: 60 − 40 = 20, so the answer should be about 20.

What You Think	What You Show	What You Write
Step 1 Subtract the ones. Since you can't subtract 6 from 5, regroup.	Regroup 1 ten into 10 ones. 15 ones − 6 ones = 9 ones.	4 15 ~~55~~ −36 9
Step 2 Subtract the tens.	4 tens − 3 tens = 1 ten.	4 15 ~~55~~ −36 19

Add to check your answer. 19 + 36 = 55

It checks.

Use place-value blocks or draw pictures to subtract.

1. 86 − 51

2. 47 − 18

3. 62 − 35

4. 41 − 11

5. 28 − 17 ______

6. 53 − 38 ______

7. **Number Sense** To subtract 91 from 99, do you need to regroup? Explain.

____

____

8. Felicia had 67 paperback books in her collection. She sold 48 of them. How many books does she have left? ______

Name ____________________

Practice
4-1

Models for Subtracting 2-Digit Numbers

Use the place-value blocks to subtract.

1. 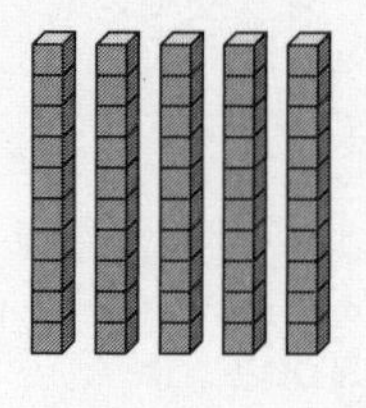

$$\begin{array}{r} 54 \\ -\ 28 \\ \hline \end{array}$$

2. 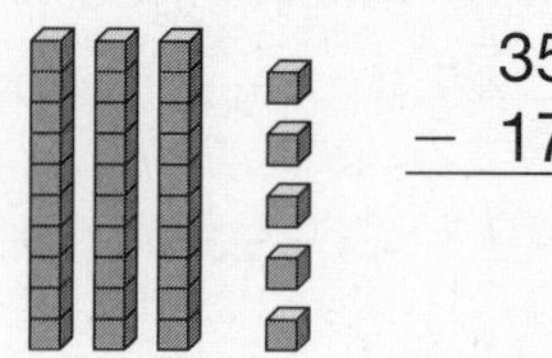

$$\begin{array}{r} 35 \\ -\ 17 \\ \hline \end{array}$$

Practice **4-1**

Use place-value blocks or draw pictures to subtract.

3. $\begin{array}{r} 31 \\ -\ 12 \\ \hline \end{array}$ **4.** $\begin{array}{r} 56 \\ -\ 39 \\ \hline \end{array}$ **5.** $\begin{array}{r} 63 \\ -\ 42 \\ \hline \end{array}$ **6.** $\begin{array}{r} 37 \\ -\ 19 \\ \hline \end{array}$ **7.** $\begin{array}{r} 60 \\ -\ 32 \\ \hline \end{array}$

8. $\begin{array}{r} 44 \\ -\ 35 \\ \hline \end{array}$ **9.** $\begin{array}{r} 73 \\ -\ 47 \\ \hline \end{array}$ **10.** $\begin{array}{r} 55 \\ -\ 27 \\ \hline \end{array}$ **11.** $\begin{array}{r} 58 \\ -\ 23 \\ \hline \end{array}$ **12.** $\begin{array}{r} 61 \\ -\ 14 \\ \hline \end{array}$

13. Draw a Picture Draw two ways to show 43 using place-value blocks.

____

14. Melissa finished page 72 of her book today. She started at page 26. How many pages did she read today? ________

15. Pedro lives 67 miles from his grandparents. After 49 miles of driving, his family stopped for gas. How many miles does Pedro's family have left to reach his grandparents' home? ________

16. There were 45 students on a bus. At the first stop, 11 students got off. Another 17 students got off at the second stop. How many students are still on the bus?

A 7 **B** 17 **C** 28 **D** 34

Name ______________________________

Reteaching
4-2

Subtracting 2-Digit Numbers

Find 62 − 26.
Estimate: 60 − 30 = 30, so the answer should be about 30.

Step 1	Step 2	Step 3
There are not enough ones to subtract.	Subtract the ones.	Subtract the tens.
6 tens 2 ones = 5 tens 12 ones	12 − 6 = 6	5 − 2 = 3
$\begin{array}{r} ^{5\,12} \\ \not{6}\not{2} \\ -\ 26 \\ \hline \end{array}$	$\begin{array}{r} ^{5\,12} \\ \not{6}\not{2} \\ -\ 26 \\ \hline 6 \end{array}$	$\begin{array}{r} ^{5\,12} \\ \not{6}\not{2} \\ -\ 26 \\ \hline 36 \end{array}$

Since 36 is close to 30, the answer is reasonable. Check your answer by adding: 36 + 26 = 62.

Subtract.

1. $\begin{array}{r} 25 \\ -\ 9 \\ \hline \end{array}$ **2.** $\begin{array}{r} 42 \\ -\ 24 \\ \hline \end{array}$ **3.** $\begin{array}{r} 74 \\ -\ 17 \\ \hline \end{array}$ **4.** $\begin{array}{r} 53 \\ -\ 22 \\ \hline \end{array}$ **5.** $\begin{array}{r} 65 \\ -\ 38 \\ \hline \end{array}$

6. 71 − 48 = ________ **7.** 92 − 56 = ________ **8.** 83 − 57 = ________

9. A total of 76 boys and 94 girls signed up to play soccer. How many more girls signed up for soccer than boys?

____

10. **Reasonableness** Melanie subtracted 76 − 35 and got 31. Is her answer reasonable? Explain.

____

____

____

Reteaching **4-2**

Name ______________________

Practice **4-2**

Subtracting 2-Digit Numbers

Subtract.

1. 34 − 16

2. 43 − 27

3. 76 − 28

4. 65 − 38

5. 82 − 47

6. 82 − 67 = ______ **7.** 63 − 35 = ______ **8.** 86 − 42 = ______

9. Reasonableness Rebecca subtracted 47 − 28 and got 19. Is her answer reasonable? Explain.

____

____

____

Practice 4-2

10. Explain It Do you need to regroup to find 73 − 35? Explain your answer.

____

____

____

11. Write a Problem Bethany has 43 apples. Write a subtraction story about the apples that would require regrouping. Then write the answer in a complete sentence.

____

____

____

12. The tree farm had 65 shade trees for sale. It sold 39 of the trees. How many shade trees did the farm have left?

A 26 **B** 36 **C** 94 **D** 104

Name ______________________________

Reteaching
4-3

Models for Subtracting 3-Digit Numbers

You can use place-value blocks to subtract.

Find 234 − 192.

Estimate: 230 − 190 = 40, so the answer should be about 40.

	What You Show	What You Write
Step 1 Show 234 with place-value blocks.		234 −192
Step 2 Subtract the ones. 4 > 2. No regrouping is needed.	4 ones − 2 ones = 2 ones	234 −192 2
Step 3 Subtract the tens. 3 tens < 9 tens, so regroup 1 hundred for 10 tens.	13 tens − 9 tens = 4 tens	1 13 234 −192 42
Step 4 Subtract the hundreds.	1 hundred − 1 hundred = 0 hundreds	1 13 234 −192 42

Find the value of the remaining blocks:

4 tens + 2 ones = 40 + 2 = 42

So, 234 − 192 = 42.

Use place-value blocks or draw pictures to subtract.

1. 156 − 28

2. 261 − 122

3. 321 − 76

4. 446 − 257

Reteaching **4-3**

Name ______________________________

Practice

4-3

Models for Subtracting 3-Digit Numbers

Use the place-value blocks to subtract.

1. 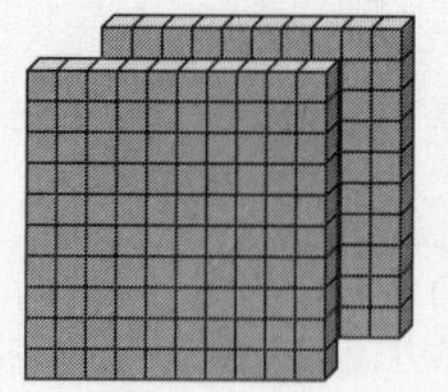 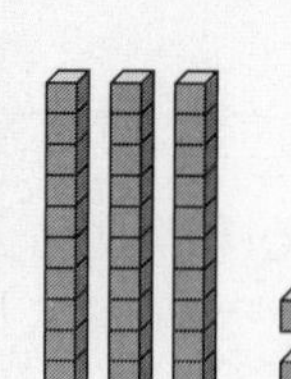

  232
− 147

2. 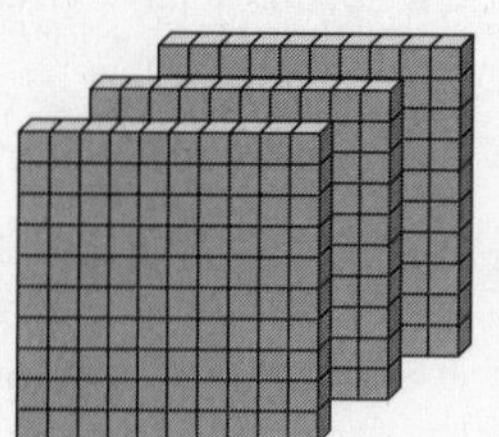

  324
− 156

Practice 4-3

Use place-value blocks or draw pictures to subtract.

3. 321 − 176

4. 242 − 86

5. 332 − 117

6. 267 − 149

7. 413 − 237

8. 165 − 137

9. 251 − 137

10. 372 − 283

11. 511 − 324

12. 346 − 138

For **13** and **14**, use the table at the right.

Pages Read

Name	Pages Read
Lance	322
Annie	263
Brad	415

13. What is the difference between the greatest and least number of pages read? __________

14. How many more pages did Lance read than Annie? __________

15. **Number Sense** Edie wanted to subtract 273 − 188. She began by finding 2 − 1. What did Edie do wrong?

____

____

16. Alice defeated Ralph 313 to 188 in a board game. By how many points did Alice win?

A 115 **B** 125 **C** 215 **D** 225

Name ___________________________

Reteaching
4-4

Subtracting 3-Digit Numbers

Find 726 − 238.

Estimate: 700 − 200 = 500, so the answer should be about 500.

Step 1

First subtract the ones.
Regroup 1 ten into 10 ones.

```
  1 16
  726
 −238
    8
```

Step 2

Subtract the tens.
Regroup 1 hundred into 10 tens.

```
   11
 6 1 16
  726
 −238
   88
```

Step 3

Subtract the hundreds.

```
   11
 6 1 16
  726
 −238
  488
```

Is your answer correct?
Check by adding:
488 + 238 = 726.
It checks.

Find each difference. Estimate and check answers for reasonableness.

1. 318 − 123

2. 441 − 187

3. 334 − 275

4. 512 − 299

5. 423 − 156 = ______

6. 327 − 159 = ______

7. The town library had 634 CDs for rent. During one week, 288 of them were rented. How many CDs were left? ______

8. **Number Sense** If you had to subtract 426 from 913, how many times would you need to regroup? How can you tell?

____

____

____

____

Reteaching **4-4**

Name ______________________________

Practice

4-4

Subtracting 3-Digit Numbers

Find each difference. Estimate and check answers for reasonableness.

1. 732 − 328

2. 621 − 153

3. 369 − 185

4. 267 − 78

5. 527 − 279

6. 917 − 436

7. 555 − 189

8. 422 − 244

9. 853 − 456

10. 451 − 363

11. 527 − 242 = ______ **12.** 746 − 437 = ______ **13.** 941 − 267 = ______

All Roads Lead to Omaha

Start	Finish	Miles
Dallas	Omaha	644
Chicago	Omaha	459
Tulsa	Omaha	387

14. Tulsa is how many miles closer to Omaha than Dallas? ______

15. Tulsa is how many miles closer to Omaha than Chicago? ______

16. **Strategy Practice** Jill is going on a trip from Chicago to Omaha to Tulsa. Bill will travel from Dallas to Omaha. How much farther will Jill travel than Bill?

a. What do you need to do first?

____

____

b. What is the next step?

____

c. Solve the problem.

______ miles

17. Texas has 254 counties. California has 58 counties and Florida has 67 counties. How many more counties does Texas have than California and Florida combined?

A 125 **B** 129 **C** 139 **D** 196

Practice 4-4

Name ______________________________

Reteaching
4-5

Subtracting Across Zero

To subtract from a number with 0 in the tens place, you need to regroup one hundred into 10 tens.

Find 207 − 98.

Step 1	Step 2	Step 3
Subtract the ones. Since there are 0 tens, you must first regroup the hundreds.	Regroup the hundreds. 2 hundreds and 0 tens = 1 hundred and 10 tens.	Regroup the tens. 10 tens and 7 ones = 9 tens and 17 ones. Subtract.
207 − 98	1 10 2̸0̸7 − 98	9 1 1̸0 17 2̸0̸7̸ − 98 109

Is your answer correct? Check by adding: 109 + 98 = 207.

Find each difference.

1. 301 − 72
2. 205 − 36
3. 400 − 228
4. 502 − 225
5. 603 − 215

6. 307 − 149 = ______
7. 702 − 259 = ______
8. 504 − 397 = ______

9. **Number Sense** Waco has an elevation of 405 feet above sea level. Texarkana has an elevation of 324 feet above sea level. How many feet greater is Waco's elevation than Texarkana's? Show your work. ______ feet

Reteaching **4-5**

Name ______________________________

Practice
4-5

Subtracting Across Zero

Find each difference.

1. 406 − 28

2. 300 − 211

3. 501 − 268

4. 705 − 347

5. 605 − 219

6. 800 − 579

7. 907 − 728

8. 603 − 347

9. 507 − 388

10. 706 − 497

11. 404 − 305 = ______

12. 501 − 223 = ______

13. 302 − 166 = ______

14. There were 600 ears of corn for sale at the produce market. At the end of the day, there were 212 ears left. How many ears of corn were sold? ______

15. Darrin has 702 CDs in his collection. Dana has 357 CDs in her collection. How many more CDs does Darrin have than Dana? ______

16. **Strategy Practice** Party Palace has an order for 505 party favors. It packaged 218 favors Saturday and 180 favors Sunday. How many more party favors does it still need to package? ______

17. **Write a Problem** Write a subtraction problem involving regrouping that has Ted reading 304 pages. Answer your question.

____

____

____

18. The Williams Tower in Houston, TX, is 901 feet tall. The Tower of the Americas in San Antonio, TX, is 622 feet tall. How much taller is the Williams Tower than the Tower of the Americas?

A 279 feet **B** 289 feet **C** 379 feet **D** 389 feet

Name ______________________________

Reteaching
4-6

Problem Solving: Draw a Picture and Write a Number Sentence

The distance from Cleveland, OH, to Pittsburgh, PA, is 129 miles. Detroit, MI, is 170 miles away from Cleveland. How much closer is Pittsburgh to Detroit than to Cleveland?

You can subtract to find how many miles closer Pittsburgh is to Cleveland than to Detroit.

170 miles	
129	?

$$\begin{array}{r} 170 \\ -\ 129 \\ \hline 41 \end{array}$$

Pittsburgh is 41 miles closer to Cleveland than to Detroit.

You can estimate $170 - 130 = 40$ to show that the answer is reasonable.

Solve.

1. Honolulu, HI, has an area of 86 square miles. Corpus Christi, TX, has an area that is 69 square miles greater than the area of Honolulu. How many square miles is Corpus Christi?

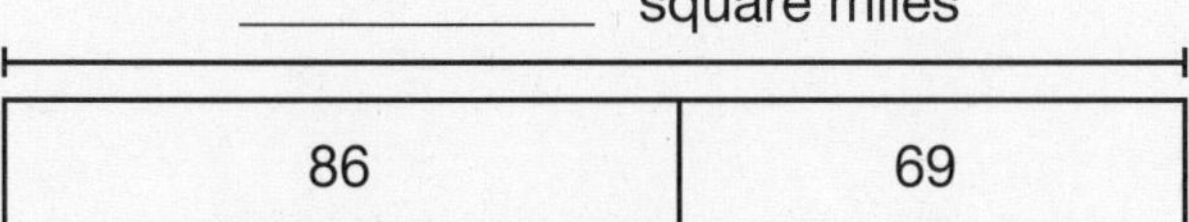

2. Bakersfield, CA, has an area of 113 square miles. Its area is 64 square miles greater than the area of Anaheim, CA. What is the area, in square miles, of Anaheim?

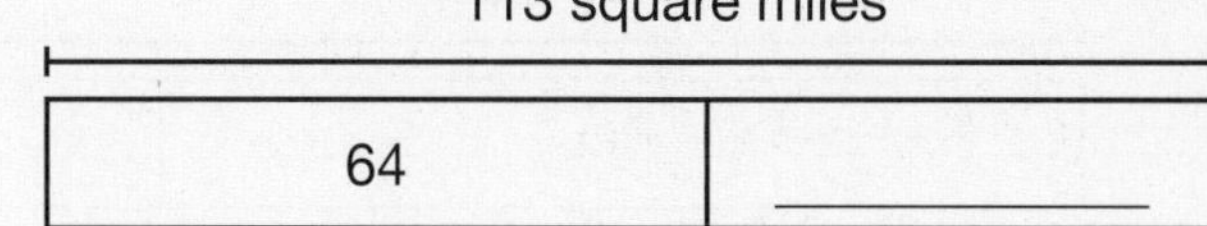

3. Writing to Explain How did you know which operation to use to solve Problem 2?

____

____

____

Reteaching **4-6**

Name ______________________

Problem Solving: Draw a Picture and Write a Number Sentence

The table below shows the areas of some of the smallest countries in the world. Use the table for **1–3.**

Area of Countries

Country	Area (in sq mi)
San Marino	24
Liechtenstein	62
Maldives	116
Palau	177

1. How many square miles greater is Maldives than San Marino?

116 square miles

24	______

2. **Draw a Picture** Draw a diagram to show how to find the difference between the areas of Liechtenstein and San Marino. Use your diagram to solve the problem.

3. Grenada is 15 square miles greater than Maldives. What is the area of Grenada?

______ square miles

116	15

4. There are 237 students at Johnson Elementary School. There are 188 students at Hoover Elementary School. How many more students are at Johnson than at Hoover?

237 students

188	______

5. **Write a Problem** Write a real-world problem that you can solve by adding or subtracting. Then give your problem to a classmate to solve.

____

____

____

Name ______________________

Multiplication as Repeated Addition

Each group below has the same number of squares. There are 5 groups of 4 squares. There are a total of 20 squares.

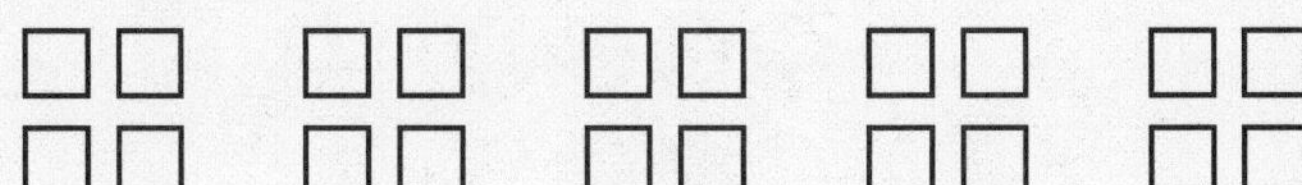

Here is the addition sentence for this problem: $4 + 4 + 4 + 4 + 4 = 20$

Here is the multiplication sentence for this problem: $5 \times 4 = 20$

Complete the addition and multiplication sentences.

1. ○○ ○○ ○○ ○○
   ○○ ○○ ○○ ○○

   4 groups of _____ $4 + 4 + 4 + 4 =$ _____ $4 \times$ _____ $= 16$

2. ○○○○ ○○○○ ○○○○ ○○○○
   ○○○ ○○○ ○○○ ○○○

   _____ groups of 7 _____ + _____ + _____ + _____ = 28

   $7 \times$ _____ = _____

Write each addition sentence as a multiplication sentence.

3. $1 + 1 + 1 + 1 + 1 = 5$ ______________________

4. $8 + 8 + 8 = 24$ ______________________

Write each multiplication sentence as an addition sentence.

5. $5 \times 5 = 25$ ______________________

6. $6 \times 2 = 12$ ______________________

7. **Explain It** Juan says, "When you put together unequal groups, you can only add." Is he correct? Explain.

   ____

Name ________________________

Multiplication as Repeated Addition

Complete.

1. 

2 groups of ____

5 + ____ = ____

2 × ____ = ____

2.

3 groups of ____

4 + ____ + ____ = ____

3 × ____ = ____

3. 4 + 4 + 4 + 4 + 4 = 5 × ____

4. ____ + ____ + ____ = 3 × 8

5. 9 + ____ + ____ = ____ × 9

6. 7 + 7 + 7 + 7 = ____ × ____

Algebra Write +, −, or × for each □.

7. 5 □ 4 = 9

8. 6 □ 2 = 12

9. 7 □ 3 = 4

10. 3 □ 3 = 9

11. 8 □ 6 = 2

12. 3 □ 3 = 6

13. **Number Sense** Marlon has 4 cards, Jake has 4 cards, and Sam has 3 cards. Can you write a multiplication sentence to find how many cards they have in all? Explain.

____

____

14. **Write a Problem** Draw a picture that shows equal groups. Then write an addition sentence and a multiplication sentence for your picture.

15. Which is equal to 6 + 6 + 6 + 6?

A 6 × 3 **B** 3 × 6 **C** 4 × 6 **D** 6 × 5

Name ______________________________

Arrays and Multiplication

An array shows objects in equal rows. This array shows 3 rows of 6 pennies.

The multiplication sentence for this array is $3 \times 6 = 18$.

You can use the Commutative (Order) Property of Multiplication to multiply the numbers in any order:
$3 \times 6 = 18$ and $6 \times 3 = 18$.

Write a multiplication sentence for each array.

1. ○○○○○○○○
○○○○○○○○

____

2. □□□□
□□□□
□□□□
□□□□

____

Complete each multiplication sentence. You may use counters or draw a picture to help.

3. $3 \times 4 = 12$ ______ $\times 3 = 12$

4. $5 \times 2 = 10$ $2 \times$ ______ $= 10$

5. Number Sense How can you use the Commutative Property to know that

○○○○○○
○○○○○○
○○○○○○

is equal to

○○○
○○○
○○○
○○○
○○○
○○○

?

____

____

____

Name ______________________

Practice
5-2

Arrays and Multiplication

Write a multiplication sentence for each array.

1. 

2.

3. 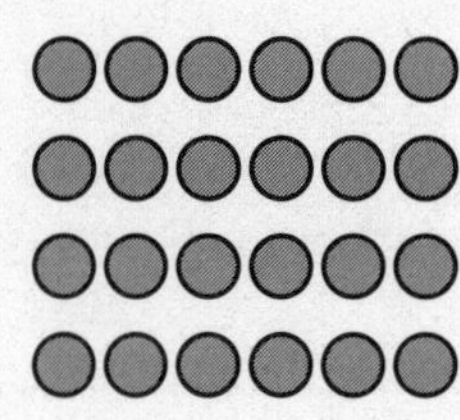

______________ ______________ ______________

Draw an array to find each multiplication fact. Write the product.

4. $3 \times 6 =$ ______

5. $4 \times 7 =$ ______

Complete each multiplication sentence.
Use counters or draw an array to help.

6. $3 \times$ ____ $= 21$

$7 \times$ ____ $= 21$

7. $4 \times 9 =$ ____

$9 \times 4 =$ ____

8. $5 \times 6 =$ ____

$6 \times 5 =$ ____

9. $4 \times 7 =$ ____

$7 \times 4 =$ ____

10. $6 \times 8 =$ ____

$8 \times 6 =$ ____

11. $9 \times 5 =$ ____

$5 \times 9 =$ ____

12. Explain It If you know that $7 \times 8 = 56$, how can you use the Commutative (Order) Property of Multiplication to find the product of 8×7?

____

____

____

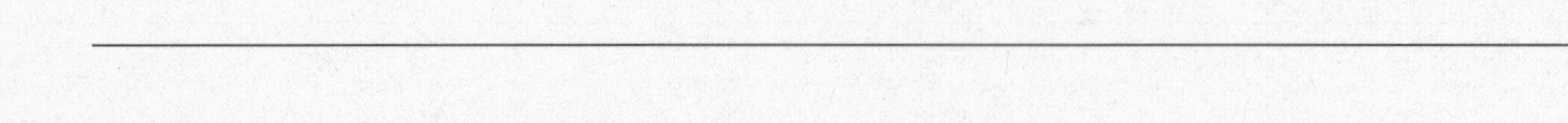

13. Which of the following is equal to 8×4?

A 4×8 **B** $4 + 8$ **C** $8 - 4$ **D** $8 + 4$

Name ______________________________

Reteaching **5-3**

Using Multiplication to Compare

Multiplication can be used to show comparisons between groups.

Erica has 3 apples. Scott has 4 times as many apples. How many apples does Scott have?

Draw Erica's apples.

$3 \times 1 = 3$

Draw Scott's apples.

$3 \times 1 = 3$

$3 \times 2 = 6$

$3 \times 3 = 9$

$3 \times 4 = 12$

Scott has 12 apples, which is 4 times as many apples as Erica.

Find each amount. You may use drawings or counters to help.

1. 4 times as many as 2 ________

2. 3 times as many as 6 ________

3. 5 times as many as 4 ________

4. 3 times as many as 7 ________

5. 2 times as many as 8 ________

6. 4 times as many as 4 ________

7. **Geometry** A triangle, △, has 3 sides. Draw a figure that has twice as many sides as a triangle.

Reteaching **5-3**

Name ______________________

Using Multiplication to Compare

Find each amount. You may use drawings or counters to help.

1. 2 times as many as 5 ______
2. 3 times as many as 7 ______
3. 4 times as many as 6 ______
4. 3 times as many as 9 ______
5. twice as many as 8 ______
6. 5 times as many as 3 ______
7. 4 times as many as 7 ______
8. 5 times as many as 6 ______
9. 4 times as many as 3 ______

10. **Reasoning** John has 5 computer games. Julian has twice as many computer games as John. How many computer games do they have in all? ______

11. George Washington is on the $1 bill. Abraham Lincoln is on the bill that is worth 5 times as much as the $1 bill. What bill is Abraham Lincoln on? ______

12. Paula has twice as many guests this week as she did last week. Last week she had 7 guests. How many guests does she have this week? ______

13. John F. Kennedy is on the coin that is worth 5 times as much as a dime. What coin is John F. Kennedy on?

    A nickel **B** quarter **C** half dollar **D** dollar

Name ______________________________

Writing Multiplication Stories

When you write a multiplication story you should:

- Always end the story with a question.
- Draw a picture to show the main idea.

Example:
Write a multiplication story for 5×9.

Josephine has 5 friends over for a snack. She gives each friend 9 grapes. How many grapes did Josephine give all together?

Josephine gave 45 grapes all together.

Write a multiplication story for each exercise. Draw a picture to find each product.

1. 4×3

____

____

2. 5×2

____

____

3. 4×6

____

____

4. Number Sense Leshon has seven $5 bills. How much money does Leshon have? Write a multiplication sentence to show the answer. ______________

Name ____________________

Writing Multiplication Stories

Write a multiplication story for each.

Draw a picture to find each product.

1. 3 × 6 **2.** 2 × 8 **3.** 4 × 3

Write a multiplication story for each picture.

4. 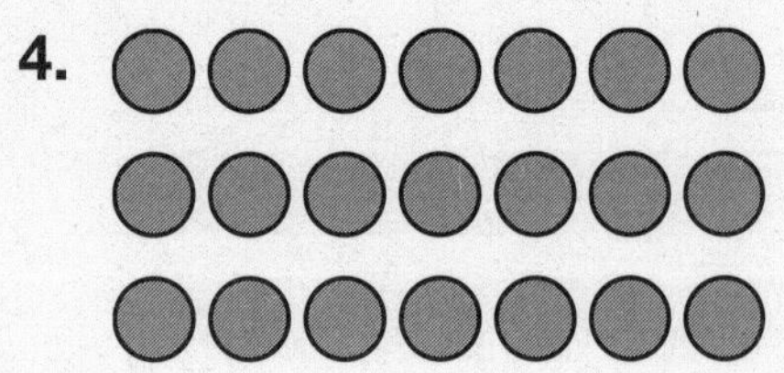

5. 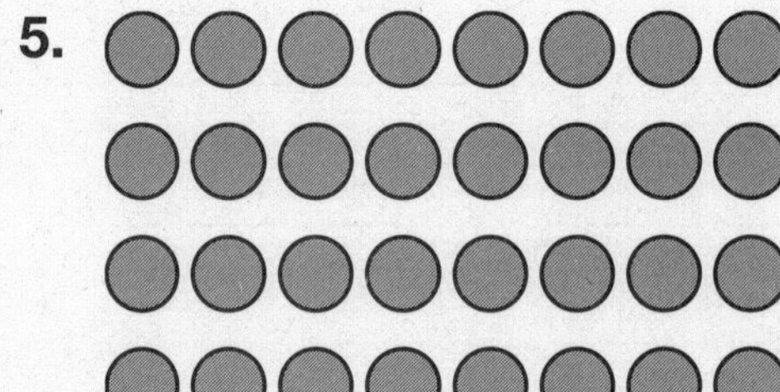

6. Algebra Hot dog buns come in packages of 8. Mrs. Wilson has a total of 40 hot dog buns. Draw a picture to find how many packages of hot dog buns Mrs. Wilson has.

7. There are 9 players on a baseball team. At the park, 4 teams are playing. How many baseball players are playing at the park?

A 27 **B** 32 **C** 36 **D** 40

Name ______________________

Problem Solving: Writing to Explain

David is making 3 pancakes for each person in his family. Today, there are 6 family members at breakfast. How many pancakes does he need to make? Explain how you can solve this problem.

You can make a table to solve this problem.

As the number of people increases by 1, the number of pancakes David needs to make increases by 3.

People	1	2	3	4	5	6
Pancakes	3	6	9	12	15	18
		3 + 3 = 6	6 + 3 = 9	9 + 3 = 12	12 + 3 = 15	15 + 3 = 18

David needs to make 18 pancakes.

1. Marcia got on an elevator on the fourth floor. She went down 2 floors. Then she went up 6 floors. Then she went down 3 floors. What floor is Marcia on now?

____

2. **Explain It** How did you find your answer to Exercise 1?

____

____

____

3. Look at the numbers below.
75, 74, 72, 69, 65, …

a. Describe the pattern.

____

____

____

b. What are the next two numbers in the pattern?

____

4. Ms. Skidmore is setting up basketball teams. There are 5 players on each team.

a. Complete the table below.

Teams	1	2	3	4	5
Players	5	10	15		

b. Describe the pattern in terms of teams and players.

____

____

Name ______________________

Practice

5-5

Problem Solving: Writing to Explain

1. Look at the numbers below.
13, 15, 19, 25, …

a. Describe the pattern.

____

____

____

b. Explain how you can find the next two numbers. What are the next two numbers?

____

____

2. Mr. Wilson is setting up volleyball teams. There are 6 players on a team.

a. Complete the table below.

Teams	1	2	3	4	5
Players	6	12	18		

b. Explain how the number of players changes as the number of teams changes.

____

____

____

3. **Algebra** The table below shows the amount of money that Louise earns in allowance each week.

a. Complete the table.

Louise's Allowance

Number of Weeks	Allowance
1	$8
2	$16
3	$24
4	______
5	______

b. How did the table help you to find the pattern?

____

____

4. Diana is training to run a marathon.

a. Complete the table for Diana's first week of training.

Diana's Training Schedule

Day	Minutes
Monday	15
Tuesday	20
Wednesday	25
Thursday	
Friday	

b. If she continues the pattern, for how many minutes will Diana run on Saturday?

____

Practice 5-5

Name ______________________________

2 and 5 as Factors

When you multiply by 2, you can use a doubles fact.
For example, 2 × 3 is the same as adding 3 + 3.

You can use a pattern to multiply by 5.

2s Facts		5s Facts	
2 × 0 = 0	2 × 5 = 10	5 × 0 = 0	5 × 5 = 25
2 × 1 = 2	2 × 6 = 12	5 × 1 = 5	5 × 6 = 30
2 × 2 = 4	2 × 7 = 14	5 × 2 = 10	5 × 7 = 35
2 × 3 = 6	2 × 8 = 16	5 × 3 = 15	5 × 8 = 40
2 × 4 = 8	2 × 9 = 18	5 × 4 = 20	5 × 9 = 45

Each multiple of 2 ends in 0, 2, 4, 6, or 8. All multiples of 2 are even.

Each multiple of 5 ends in 0 or 5.

Find each product.

1. 3 × 2 = ______ **2.** 4 × 2 = ______ **3.** 6 × 2 = ______

4. 4 × 5 = ______ **5.** 3 × 5 = ______ **6.** 7 × 5 = ______

7. 5 × 2 = ______ **8.** 6 × 5 = ______ **9.** 8 × 2 = ______

10. 9 × 5 = ______

11. 2 × 7 = ______

12. 2 × 2 = ______

13. 5 × 5 = ______

14. 0 × 2 = ______

15. What is 9 times 2? ______

16. What is 5 times 8? ______

17. Explain It Is 25 a multiple of 2 or 5? How do you know?

____

____

Name ____________________

Practice
5-6

2 and 5 as Factors

Find each product.

1. 2×5 ______ **2.** 4×5 ______ **3.** 3×2 ______ **4.** 8×5 ______ **5.** 7×2 ______

6. $\begin{array}{r} 9 \\ \times 2 \\ \hline \end{array}$ **7.** $\begin{array}{r} 6 \\ \times 5 \\ \hline \end{array}$ **8.** $\begin{array}{r} 5 \\ \times 9 \\ \hline \end{array}$ **9.** $\begin{array}{r} 2 \\ \times 6 \\ \hline \end{array}$ **10.** $\begin{array}{r} 5 \\ \times 5 \\ \hline \end{array}$

11. Multiply 7 and 5. ______

12. Find 8 times 2. ______

Algebra Compare. Use $<$, $>$, or $=$.

13. $3 \times 5 \bigcirc 4 \times 5$ **14.** $6 \times 3 \bigcirc 6 \times 2$ **15.** $8 \times 2 \bigcirc 2 \times 8$

16. $6 \times 5 \bigcirc 5 \times 6$ **17.** $4 \times 2 \bigcirc 5 \times 2$ **18.** $7 \times 5 \bigcirc 5 \times 6$

19. Tara walks 2 miles each day. How many miles does she walk in a week?

______

20. There are 5 days in each school week. How many school days are there in 9 weeks?

______

21. Explain It How can adding doubles help you to multiply by 2? Give an example in your explanation.

______

______

______

______

22. If the ones digit of a number greater than 1 is 0, what factor or factors must that number have?

A 2 only **B** 5 only **C** 2 and 5 **D** Neither 2 or 5

Practice 5-6

Name ____________________

10 as a Factor

The table shows the multiplication facts for 10.

10s Facts	
10 × 0 = 0	10 × 5 = 50
10 × 1 = 10	10 × 6 = 60
10 × 2 = 20	10 × 7 = 70
10 × 3 = 30	10 × 8 = 80
10 × 4 = 40	10 × 9 = 90

All multiples of 10 end with zero, such as 110; 2,350; and 467,000.

Find 10 × 5.

To find the answer, you can skip count or you can write a zero after the 5.

1 2 3 4 5

0 10 20 30 40 50

or

Tens	Ones
	5

× 10 =

Tens	Ones
5	0

5 × 10 = 50

1. 10 × 2 = ______ **2.** 5 × 10 = ______ **3.** 10 × 8 = ______

4. 2 × 8 = ______ **5.** $10 × 6 = ______ **6.** 7 × 5 = ______

7. $10 × 4 = ______ **8.** 9 × 2 = ______ **9.** 8 × 9 = ______

10. 10 × 3

11. $4 × 5

12. 2 × 2

13. $10 × 5

14. $8 × 5

15. 10 × 4

16. Critical Thinking When you multiply a whole number by 10, what is always true about the ones place in the product?

____

Name ___________________________

Practice
5-7

10 as a Factor

Find each product.

1. 3 × 10 ______ **2.** 7 × 10 ______ **3.** 10 × 5 ______ **4.** 7 × 5 ______ **5.** 10 × 8 ______

6. 9 × 10 ______ **7.** 6 × 1 ______ **8.** 10 × 2 ______ **9.** 9 × 7 ______ **10.** 4 × 10 ______

11. 1 × 10 ______ **12.** 6 × 10 ______ **13.** 5 × 4 ______ **14.** 10 × 10 ______ **15.** 10 × 3 ______

16. $\begin{array}{r} 8 \\ \times\ 5 \\ \hline \end{array}$ **17.** $\begin{array}{r} 10 \\ \times\ 9 \\ \hline \end{array}$ **18.** $\begin{array}{r} 10 \\ \times\ 8 \\ \hline \end{array}$ **19.** $\begin{array}{r} 10 \\ \times\ 4 \\ \hline \end{array}$ **20.** $\begin{array}{r} 10 \\ \times\ 7 \\ \hline \end{array}$

21. $\begin{array}{r} 10 \\ \times\ 6 \\ \hline \end{array}$ **22.** $\begin{array}{r} 5 \\ \times\ 2 \\ \hline \end{array}$ **23.** $\begin{array}{r} 10 \\ \times\ 1 \\ \hline \end{array}$ **24.** $\begin{array}{r} 10 \\ \times\ 5 \\ \hline \end{array}$ **25.** $\begin{array}{r} 9 \\ \times\ 0 \\ \hline \end{array}$

26. Mary Ann earns $10 each day walking the neighborhood dogs. How much will she earn in 7 days?

______

27. A game of basketball requires 10 players. At the park, there are 5 games being played. How many total players are at the park?

______

28. **Strategy Practice** Mr. Keyes made four rows of 10 cookies. Seven of the cookies in the first row were eaten. How many cookies remain?

______

29. Which is **NOT** a multiple of 10?

A 30
B 55
C 70
D 90

Practice 5-7

Name ______________________

9 as a Factor

You can use two patterns to help you remember 9s facts.

9s Facts
$9 \times 0 = 0$
$9 \times 1 = 9$
$9 \times 2 = 18$
$9 \times 3 = 27$
$9 \times 4 = 36$
$9 \times 5 = 45$
$9 \times 6 = 54$
$9 \times 7 = 63$
$9 \times 8 = 72$
$9 \times 9 = 81$

1. The tens digit will be 1 less than the factor being multiplied by 9.

2. The sum of the digits of the product will always be 9, unless the other factor is 0.

Find 9×7.

The tens digit must be 1 less than 7.
The tens digit is 6.

The sum of the digits must be 9.
$9 - 6 = 3$, so the ones digit is 3.

The product is 63.

Find each product.

1. $9 \times 3 =$ ______ **2.** $2 \times 9 =$ ______ **3.** $1 \times 9 =$ ______

4. $5 \times 9 =$ ______ **5.** $5 \times 8 =$ ______ **6.** $6 \times 9 =$ ______

7. $2 \times 7 =$ ______ **8.** $0 \times 9 =$ ______ **9.** $4 \times 9 =$ ______

10. $\begin{array}{r} 9 \\ \times 9 \\ \hline \end{array}$ **11.** $\begin{array}{r} 9 \\ \times 5 \\ \hline \end{array}$ **12.** $\begin{array}{r} 8 \\ \times 9 \\ \hline \end{array}$ **13.** $\begin{array}{r} 7 \\ \times 9 \\ \hline \end{array}$ **14.** $\begin{array}{r} 9 \\ \times 2 \\ \hline \end{array}$

15. Multiply 6 and 9. ______ **16.** Multiply 0 and 9. ______

17. Explain It Look at the table of 9s facts. Do you see another number pattern in the multiples of 9? Explain.

____

____

Name ______________________

Practice
5-8

9 as a Factor

Find each product.

1. 9×4 ______ **2.** 7×9 ______ **3.** 9×9 ______ **4.** 9×8 ______ **5.** 5×3 ______

6. 9×5 **7.** 2×9 **8.** 6×9 **9.** 2×7 **10.** 8×9

11. Multiply 4 and 9. ______ **12.** Find 3 times 9. ______

Algebra Complete. Use +, −, or ×.

13. $2 \times 9 = 10 \square 8$ **14.** $20 + 16 = 9 \square 4$ **15.** $9 \times 5 = 50 \square 5$

16. $9 \times 8 = 70 \square 2$ **17.** $10 \square 1 = 1 \times 9$ **18.** $9 \square 3 = 20 + 7$

19. Paula's hair was put into 9 braids. Each braid used 3 beads. How many beads were used in all?

____

20. A baseball game has 9 innings. A doubleheader is 2 games in the same day. How many innings are there in a doubleheader?

____

21. Write a Problem Write a multiplication story for 9×8. Include the product in your story.

____

____

22. Which number below is a multiple of 9?

A 35 **B** 46 **C** 54 **D** 65

Name ______________________

Reteaching
5-9

Multiplying with 0 and 1

Zero and one have special multiplication properties.

The Identity (One) Property of Multiplication		The Zero Property of Multiplication	
When you multiply a number and 1, the product is that number.		When you multiply a number and 0, the product is 0.	
Examples:		Examples:	
$4 \times 1 = 4$	$16 \times 1 = 16$	$5 \times 0 = 0$	$123 \times 0 = 0$
$1 \times 9 = 9$	$13 \times 1 = 13$	$17 \times 0 = 0$	$0 \times 58 = 0$
$251 \times 1 = 251$	$1 \times 48 = 48$	$0 \times 51 = 0$	$74 \times 0 = 0$

1. $1 \times 2 =$ ______ **2.** $0 \times 3 =$ ______ **3.** $4 \times 1 =$ ______

4. $8 \times 0 =$ ______ **5.** $6 \times 1 =$ ______ **6.** $1 \times 7 =$ ______

7. 1×7 **8.** 6×0 **9.** 8×1

10. 10×0 **11.** 1×2 **12.** 0×9

Complete each number sentence. Write <, >, or = for each ◯.

13. 8×2 ◯ 4×4 **14.** 19×1 ◯ 37×0 **15.** 7×2 ◯ $13 + 1$

Complete each number sentence. Write × or + for each ◯.

16. 5 ◯ 0 = 5 **17.** 5 ◯ 1 = 6 **18.** 1 ◯ 5 = 5

19. Write a Problem Write a multiplication sentence that shows the Zero Property of Multiplication. Explain why it shows this property.

____

Reteaching 5-9

Name ______________________

Practice 5-9

Multiplying with 0 and 1

Find each product.

1. 1×4 ______ 2. 0×5 ______ 3. 6×1 ______ 4. 0×3 ______ 5. 5×1 ______

6. $\begin{array}{r} 1 \\ \times 1 \\ \hline \end{array}$ 7. $\begin{array}{r} 0 \\ \times 9 \\ \hline \end{array}$ 8. $\begin{array}{r} 1 \\ \times 8 \\ \hline \end{array}$ 9. $\begin{array}{r} 6 \\ \times 1 \\ \hline \end{array}$ 10. $\begin{array}{r} 7 \\ \times 0 \\ \hline \end{array}$

11. Multiply 1 and 7. ______

12. Find 0 times 8. ______

Algebra Complete. Write $<$, $>$, or $=$ for each ◯.

13. 1×6 ◯ 3×0

14. 5×0 ◯ 1×7

15. 1×3 ◯ 3×1

Algebra Complete. Write $\times$, $+$, or $-$ for each ☐.

16. 1 ☐ 7 = 7

17. 8 ☐ 0 = 8

18. 6 ☐ 1 = 5

19. Sara keeps 4 boxes under her bed. Each box is for holding a different type of seashell. There are 0 shells in each box. Write a multiplication sentence to show how many shells Sara has in all.

____

20. **Explain It** Is the product of 0×0 the same as the sum of $0 + 0$? Explain.

____

____

21. **Geometry** A pentagon has 5 sides. Lonnie has a table shaped like a pentagon. How many chairs does Lonnie need if he wants 1 chair on each side?

______

22. Which multiplication problem below has the greatest product?

A 5×1 **B** 6×0 **C** 0×7 **D** 8×0

Name ____________________

Reteaching
5-10

Problem Solving: Two-Question Problems

Sometimes you need the answer to one question to help you answer another question.

Ms. Williams bought 3 pizzas for $8 each. She gave the cashier $30. How much change did she receive?

First, find the cost of the pizzas.

_____ in all

$8	$8	$8

$\$8 \times 3 = \$24$

The pizzas cost $24.

Next, find the change.

$30 in all

$24	___

$\$30 - \$24 = \$6$

Ms. Williams received $6 in change.

1a. Ray bought a pair of sunglasses for $22 and a hat for $19. How much money did the items cost?

_____ in all

$22	$19

1b. Ray gave the cashier a $50 bill. How much change should Ray receive?

$50 in all

$41	___

2. Explain It Cindy bought 4 lunch specials for $7 each. She gave the cashier $40. How much change should Cindy receive? Explain how you found your answer.

____

____

____

____

Reteaching 5-10

Name ______________________________

Problem Solving: Two-Question Problems

Use the answer from the first problem to solve the second problem.

1a. Lynette bought a book for $13 and a DVD for $22. How much money did the items cost?

______ in all

$22	$13

1b. Suppose Lynette paid the cashier with a $50 bill. How much change should Lynette get?

$50 in all

______	______

2a. Melissa bought 2 T-shirts for $9 each. How much money did Melissa spend on T-shirts?

____

b. Melissa had $32 in her purse. How much money does she have left?

____

3a. Curt bought 3 tickets to the movies for $8 each. How much money did Curt spend on movie tickets?

____

b. Curt also bought a large popcorn for $5. How much money did Curt spend altogether?

____

4. Lenny bought 4 packs of baseball cards for $3 each. He paid the cashier with a $20 bill. How much change will Lenny receive?

A $7

B $8

C $12

D $13

5. Write a Problem Write two problems that can be solved by using the answer from the first problem to solve the second problem.

____

____

____

____

____

Name ______________________

3 as a Factor

You can use an array to show 3s facts.

3s Facts

$3 \times 0 = 0$	$3 \times 5 = 15$
$3 \times 1 = 3$	$3 \times 6 = 18$
$3 \times 2 = 6$	$3 \times 7 = 21$
$3 \times 3 = 9$	$3 \times 8 = 24$
$3 \times 4 = 12$	$3 \times 9 = 27$

Multiply 2×3 using arrays.

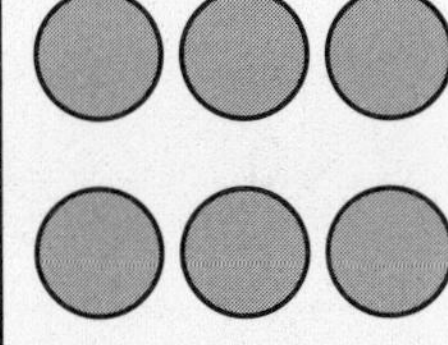

$2 \times 3 = 6$

You can also use a 2s and a 1s fact to find a 3s fact.

Find 7×3.

a. Find a 2s fact with 7: $2 \times 7 = 14$

b. Find a 1s fact with 7: $1 \times 7 = 7$

c. Add the facts: $14 + 7 = 21$

Find each product.

1. 3×2 ______ **2.** 3×4 ______ **3.** 3×5 ______ **4.** 3×1 ______ **5.** 3×9 ______

6. 6×9 ______ **7.** 7×3 ______ **8.** 0×3 ______ **9.** 8×5 ______ **10.** 3×3 ______

11. Number Sense How can you use a 2s fact and a 1s fact to find 3×8?

____

____

Name ______________________

Practice
6-1

3 as a Factor

Find the product.

1. 1×3 ______

2. 3×7 ______

3. 6×3 ______

4. 8×3 ______

5. 10×5 ______

6. 3×2 ______

7. 4×3 ______

8. 3×0 ______

9. 2×7 ______

10. 3×3 ______

11. 5×3

12. 10×3

13. 2×3

14. 3×9

15. 9×3

16. A bicycle store also sells tricycles. It has 6 tricycles in stock. How many wheels do the tricycles have in all? ______

17. There were 5 people who bought tickets to a football game. They bought 3 tickets each. How many tickets were bought all together? ______

18. Number Sense What addition sentence is equal to 4×3? ______

19. Geometry How many small squares are in the figure below? ______

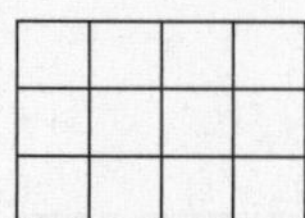

20. Reasonableness Maria said $7 \times 3 = 21$. Connie said $3 \times 7 = 21$. Who is correct? Explain.

______

______

______

21. Which number is a multiple of 3?

A 16 **B** 20 **C** 24 **D** 28

Practice 6-1

Name ______________________________

4 as a Factor

If you know a 2s multiplication fact, you can find a 4s multiplication fact.

4s Facts

$4 \times 0 = 0$	$4 \times 5 = 20$
$4 \times 1 = 4$	$4 \times 6 = 24$
$4 \times 2 = 8$	$4 \times 7 = 28$
$4 \times 3 = 12$	$4 \times 8 = 32$
$4 \times 4 = 16$	$4 \times 9 = 36$

You can double a 2s fact or add a 2s fact by itself to find a 4s fact.

When you double an array of 2×1, you get an array of 4×1.

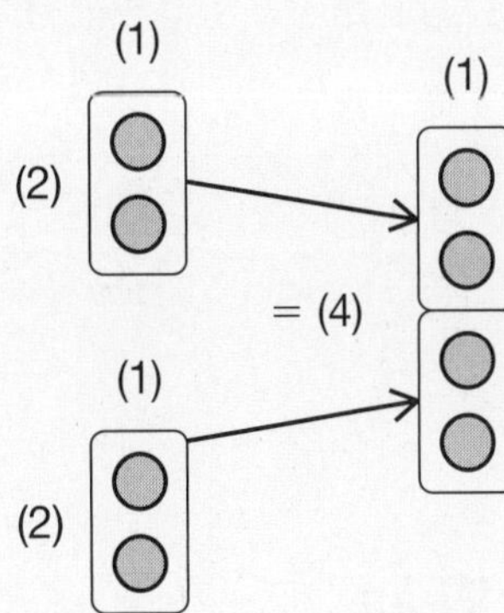

Find 4×3 by doubling a 2s fact.

a. Find a 2s fact with 3 as a factor.

$2 \times 3 = 6$

b. Double it.

$2 \times 6 = 12$

Find 4×3 by adding a 2s fact by itself.

a. Find a 2s fact with 3 as a factor.

$2 \times 3 = 6$

b. Add the fact to itself.

$6 + 6 = 12$

Find each product.

1. 4×6 ________ **2.** 8×4 ________ **3.** 6×5 ________ **4.** 9×4 ________ **5.** 4×1 ________

6. 4×3 ________ **7.** 4×7 ________ **8.** 12×2 ________ **9.** 0×4 ________ **10.** 4×4 ________

11. Number Sense How can you use 2×8 to find 4×8?

____

____

Name ______________________

Practice **6-2**

4 as a Factor

Find the product.

1. 2×4 ______ **2.** 4×5 ______ **3.** 3×4 ______ **4.** 4×4 ______ **5.** 5×8 ______

6. 4×6 ______ **7.** 1×4 ______ **8.** 3×9 ______ **9.** 0×4 ______ **10.** 4×7 ______

11. 10×4 **12.** 1×4 **13.** 2×4 **14.** 4×9 **15.** 8×4

Practice **6-2**

16. **Number Sense** What multiplication fact can you double to find 4×7?

______

17. Each square table can seat 4 people. How many people can be seated at 8 square tables?

______

18. Jillian sold 4 books of raffle tickets. Each book had 9 tickets. How many tickets did Jillian sell all together?

______

19. The soccer team has practice 4 times each week during the season. If the season is 10 weeks long, how many practices does the team have?

______

20. **Writing to Explain** If you know that $4 \times 5 = 20$, how can you use the Commutative (Order) Property to find 5×4?

____

____

____

21. Aaron changed the tires on 5 cars. Each car had 4 tires. How many tires did Aaron change?

A 12 **B** 16 **C** 20 **D** 24

Name ______________________________

6 and 7 as Factors

You can use multiplication facts that you already know to find other multiplication facts.

6s Facts

$6 \times 0 = 0$	$6 \times 5 = 30$
$6 \times 1 = 6$	$6 \times 6 = 36$
$6 \times 2 = 12$	$6 \times 7 = 42$
$6 \times 3 = 18$	$6 \times 8 = 48$
$6 \times 4 = 24$	$6 \times 9 = 54$

You can use a 3s fact to find a 6s fact. Find the 3s fact and then add the product to itself.

Find 6×9.

a. Find the 3s fact with 9: $3 \times 9 = 27$.

b. Add the product to itself: $27 + 27 = 54$.

7s Facts

$7 \times 0 = 0$	$7 \times 5 = 35$
$7 \times 1 = 7$	$7 \times 6 = 42$
$7 \times 2 = 14$	$7 \times 7 = 49$
$7 \times 3 = 21$	$7 \times 8 = 56$
$7 \times 4 = 28$	$7 \times 9 = 63$

You can use a 2s and a 5s fact to find a 7s fact.

Find 7×5.

a. Find the 2s fact with 5: $2 \times 5 = 10$.

b. Find the 5s fact with 5: $5 \times 5 = 25$.

c. Add the products: $10 + 25 = 35$.

Find each product.

1. 2×7 ______ **2.** 6×7 ______ **3.** 7×9 ______ **4.** 6×4 ______ **5.** 6×8 ______

6. 7×7 ______ **7.** 6×2 ______ **8.** 8×7 ______ **9.** 3×7 ______ **10.** 6×6 ______

11. $\begin{array}{r} 5 \\ \times\ 6 \\ \hline \end{array}$ **12.** $\begin{array}{r} 7 \\ \times\ 4 \\ \hline \end{array}$ **13.** $\begin{array}{r} 6 \\ \times\ 9 \\ \hline \end{array}$ **14.** $\begin{array}{r} 7 \\ \times\ 3 \\ \hline \end{array}$

15. Number Sense Harold says, "To find 6×8, I can use the facts for 5×4 and 1×4." Do you agree? Explain.

____

____

Name ______________________________

Practice
6-3

6 and 7 as Factors

Find the product.

1. 5 × 6 ______ **2.** 6 × 3 ______ **3.** 6 × 8 ______ **4.** 3 × 7 ______ **5.** 7 × 10 ______

6. 7 × 4 ______ **7.** 6 × 4 ______ **8.** 5 × 7 ______ **9.** 7 × 8 ______ **10.** 6 × 6 ______

11. 7 × 6 **12.** 10 × 6 **13.** 10 × 7 **14.** 7 × 7 **15.** 2 × 6

Practice **6-3**

16. Number Sense What multiplication fact can be found by using the arrays for 2 × 9 and 5 × 9?

______

17. The chicken eggs Raul's science class is watching take 3 weeks to hatch. How many days will it be until the eggs hatch?

______

18. Emily cut 7 apples into slices. There are 6 slices from each apple. How many apple slices does she have in all?

______

19. At a barbeque there are 6 tables set up. Each table can seat 8 people. How many people can be seated at the tables all together?

______

20. Writing to Explain How could you use 5 × 6 = 30 to find the product of 6 × 6?

____

____

____

21. Barry takes 7 minutes to ride his bicycle one mile. At this rate, how long would Barry take to ride his bicycle 4 miles?

A 21 minutes **B** 24 minutes **C** 27 minutes **D** 28 minutes

Name ______________________________

Reteaching
6-4

8 as a Factor

You can double a 4s fact to multiply with 8.

8s Facts

$8 \times 0 = 0$	$8 \times 5 = 40$
$8 \times 1 = 8$	$8 \times 6 = 48$
$8 \times 2 = 16$	$8 \times 7 = 56$
$8 \times 3 = 24$	$8 \times 8 = 64$
$8 \times 4 = 32$	$8 \times 9 = 72$

Find 8×6.

a. Find $4 \times 6 = 24$.

b. Add the product to itself: $24 + 24 = 48$

o o o o o o
o o o o o o
o o o o o o
o o o o o o } $4 \times 6 = 24$

$24 + 24 = 48$

o o o o o o
o o o o o o
o o o o o o
o o o o o o } $4 \times 6 = 24$

So, $8 \times 6 = 48$.

Find each product.

1. 2×8 ______ **2.** 4×8 ______ **3.** 8×5 ______ **4.** 9×7 ______ **5.** 8×8 ______

6. 0×8 ______ **7.** 6×7 ______ **8.** 9×8 ______ **9.** 1×8 ______ **10.** 6×8 ______

11. A gallon is equal to 8 pints. How many pints are in 5 gallons?

______

12. **Writing to Explain** How can you use 4s facts to find 7×8? Give the product in your explanation.

____

____

Reteaching **6-4**

Name ____________________

Practice
6-4

8 as a Factor

Find the product.

1. 1×8 ______ **2.** 8×0 ______ **3.** 4×6 ______ **4.** 2×8 ______ **5.** 8×7 ______

6. 8×3 ______ **7.** 4×8 ______ **8.** 8×9 ______ **9.** 8×5 ______ **10.** 8×8 ______

11. 10×8 **12.** 7×8 **13.** 7×6 **14.** 8×3 **15.** 9×8

Practice 6-4

16. An octopus has 8 arms. At the zoo, there are 3 octopuses in one tank. How many arms do the octopuses have all together? ______

17. Number Sense How can you use 4×7 to find 8×7? Find the product.

______

______

18. Writing to Explain Jose said all of the multiples of 8 are also multiples of 2. Jamila said that all of the multiples of 8 are also multiples of 4. Who is correct? Explain.

______

______

19. A package of fruit juice contains 8 boxes. How many boxes are there in 5 packages? ______

20. What is the next number in the pattern below?
16, 24, 32, 40, 48 ______

21. Each package of rolls contains 8 rolls. Ted bought 6 packages. How many rolls did he buy in all?

A 42 **B** 48 **C** 49 **D** 54

Name ______________________________

11 and 12 as Factors

You can break apart numbers to multiply by 2-digit numbers.

To multiply by 11:

Think of 11 as 10 + 1.

$2 \times 11 = (2 \times 10) + (2 \times 1) = 22$

$3 \times 11 = (3 \times 10) + (3 \times 1) = 33$

$4 \times 11 = (4 \times 10) + (4 \times 1) = 44$

$5 \times 11 = (5 \times 10) + (5 \times 1) = 55$

$6 \times 11 = (6 \times 10) + (6 \times 1) = 66$

$7 \times 11 = (7 \times 10) + (7 \times 1) = 77$

$8 \times 11 = (8 \times 10) + (8 \times 1) = 88$

$9 \times 11 = (9 \times 10) + (9 \times 1) = 99$

$10 \times 11 = (10 \times 10) + (10 \times 1) = 110$

$11 \times 11 = (11 \times 10) + (11 \times 1) = 121$

$12 \times 11 = (12 \times 10) + (12 \times 1) = 132$

To multiply by 12:

Think of 12 as 10 + 2.

$2 \times 12 = (2 \times 10) + (2 \times 2) = 24$

$3 \times 12 = (3 \times 10) + (3 \times 2) = 36$

$4 \times 12 = (4 \times 10) + (4 \times 2) = 48$

$5 \times 12 = (5 \times 10) + (5 \times 2) = 60$

$6 \times 12 = (6 \times 10) + (6 \times 2) = 72$

$7 \times 12 = (7 \times 10) + (7 \times 2) = 84$

$8 \times 12 = (8 \times 10) + (8 \times 2) = 96$

$9 \times 12 = (9 \times 10) + (9 \times 2) = 108$

$10 \times 12 = (10 \times 10) + (10 \times 2) = 120$

$11 \times 12 = (11 \times 10) + (11 \times 2) = 132$

$12 \times 12 = (12 \times 10) + (12 \times 2) = 144$

Use patterns to find each product.

1. $2 \times 11 =$ ______
$2 \times 12 =$ ______

2. $8 \times 11 =$ ______
$8 \times 12 =$ ______

3. $4 \times 11 =$ ______
$4 \times 12 =$ ______

4. $9 \times 11 =$ ______
$9 \times 12 =$ ______

5. 11×6

6. 11×10

7. 12×10

8. 11×11

9. 12×12

10. **Explain It** How can you use a pattern to find 12×11? Give the product.

____

____

____

Name ______________________________

Practice
6-5

11 and 12 as Factors

Use patterns to find each product.

1. $4 \times 11 =$ ______ **2.** $6 \times 11 =$ ______ **3.** $9 \times 11 =$ ______ **4.** $5 \times 11 =$ ______

$4 \times 12 =$ ______ $6 \times 12 =$ ______ $9 \times 12 =$ ______ $5 \times 12 =$ ______

5. 11×8 **6.** 12×10 **7.** 11×11 **8.** 12×11 **9.** 12×12

10. A dozen is another way of saying 12. How many eggs are there in a package of two dozen?

______

11. A soccer team has 11 players. There are 8 teams playing. How many people are playing soccer?

______

12. There are 6 volleyball games being played in the gym. Each game has a total of 12 players. How many people are playing volleyball in all?

______

13. Strategy Practice Maureen runs 6 miles each day. Eileen runs 9 miles each day. How many more miles does Eileen run than Maureen in 11 days?

______

14. Explain It How can you use a pattern to find the product of 5×12?

____

____

____

____

15. A jury has 12 people on it. There are enough citizens for 7 juries. How many people are there all together?

A 70

B 77

C 84

D 91

Practice 6-5

Name ______________________

Reteaching 6-6

Multiplying with 3 Factors

You can use the Associative Property of Multiplication to multiply three factors. The Associative Property states that the way the factors are grouped does not change the product.

The Associative Property of Multiplication is applied like the Associative Property of Addition.

Addition	**Multiplication**
$4 + 3 + 3 = 4 + (3 + 3)$	$4 \times 3 \times 3 = 4 \times (3 \times 3)$
$4 + 6$	4×9
10	36

Find the product that is easy to find. Then multiply by the third number.

Find each product. You may draw a picture to help.

1. $3 \times 2 \times 1$ ______ **2.** $2 \times 3 \times 5$ ______ **3.** $3 \times 3 \times 2$ ______ **4.** $7 \times 3 \times 2$ ______

5. $4 \times 2 \times 7$ ______ **6.** $3 \times 4 \times 5$ ______ **7.** $2 \times 2 \times 6$ ______ **8.** $2 \times 5 \times 7$ ______

9. Each package of fruit juice has 2 rows. There are 6 boxes in each row. Mrs. Stokes bought 3 packages. How many boxes of fruit juice did Mrs. Stokes buy? Write a number sentence with your answer.

____

____

10. Explain It How do you know that $4 \times 2 \times 2$ is the same as 4×4? Explain.

____

Reteaching **6-6**

Name ______________________________

Multiplying with 3 Factors

Find the product. You may draw a picture to help.

1. $2 \times 3 \times 3$ ______

2. $2 \times 2 \times 4$ ______

3. $8 \times 2 \times 2$ ______

4. $6 \times 2 \times 3$ ______

5. $3 \times 3 \times 4$ ______

6. $5 \times 2 \times 5$ ______

7. $5 \times 4 \times 2$ ______

8. $4 \times 2 \times 3$ ______

Find the missing number.

9. $4 \times 4 \times 3 = 48$,
so $4 \times (4 \times 3) = \square$

10. $(5 \times 2) \times 8 = \square$

11. Sarah and Amanda each have 2 bags with 4 marbles in each. How many marbles do they have altogether?

______

12. Jesse bought 2 sheets of stamps. On each sheet there are 5 rows of stamps with 6 stamps in each row. How many stamps did Jesse buy?

______

13. Reasonableness Is the product of $6 \times 2 \times 4$ less than 50? Explain.

____

____

14. Which number makes this number sentence true?

$8 \times 2 \times 4 = 8 \times (\blacksquare \times 4)$

A 2 **B** 4 **C** 8 **D** 64

15. Write three ways to find $3 \times 2 \times 4$.

____

____

Name ______________________

Reteaching
6-7

Problem Solving: Multiple-Step Problems

Enzo's puts 3 meatballs in each of its meatball subs. Carlos's uses 2 times as many meatballs for its meatball subs. Mr. Kerwin orders 4 meatball subs from Carlos's. How many meatballs will be in his subs?

Find and solve the hidden question.

How many meatballs does Carlos's put in each meatball sub?

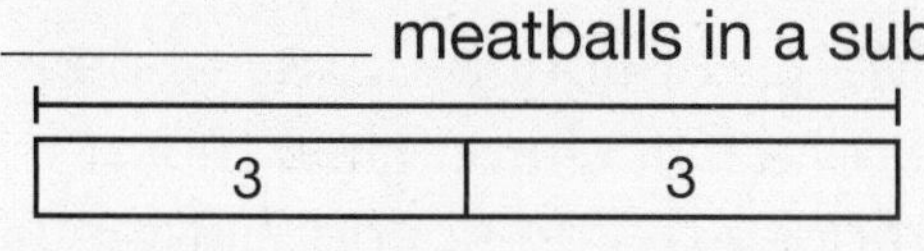

$3 \times 2 = 6$

Carlos's puts 6 meatballs in each of its meatball subs.

Use the answer to the hidden question to solve the problem.

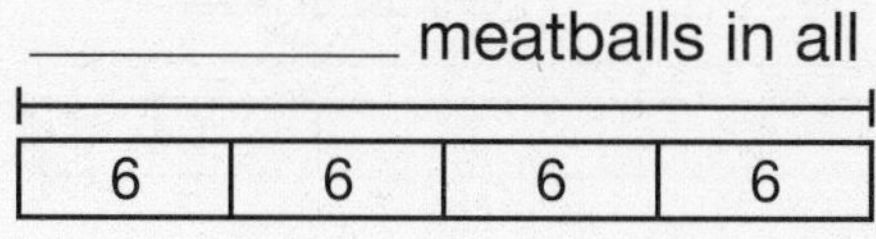

$6 \times 4 = 24$

Mr. Kerwin will have 24 meatballs altogether in his 4 meatball subs.

1. Meredith bought a book for \$8, a magazine for \$5, and bottled water for \$2. She paid with a \$20 bill. How much change should she get?

   Tip: Find the total cost of the three items.

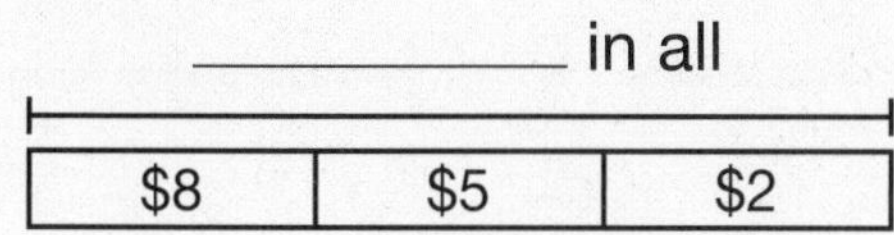

\$20 in all

\$15	?

____

2. Sue bought 3 T-shirts for \$8 each. She paid with a \$50 bill. How much change should she get?

____

3. **Writing to Explain** What steps did you take to answer Exercise 2?

____

____

____

____

____

Reteaching **6-7**

Name ____________________

Practice
6-7

Problem Solving: Multiple-Step Problems

Use the pictures for **1** through **4**.

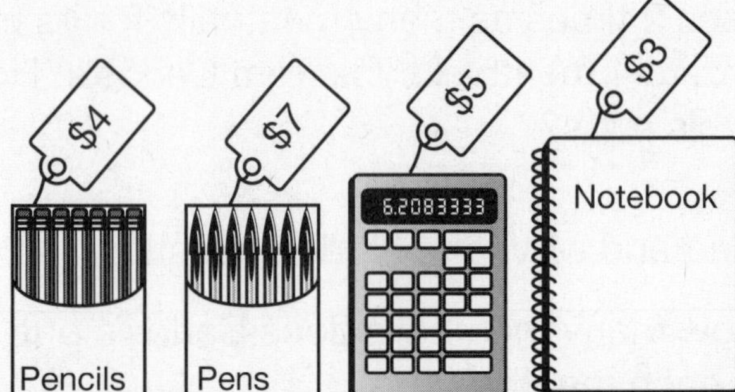

1. Teri bought 3 boxes of pencils. She paid with a $20 bill. How much change did she receive?

Tip First find the cost of the pencils.

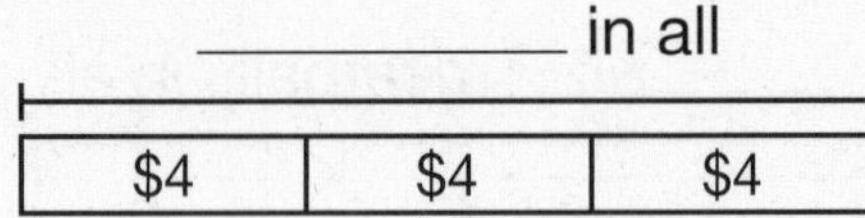

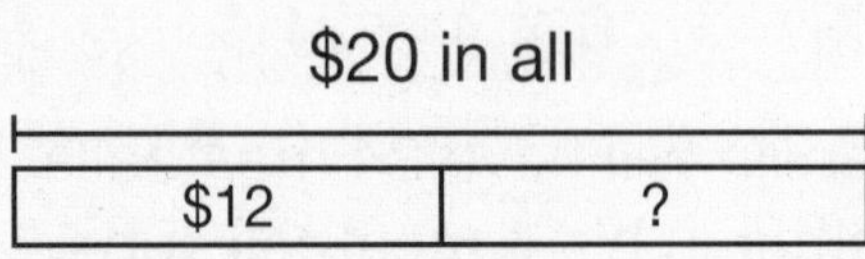

______

2. Martin bought 3 boxes of pens and a calculator. How much money did he spend all together?

Tip First find the cost of the pens.

______

3. Joey bought 2 notebooks and 2 boxes of pencils. How much money did he spend all together?

______

4. Allie bought 3 notebooks and 2 boxes of pens. She paid with $40. How much change did she receive?

______

5. **Write a Problem** Write a real-world problem involving multiple steps. Then solve your problem.

______

______

______

______

6. **Number Sense** Bert has $50 in his wallet. Then he buys 2 CDs for $13 each. How much money does he have left?

A $12 **B** $24 **C** $26 **D** $37

Practice 6-7

Name ______________________________

Division as Sharing

Division shows how many items are in each group or how many equal groups there are.

There are 15 counters that are going to be put into 5 groups. How many counters will be in each group?

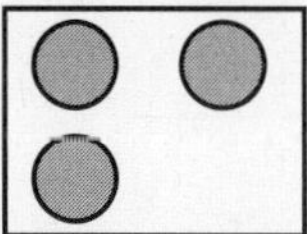 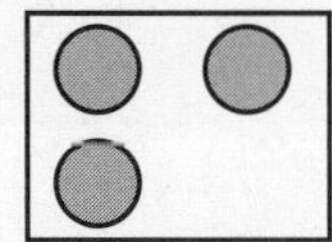 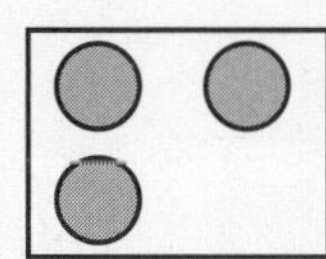 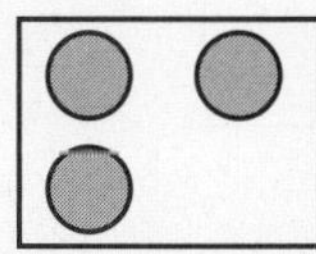 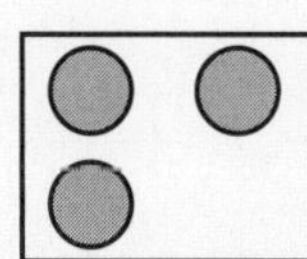

There are 15 counters. There are 5 groups.
There are 3 counters in each group.
So, $15 \div 5 = 3$.

Use counters or draw a picture to solve.

1. 12 tennis balls, 4 cans
   How many tennis balls in each can?
   ____

2. 20 cookies, 5 bags
   How many cookies in each bag?
   ____

3. 16 apples, 2 baskets
   How many apples in each basket?
   ____

4. 20 fingers, 4 hands
   How many fingers on each hand?
   ____

5. One box contains 12 granola bars. Two bars are in each package. How many packages are in each box of granola bars?
   ____

6. **Number Sense** Could you divide 14 shirts into two equal groups? Why or why not?

   ____

   ____

Name ____________________

Practice 7-1

Division as Sharing

Use counters or draw a picture to solve.

1. 24 people, 4 rows
   How many people in each row?

______

2. 18 marbles, 2 people
   How many marbles for each person?

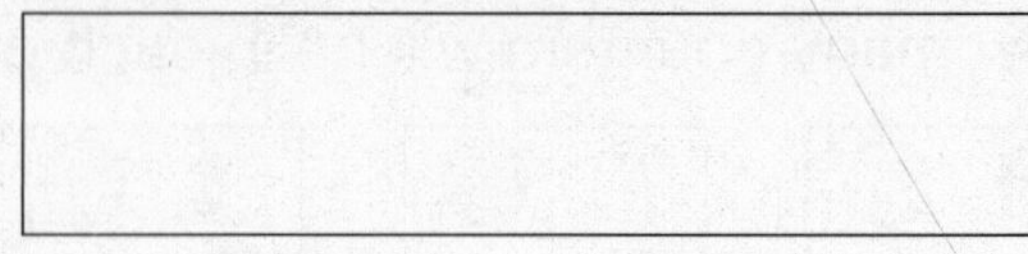

______

3. 25 apples, 5 trees
   How many apples on each tree?

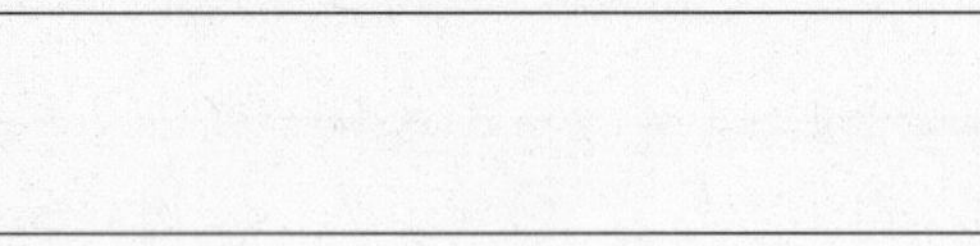

______

4. 21 books, 3 shelves
   How many books on each shelf?

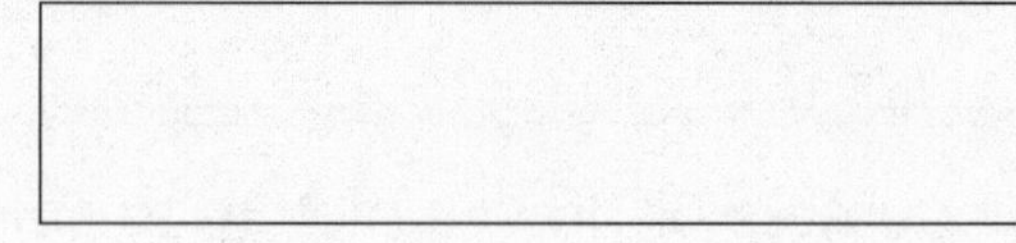

______

Practice 7-1

Complete each division sentence.

5.

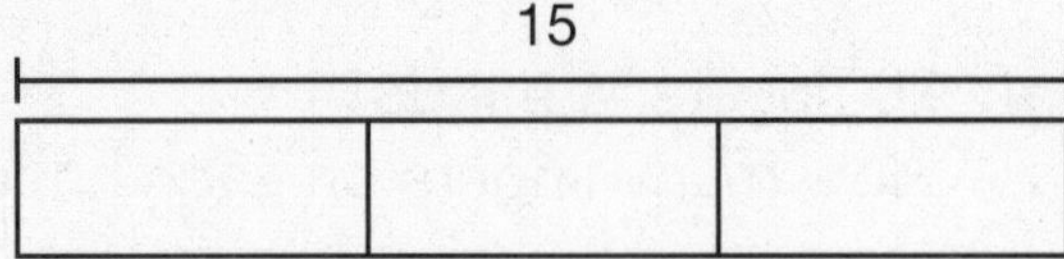

$15 \div 3 = \square$

6.

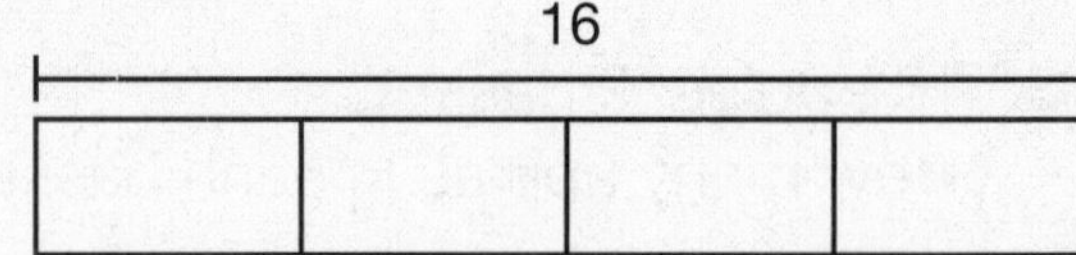

$16 \div 4 = \square$

7. **Explain It** Ron and Pam each have 20 pennies. Ron will put his pennies into 4 groups. Pam will put her pennies into 5 groups. Who will have more pennies in each group? Explain.

______

______

8. There are 28 days in February. There are 7 days in a week. How many weeks are there in February?

   A 3 **B** 4 **C** 5 **D** 6

Name ______________________________

Understanding Remainders

In a division problem, the remainder is the number left after division is completed. The remainder must always be less than the divisor.

Jamal has 22 marbles. He is going to put 6 marbles in each bag. How many bags can he fill? How many marbles will be left over?

Jamal can fill 3 bags. There will be 4 marbles left over.

There are 3 ways to interpret a remainder.

The remainder can be ignored.	The remainder is the answer.	Add 1 to the quotient.
How many bags did Jamal fill? 3	*How many marbles are not in bags?* 4	*How many bags does Jamal need for all the marbles?* 4

Use counters or draw a picture to find each number of groups and the number left over.

1. 17 apples
3 apples in each bag

17 ÷ 3 = ☐ with ☐ left over

2. 21 cards
5 cards in each sleeve

21 ÷ 5 = ☐ with ☐ left over

3. 19 CDs
4 CDs on each shelf

19 ÷ 4 = ☐ with ☐ left over

4. 16 ÷ 5 = ☐ with ☐ left over

5. 34 ÷ 6 = ☐ with ☐ left over

6. 31 ÷ 8 = ☐ with ☐ left over

7. Explain It Why must the remainder be less than the divisor?

____

Name ______________________

Practice 7-2

Understanding Remainders

Use counters or draw a picture to find each number of groups and the number left over.

1. 15 cards
4 cards in each envelope
$15 \div 4 =$ ☐ with ☐ left over

2. 17 books
5 books in each box
$17 \div 5 =$ ☐ with ☐ left over

3. 25 marbles
6 marbles in each bag
$25 \div 6 =$ ☐ with ☐ left over

4. 22 photos
3 photos on each page
How many pages can be filled?
______

5. 14 DVDs
5 DVDs on each shelf
How many DVDs will be put on the third shelf?
______

6. 27 postcards
5 postcards in each pile
How many postcards are in the sixth pile?
______

7. $17 \div 2 =$ ☐ with ☐ left over

8. $26 \div 8 =$ ☐ with ☐ left over

9. $34 \div 7 =$ ☐ with ☐ left over

10. **Explain It** There are 25 students in Ms. Morris's class. She wants to divide the class into 3, 4, or 5 equal teams. Which number of teams can she have? Explain.
______
______

11. How many complete teams can be made with 18 people and 4 people on each team?
A 4
B 5
C 6
D 14

12. There are 14 girls trying out for cheerleading. Each team will have 6 cheerleaders. How many girls will not make a team?
______

13. **Reasoning** The Wolfpack team has 26 players. Team members will travel to their next game in cars. Each car can hold 4 players. How many cars are needed?
______

Practice 7-2

Name ______________________________

Division as Repeated Subtraction

You can think of division as repeated subtraction.

Emily has 20 raffle tickets. There are 5 tickets in each book.
How many books of raffle tickets does Emily have?

Start with 20 tickets. Subtract 5.	$20 - 5 = 15$
Subtract 5 more tickets.	$15 - 5 = 10$
Subtract 5 more tickets.	$10 - 5 = 5$
Subtract 5 more tickets.	$5 - 5 = 0$
You have reached 0.	

You have subtracted 5 four times.
So, $20 \div 5 = 4$.

Emily has 4 books of raffle tickets.

Use counters or draw a picture to solve.

1. 10 markers
5 markers in each box
How many boxes?

____

2. 8 hamsters
2 hamsters in each cage
How many cages?

____

3. 16 books
4 books on each shelf
How many shelves?

____

4. 18 players
3 players on each team
How many teams?

____

5. Annie had 16 balloons. She shares them equally with Connie.
How many balloons does each girl have now?

____

6. **Explain It** Show how you can use repeated subtraction to find how many groups of 7 are in 28.
Then write the division sentence for the problem.

____

____

Name ____________________

Division as Repeated Subtraction

Use counters or draw a picture to solve.

1. 18 pens
3 pens in each box
How many boxes?

______

2. 24 students
3 students on each team
How many teams?

______

3. 35 stickers
5 stickers on each sheet
How many sheets?

______

4. 30 leaves
6 leaves painted on each vase
How many vases?

______

5. Number Sense What division sentence means the same as the following subtraction sentences?

$12 - 4 = 8$
$8 - 4 = 4$
$4 - 4 = 0$

______

6. Tandem bicycles are ridden by 2 people. If 14 people rented tandem bicycles, how many bicycles were rented?

______

7. Explain It Tamara says that $15 \div 3 = 5$. Is she correct? Explain.

______

______

______

8. Keisha has to carry 32 boxes to her room. She can carry 4 boxes on each trip. How many trips will she take?

A 6 **B** 7 **C** 8 **D** 9

Name ______________________

Writing Division Stories

Eddie was asked to write a division story using 12 ÷ 4.

Eddie wrote his story this way.

Cami has 12 crayons and some cans.
She puts 4 crayons into each can.

How many cans did Cami use?

Think of a situation where the larger number can be put into groups.

Write your question.

You can show Eddie's story this way.

Cami used 3 cans.

Write a division story for each number sentence.
Then use counters or draw a picture to solve.

1. 10 ÷ 2 = ☐

____

____

____

2. 21 ÷ 3 = ☐

____

____

____

3. 18 ÷ 3 = ☐

____

____

____

4. 16 ÷ 4 = ☐

____

____

____

5. Explain It Sheila wrote a division story. She asked how many equal groups 24 flowers could be put into. What information must she give about the groups?

____

____

Name ______________________

Practice
7-4

Writing Division Stories

Write a division story for each number sentence.
Then use counters or draw a picture to solve.

1. 54 ÷ 6 = ☐

2. 36 ÷ 9 = ☐

3. 42 ÷ 7 = ☐

4. 25 ÷ 5 = ☐

5. There are 40 relatives at a party. There are 5 tables that each seat the same number of people. How many people can sit at each table?

______

6. A softball pitcher needs to get 3 outs in an inning. If a pitcher gets 21 outs, how many innings did she pitch?

______

7. Explain It There are 16 people at a party. They want to set up relay teams with exactly 3 people each. Can they do it? Explain.

8. Which division sentence will give an answer that is not in equal groups?

A 26 ÷ 4 **B** 35 ÷ 7 **C** 42 ÷ 6 **D** 45 ÷ 5

Name ______________________

Problem Solving: Use Objects and Draw a Picture

Sometimes, drawing a picture will help you solve a problem. It will help you "see" the problem and perhaps the solution.

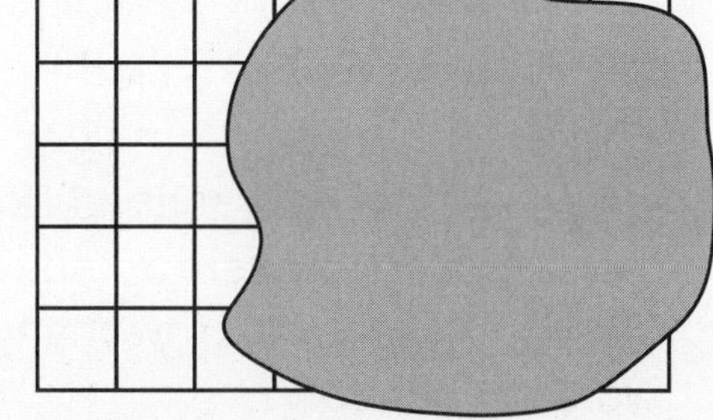

Some orange juice spilled on a tile floor and covered up part of the floor. The tile floor was in the shape of a rectangle. There were 40 square tiles in the whole floor. How many tiles were in each row?

Draw a picture to show what you know.

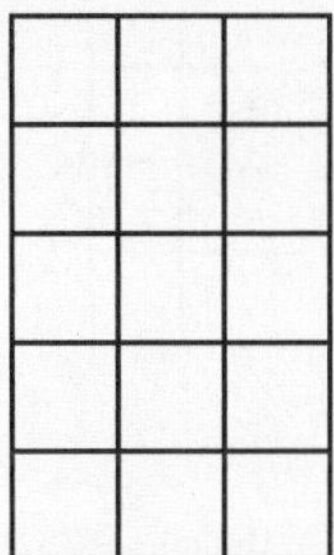

Finish the picture to solve the problem.

There should be 40 tiles in all.

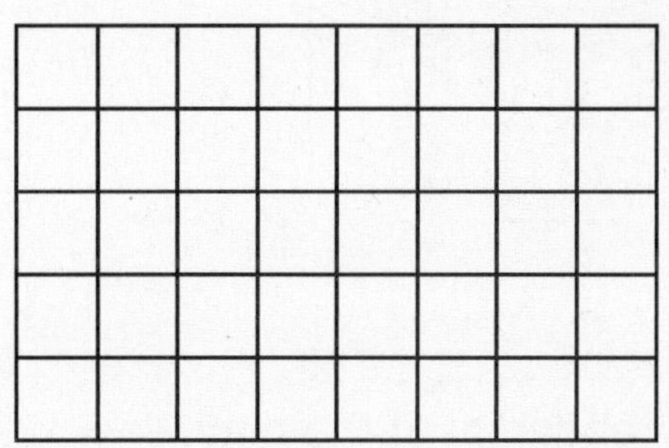

So there are 8 tiles in each row.

Solve. Use objects or draw a picture.

1. Mr. Robbins spilled stain on part of a tiled floor. The whole section of floor was shaped like a rectangle. There were 45 squares in the section. How many squares were in each row?

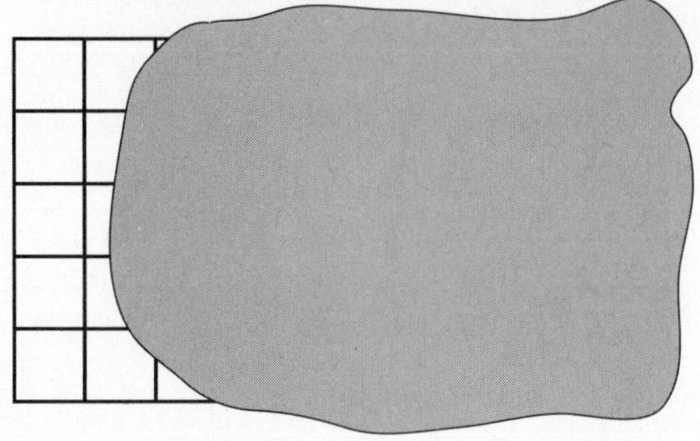

____

2. Kate is painting a wall. She painted over part of a section of 30 square tiles. The whole section of tiles was shaped like a rectangle. How many rows of tiles were in the whole section?

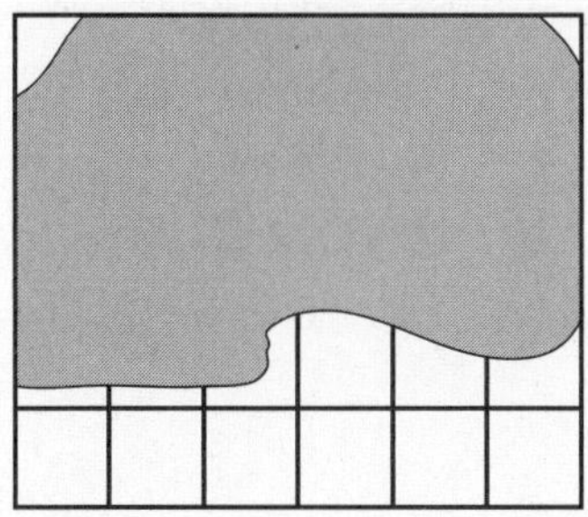

____

Name ______________________

Practice
7-5

Problem Solving: Use Objects and Draw a Picture

Solve. Use objects or draw a picture.

1. Ron painted part of a tiled section of his bathroom floor. The whole section was shaped like a rectangle. There were 35 square tiles in the section. How many tiles were in each row?

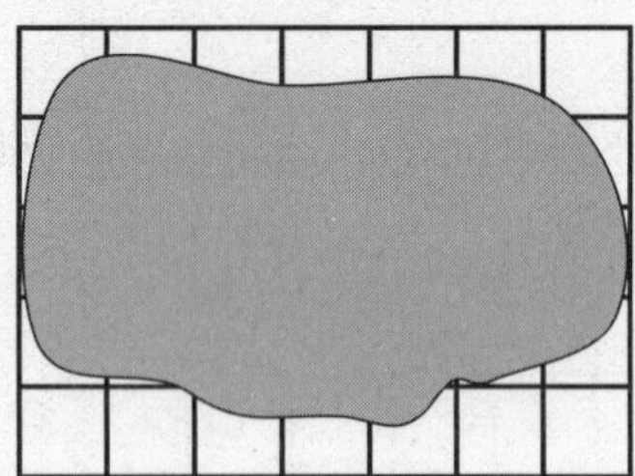

______

2. Some syrup spilled on a checkerboard-style table. The syrup covered some of the tiles. There were 36 squares on the table. How many of the squares had syrup on them?

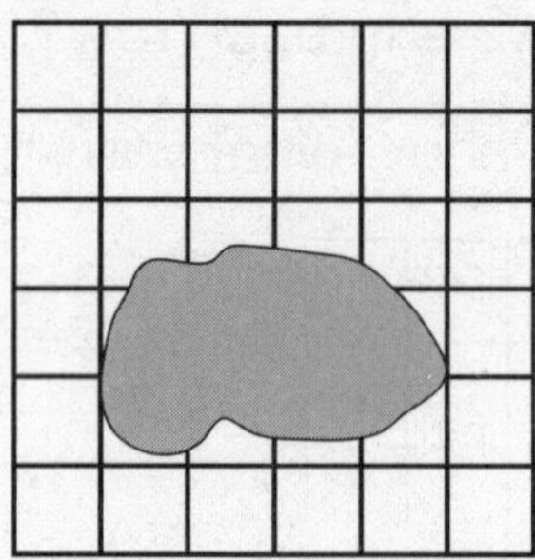

______

3. Dress rehearsal of the play was attended by 142 people. Opening night was attended by 238 people. How many people saw the two shows in all?

______ people in all

142	238

4. Carol and Deanna drove 320 miles altogether this weekend. They drove 196 miles Sunday. How many miles did they drive Saturday?

320 miles in all

	196

5. **Write a Problem** Write and solve a real-world problem that you can solve by using objects or drawing a picture.

____

____

Name ______________________

Reteaching
8-1

Relating Multiplication and Division

You can use multiplication facts to understand division.
Fact families show how multiplication and division are related.

Here is the fact family for 3, 8, and 24:

$3 \times 8 = 24$ $\quad$ $24 \div 3 = 8$

$8 \times 3 = 24$ $\quad$ $24 \div 8 = 3$

Complete. Use counters or draw a picture to solve.

1. $3 \times \square = 6$

$6 \div 3 = \square$

2. $7 \times \square = 14$

$14 \div 7 = \square$

3. $5 \times \square = 20$

$20 \div 5 = \square$

4. $4 \times \square = 24$

$24 \div 4 = \square$

5. **Number Sense** What other number is a part of this fact family? 3, 4, ______

6. There are 28 days in 4 weeks. What fact family would you use to find the number of days in 1 week?

____

7. There are 12 inches in 1 foot. What fact family would you use to find the number of inches in 2 feet?

____

Reteaching **8-1**

Name ______________________

Practice

8-1

Relating Multiplication and Division

Complete. Use counters or draw a picture to help.

1. $5 \times \square = 15$

$15 \div 5 = \square$

2. $6 \times \square = 24$

$24 \div 6 = \square$

3. $7 \times \square = 35$

$35 \div 7 = \square$

4. $5 \times \square = 25$

$25 \div 5 = \square$

5. $3 \times \square = 12$

$12 \div 3 = \square$

6. $3 \times \square = 27$

$27 \div 3 = \square$

7. **Number Sense** Write a fact family for 3, 6, and 18.

____

____

8. Patrick purchased 12 books. He needed 4 books for each of his projects at school. How many projects did he have?

______

9. **Draw a Picture** Draw an array. Then write a fact family to describe your array.

____

____

10. **Explain It** Evan told his class that the people in his family have 14 legs altogether. Quinton said that there must be 7 people in Evan's family. Is Quinton correct? Explain.

____

____

11. Which number makes this number sentence true? $\blacksquare \div 6 = 8$

A 2 **B** 14 **C** 24 **D** 48

Practice **8-1**

Name ______________________

Fact Families with 2, 3, 4, and 5

You can use multiplication facts to help you find division facts.

Darren and Molly have 16 sheets of paper. Each will get the same number of sheets of paper. How many will each get?

Peter has 24 pennies. He puts the pennies into 4 equal piles. How many pennies are in each pile?

What You Think	What You Write	What You Think	What You Write
2 times what number equals 16? $2 \times \mathbf{8} = 16$	$16 \div 2 = \mathbf{8}$ Darren and Molly will each get 8 sheets of paper.	4 times what number equals 24? $4 \times \mathbf{6} = 24$	$24 \div 4 = \mathbf{6}$ Peter has 6 pennies in each pile.

Find each quotient.

1. $14 \div 2$ ____ **2.** $35 \div 5$ ____ **3.** $15 \div 3$ ____ **4.** $32 \div 4$ ____ **5.** $24 \div 3$ ____

6. $2\overline{)12}$ **7.** $3\overline{)27}$ **8.** $5\overline{)25}$ **9.** $4\overline{)20}$ **10.** $4\overline{)40}$

11. Number Sense Write a fact family using the numbers 5, 6, and 30.

____

____

Name ______________________________

Practice
8-2

Fact Families with 2, 3, 4, and 5

Find each quotient.

1. 14 ÷ 2 ______ **2.** 12 ÷ 3 ______ **3.** 16 ÷ 4 ______ **4.** 30 ÷ 5 ______ **5.** 21 ÷ 3 ______

6. $2\overline{)20}$ **7.** $4\overline{)32}$ **8.** $5\overline{)40}$ **9.** $3\overline{)18}$ **10.** $4\overline{)32}$

11. Find 18 divided by 3. ______ **12.** Divide 60 by 6. ______ **13.** Find 35 divided by 5. ______

Algebra Find each missing number.

14. 45 ÷ ☐ = 5 **15.** 30 ÷ 3 = ☐ **16.** ☐ ÷ 2 = 7

Number Sense Write < or > to compare.

17. 5 × 2 ◯ 8 ÷ 2 **18.** 3 × 6 ◯ 6 ÷ 3 **19.** 4 + 8 ◯ 4 × 8

20. Gabriella and 4 friends shared a pack of 15 glue sticks equally. How many glue sticks did each person get?

______

21. Erica counted 45 fingers when the students were asked who wants to play kickball. How many hands went up?

______

22. **Explain It** Franklin says that if he divides 50 by 5, he will get 10. Jeff says he should get 9. Who is correct? Explain.

____

____

23. Which fact does not belong in the same fact family as 24 ÷ 4 = 6?

A 4 × 6 = 24 **B** 6 + 4 = 10 **C** 24 ÷ 6 = 4 **D** 6 × 4 = 24

Practice **8-2**

Name ______________________

Fact Families with 6 and 7

Multiplication facts can help you to find division facts when 6 or 7 is the divisor.

Find 35 ÷ 7.

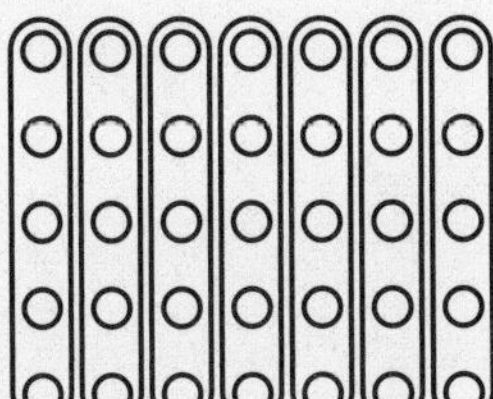

There are 48 marbles. They come in packages of 6. How many packages of marbles are there?

Find 48 ÷ 6.

What You Think	What You Write	What You Think	What You Write
What number times 7 equals 35? 7 × **5** = 35	35 ÷ 7 = **5**	What number times 6 equals 48? 6 × **8** = 48	48 ÷ 6 = **8** There are 8 packages of marbles.

Find each quotient.

1. 30 ÷ 6 ______ **2.** 28 ÷ 7 ______ **3.** 36 ÷ 6 ______ **4.** 21 ÷ 7 ______ **5.** 42 ÷ 6 ______

6. $7\overline{)49}$ **7.** $6\overline{)54}$ **8.** $7\overline{)70}$ **9.** $6\overline{)48}$ **10.** $7\overline{)56}$

11. Number Sense Name a number that can be evenly divided by 6 and by 7.

____

12. Reasoning Using 6 as one of the numbers, write a fact family with only two facts.

____

Name ______________________

Practice 8-3

Fact Families with 6 and 7

Find each quotient.

1. 24 ÷ 6 ______ **2.** 42 ÷ 7 ______ **3.** 36 ÷ 4 ______ **4.** 63 ÷ 7 ______ **5.** 40 ÷ 5 ______

6. $6\overline{)48}$ **7.** $7\overline{)49}$ **8.** $2\overline{)12}$ **9.** $6\overline{)36}$ **10.** $3\overline{)27}$

11. Find 70 divided by 7. ______ **12.** Divide 66 by 6. ______ **13.** Find 48 divided by 6. ______

Practice **8-3**

14. Explain It How can you use a multiplication fact to find a division fact?

____

____

15. Sierra's karate class lasts 56 days.
How many weeks does the class last? ______

16. Explain It Wendell has a box with 36 cherries. He divides the cherries equally among 5 friends and himself. Bonnie received 6 cherries. She thinks she should have received one more. Is she correct? Explain.

____

____

____

17. Mr. Kline brought 30 boxes of fruit juice to a soccer game. Fruit juice comes in packages of 6. How many packages did Mr. Kline bring? ______

18. Katie bought 42 baseball cards. The cards come in packs of 7. How many packs of cards did Katie buy?

A 5 **B** 6 **C** 7 **D** 8

Name ___________________________________

Reteaching
8-4

Fact Families with 8 and 9

Multiplication facts can help you to find division facts when 8 or 9 is the divisor.

There are 32 counters. There are 8 counters in each row. How many rows are there?

There are 45 counters. There are 9 rows. How many counters are in each row?

What You Think	What You Write	What You Think	What You Write
8 times what number equals 32? $8 \times \mathbf{4} = 32$	$32 \div 8 = \mathbf{4}$ There are 4 rows of counters.	9 times what number equals 45? $9 \times \mathbf{5} = 45$	$45 \div 9 = \mathbf{5}$ There are 5 counters in each row.

Find each quotient.

1. $54 \div 9$ ______ **2.** $24 \div 8$ ______ **3.** $56 \div 8$ ______ **4.** $36 \div 9$ ______ **5.** $63 \div 9$ ______

6. $9\overline{)72}$ **7.** $8\overline{)48}$ **8.** $8\overline{)40}$ **9.** $8\overline{)80}$ **10.** $9\overline{)81}$

11. Number Sense What multiplication fact could you use to find a number that can be divided evenly by 8 and by 9?

____

Reteaching **8-4**

Name ______________________

Practice **8-4**

Fact Families with 8 and 9

Find each quotient.

1. 48 ÷ 8 ______ **2.** 18 ÷ 9 ______ **3.** 49 ÷ 7 ______ **4.** 64 ÷ 8 ______ **5.** 45 ÷ 9 ______

6. $6\overline{)42}$ **7.** $8\overline{)72}$ **8.** $9\overline{)36}$ **9.** $5\overline{)15}$ **10.** $8\overline{)56}$

11. Find 81 divided by 9. ______ **12.** Divide 40 by 8. ______ **13.** Find 90 divided by 9. ______

Algebra Write < or > to compare.

14. 63 ÷ 9 ◯ 8 **15.** 32 ÷ 8 ◯ 8 **16.** 54 ÷ 9 ◯ 5

17. Reasoning It costs $7 for a matinee and $8 for an evening movie. With $56, would you be able to buy more matinee tickets or evening tickets? Explain.

____

____

18. Teri scored 64 points in the first 8 basketball games she played in. She scored the same number of points in each game. How many points did she score in each game? ______

19. Explain It Adam made 19 paper cranes Monday and 8 more Tuesday. He gave 9 friends an equal number of cranes. How many cranes did each friend receive? Explain how you found your answer.

____

____

____

20. A short story consists of 81 pages. Andrea will read 9 pages each day. How many days will it take Andrea to finish the story?

A 6 **B** 7 **C** 8 **D** 9

Name ______________________

Dividing with 0 and 1

There are special rules to follow when dividing by 1 or 0.

Rule	Example	What You **Think**	What You **Write**
When any number is divided by 1, the quotient is that number.	7 ÷ 1 = ?	1 times what number = 7? 1 × 7 = 7 So, 7 ÷ 1 = 7	7 ÷ 1 = 7 or $1\overline{)7}$ with quotient 7
When any number (except 0) is divided by itself, the quotient is 1.	8 ÷ 8 = ?	8 times what number = 8? 8 × 1 = 8 So, 8 ÷ 8 = 1	8 ÷ 8 = 1 or $8\overline{)8}$ with quotient 1
When zero is divided by a number (except 0), the quotient is 0.	0 ÷ 5 = ?	5 times what number = 0? 5 × 0 = 0 So, 0 ÷ 5 = 0	0 ÷ 5 = 0 or $5\overline{)0}$ with quotient 0
You cannot divide a number by 0.	9 ÷ 0 = ?	0 times what number = 9? There is no number that works, so 9 ÷ 0 cannot be done.	9 ÷ 0 cannot be done

Find each quotient.

1. 25 ÷ 1 ______ **2.** 9 ÷ 9 ______ **3.** 0 ÷ 8 ______ **4.** 6 ÷ 6 ______ **5.** 4 ÷ 1 ______

6. $1\overline{)7}$ **7.** $12\overline{)12}$ **8.** $17\overline{)0}$ **9.** $5\overline{)5}$ **10.** $1\overline{)9}$

Compare. Use <, >, or =.

11. 15 ÷ 1 ◯ 15 ÷ 15 **12.** 0 ÷ 12 ◯ 12 ÷ 12

Reteaching **8-5**

Name ______________________

Practice
8-5

Dividing with 0 and 1

Find each quotient.

1. $0 \div 6$ ____ **2.** $8 \div 8$ ____ **3.** $6 \div 1$ ____ **4.** $0 \div 5$ ____ **5.** $9 \div 9$ ____

6. $1\overline{)5}$ **7.** $4\overline{)0}$ **8.** $6\overline{)6}$ **9.** $1\overline{)8}$ **10.** $1\overline{)3}$

11. $3\overline{)24}$ **12.** $6\overline{)42}$ **13.** $8\overline{)72}$ **14.** $5\overline{)30}$ **15.** $7\overline{)63}$

16. Find 0 divided by 2. ____ **17.** Divide 7 by 1. ____ **18.** Find 4 divided by 4. ____

Algebra Write <, >, or = to compare.

19. $6 \div 6$ ◯ $8 \div 8$ **20.** $0 \div 5$ ◯ $5 \div 5$ **21.** $9 \div 1$ ◯ $7 \div 1$

22. Tickets for rides cost $1 each at the fair. Bob has $6 to buy tickets. How many tickets can Bob buy? ____

23. **Reasoning** Nikki is the goalie on her soccer team. She has allowed 0 goals in 8 games. How many goals has she allowed in each game? ____

24. **Explain It** Why is $10 - 0 = 10$, but $0 \div 10 = 0$? Explain.

____

____

____

25. Which has the greatest quotient?

A $6 \div 6$ **B** $5 \div 1$ **C** $0 \div 3$ **D** $8 \div 8$

Practice **8-5**

Name ___________________________

Reteaching **8-6**

Problem Solving: Draw a Picture and Write a Number Sentence

You can draw a picture to help you divide.

Neil has 54 CDs. He has the CDs equally placed among 6 shelves. How many CDs can go on each shelf?

Draw a diagram to show the problem. Make 6 rows with the same number of CDs until you reach 54.

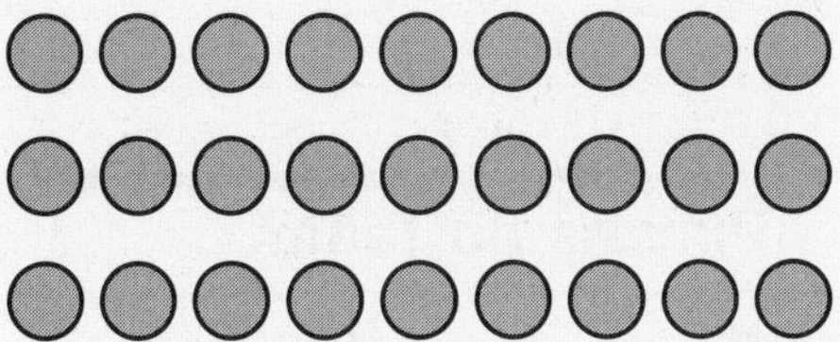

Write a number sentence: $54 \div 6 = 9$.

Check your answer by using multiplication: $6 \times 9 = 54$.

Neil can put 9 CDs on each shelf.

Draw a diagram to show what you know.
Then write a number sentence and solve.

1. There are 5 cars taking students to a museum. Each car can seat 4 students. How many students can go to the museum?

   ____

2. There are 16 players competing in the beach volleyball tournament. There are 8 teams competing. How many players are on each team?

   ____

3. **Explain It** Sandy said she could use addition to answer question 1. How could this be done?

   ____

   ____

Reteaching **8-6**

Name ________________________________

Practice **8-6**

Problem Solving: Draw a Picture and Write a Number Sentence

In **1** and **2**, draw a diagram to show what you know. Then write a number sentence and solve.

1. Maria bought 5 cans of tennis balls. Each can contained 3 tennis balls. How many tennis balls did Maria buy altogether?

____

2. In Ms. Ramirez's class, there are 28 students. They sit in 4 equal rows. How many students are in each row?

____

In **3** and **4**, use the chart.

Players on Team	
Sport	**Players**
Tennis	2
Basketball	5
Softball	10

3. A community center has 3 tennis teams and 5 basketball teams. No one is on both teams. How many athletes are there?

____

4. **Number Sense** Fabio said that there are 3 times as many people on a basketball team as on a tennis team. Is he correct? Explain why or why not.

____

____

____

Write a number sentence and solve. Use this information for **5** and **6**.

Marshall sleeps 8 hours each day.

5. How many hours does Marshall sleep in one week? ________________

6. How many hours is Marshall awake each day? ________________

7. Tricia spent $12 to rent ice skates. She rented them for 4 hours. Which number sentence can you write to find how much it costs to rent skates for one hour?

A $12 − 4 = ■ **B** $12 + 4 = ■ **C** $12 × 4 = ■ **D** $12 ÷ 4 = ■

Name ______________________

Repeating Patterns

Patterns can grow or patterns can repeat.
Repeating patterns can use numbers or shapes.
You can extend a pattern by finding a rule for the pattern.

Repeating Patterns with Shapes

Use this pattern.
What is the next shape?

Assign each shape a number. When a shape repeats use the same number.

The next shape is the second shape.

Repeating Patterns with Numbers

Use the pattern below. What is the 12th number in this pattern?

4, 7, 3, 5, 4, 7, 3, 5, 4, 7, ...

Find the pattern.
The pattern is 4, 7, 3, 5, and then it repeats.

Extend the pattern until reaching the 12th number.

4, 7, 3, 5, 4, 7, 3, 5, 4, 7, 3, 5

The 12th number is 5.

1. Draw the next three shapes in the pattern.

____

2. What are the next three numbers in the pattern below?
5, 8, 3, 1, 5, 8, 3, 1, 5, 8

____

3. Explain It In the pattern in Exercise 2, how could you find the 15th number? What is that number?

____

____

____

Name ______________________

Repeating Patterns

Draw the next three shapes to continue the pattern.

1. 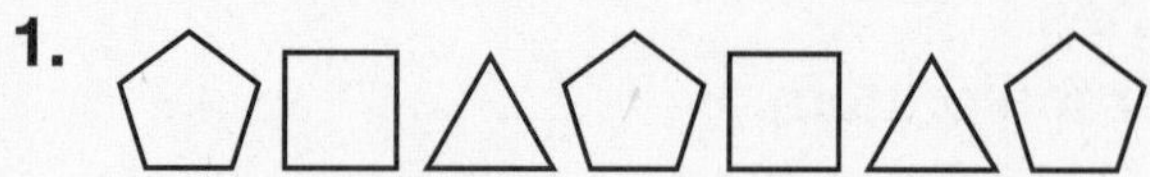

____

2. 

____

Write the next three numbers to continue the pattern.

3. 4, 6, 2, 8, 4, 6, 2, 8, 4, ...

____

4. 3, 3, 5, 3, 3, 5, 3, 3, 5, ...

____

5. **Draw a Picture** What is the 12th shape in the pattern below?

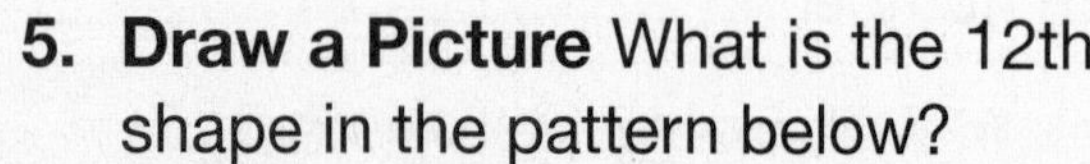

____

6. **Strategy Practice** Penny has made a pattern of shapes on her bedroom walls. She drew a rectangle, 2 circles, a rectangle, and then 2 more circles until she drew 24 circles. How many shapes did she draw in all?

____

7. Mrs. Washington placed students in a line. The order was 1 boy, 2 girls, 2 boys, and continued. Was the 10th student a boy or a girl?

____

8. What is the 15th number in the pattern below?
3, 6, 5, 2, 3, 6, 5, 2, ...

A 2 **B** 3 **C** 5 **D** 6

Practice 9-1

Name ______________________

Number Sequences

A number sequence is a pattern that increases or decreases while following a rule.

What are the next three numbers in this pattern?

36, 42, 48, 54, ...

Step 1

Find the pattern.

You can subtract to find the pattern.

$54 - 48 = 6$

$48 - 42 = 6$

$42 - 36 = 6$

Each number is 6 more than the number before it. So, a rule for the pattern is "add 6."

Step 2

Use this rule to extend the pattern.

Start with 54. Add 6.

$54 + 6 = 60$

$60 + 6 = 66$

$66 + 6 = 72$

So, the next three numbers are 60, 66, and 72.

Find the next three numbers in each pattern.
Write a rule for the pattern.

1. 35, 40, 45, ■, ■, ■
____

2. 43, 39, 35, ■, ■, ■
____

3. 32, 39, 46, ■, ■, ■
____

4. 13, 21, 29, ■, ■, ■
____

5. 75, 65, 55, ■, ■, ■
____

6. 51, 45, 39, ■, ■, ■
____

7. **Critical Thinking** How can you use subtraction to complete an addition pattern? Use Exercise 3 as an example.

____

____

____

Name ______________________________

Practice
9-2

Number Sequences

Find the missing numbers in each pattern. Write a rule for the pattern.

1. 19, 23, 27, ■, ■

2. 32, 26, 20, ■, ■

3. 125, 150, 175, ■, ■

4. 8, 15, ■, ■, 36

5. 90, 80 ■, ■, 50

6. 84, 69, 54, ■, ■

7. 30, 50, ■, 90, ■

8. 65, 56, ■, 38, ■

9. 35, ■, 57, 68, ■

10. **Reasoning** The house numbers on Carr Memorial Avenue follow a pattern. The first four houses on the left side of the street are numbered 8, 14, 20, and 26. How many more houses are on the left side of the street with numbers less than 50?

11. Noreen is beginning an exercise program. The first week she exercises 25 minutes each day. The second week she exercises 30 minutes a day and the third week she increases it to 35 minutes a day. If the pattern continues, how long will she exercise each day in the fifth week?

12. **Explain It** What do you need to do to extend a pattern?

13. John said that 52 is part of the pattern below.
Mary said that 66 is part of the pattern below.
Who is correct?
18, 26, 34, 42, …

A Neither is correct.

B Both are correct.

C Only John is correct.

D Only Mary is correct.

Name ______________________________

Extending Tables

A table is an organized way to show a pattern.

Weeks	Days
1	7
3	21
5	35
6	42
8	?

Each pair of values follows some rule. If you can find a rule that works for all the pairs, you can extend the table.

What is the missing number in this table?

Step 1

Find a rule for the pattern.

The first 4 weeks are shown.
You can divide to find the pattern.

$42 \div 6 = 7$
$35 \div 5 = 7$
$21 \div 3 = 7$
$7 \div 1 = 7$

There are 7 days in one week.

Step 2

Use your rule to find the missing number.

Multiply the days in 1 week by the number of weeks.

$8 \times 7 = 56$

The missing number is 56.

Complete each table.

1.

Cars	Wheels
1	4
2	8
3	
4	16
8	32

2.

Old Price	New Price
\$63	\$53
\$48	\$38
	\$31
\$37	\$27
\$26	\$16

3.

Weight of Salad in Ounces	6	10	14	18
Total Weight of Container in Ounces	9	13	17	

Name ______________________

Practice 9-3

Extending Tables

Find the missing numbers.

1.

Number of Cats	Number of Legs
1	4
2	
3	12
4	16
	32

2.

Money Earned	Money Saved
$25	$15
$32	$22
$43	
	$47
$73	$63

3.

Touchdowns	Points
1	6
2	12
3	
	36
8	48

For **4** and **5**, use the table at the right.

T-shirts	Cost
1	$8
3	$24
5	$40

4. How much money would 9 T-shirts cost?

____

5. Strategy Practice How much more money do 10 T-shirts cost than 6 T-shirts? Explain how you determined your answer.

____

____

____

6. Number Sense Bob has 3 bookshelves that hold a total of 27 books. He adds a fourth shelf and now has 36 books. If he adds 2 more shelves, how many books can he have in total?

____

7. What is the missing number in the table below?

In	3	5	8	15
Out	9	11	14	

A 21 **B** 25 **C** 30 **D** 45

Practice 9-3

Name ______________________

Writing Rules for Situations

Reteaching
9-4

When working with tables, it is important to find a rule that works for all pairs of numbers. The rule tells how to find one of the numbers in a pair.

Old Price	New Price
$15	$10
$22	$17
$28	$23
$37	$32
$51	$46

Each pair of numbers follows a rule. If you can find a rule that works, you can extend the table.

Step 1

Find the pattern. Check the first pair of numbers to see how the first number changed to become the second number.

15 − 10 = 5

A rule of the first pair of numbers is "subtract 5."

Step 2

See if this rule works for all the values.

22 − 17 = 5 37 − 32 = 5

28 − 23 = 5 51 − 46 = 5

The rule "subtract 5" works for every pair of values.

Find the missing numbers in each table. Write a rule for the table.

1.

Earned	Spent
$21	$14
$30	$23
$42	
$48	$41
$59	

____

2.

Teams	Players
3	27
8	72
6	
9	
2	18

____

3.

Tickets	Cost
2	$1
6	$3
12	
10	$5
20	

____

4. **Number Sense** Joe said that by using the information in Exercise 2 there would be 250 players if there were 25 teams. Is that correct? Explain.

____

____

Reteaching 9-4

Name ______________________

Practice
9-4

Writing Rules for Situations

Find the missing numbers in each table.
Write a rule for the table.

1.

Max's Age	Carol's Age
7	13
10	
14	20
18	24
	31

____

2.

Tricycles	Wheels
5	15
3	9
7	
	27
2	6

____

3.

Old Price	New Price
$25	$18
$16	$9
	$32
$53	$46
$72	

____

For **4** and **5**, use the table at the right.

Players	Teams
24	4
48	8
36	6
30	5

4. The table shows the number of players on a volleyball team. What is a rule for the table?

____

5. **Explain It** If there are 12 teams, how many players will there be? Explain how you found your answer.

____

____

6. How many miles can Nick travel in 5 hours? 6 hours?

Hours	1	2	3	4
Miles	60	120	180	240

____

7. The table shows how many CDs Jim and Ken each own after joining a CD club. Which is a rule that works for this table?

Jim	8	12	20	30
Ken	16	20	28	38

A Add 8
B Multiply by 2
C Subtract 10
D Divide by 2

Practice 9-4

Name ______________________

Translating Words to Expressions

You can use phrases that are given in a problem to determine which sign to use. This will help you to solve word problems. Below are examples of addition, subtraction, multiplication, and division phrases.

Word phrase	Numerical expression
3 hours studied Monday and 2 more today	$3 + 2$
Word phrase	**Numerical expression**
6 DVDs fewer than 15	$15 - 6$
Word phrase	**Numerical expression**
6 times the $5 earned	$6 \times \$5$
Word phrase	**Numerical expression**
15 people in 3 equal rows	$15 \div 3$

Write a numerical expression for each word phrase.

1. 16 less than 35 ______________

2. 12 more than 17 ______________

3. 4 times as many as 7 ______________

4. 18 that are in 2 equal groups ______________

5. **Write a Problem** Write a word problem involving the number of pages in a book. Then write the numerical expression that you would need to use to solve your problem.

____

____

Name ______________________

Practice 9-5

Translating Words to Expressions

Write a numerical expression for each word phrase.

1. a total of 21 that is split into 3 equal groups

____

2. the difference when 9 is taken away from 24

____

3. the sum of 32 and 27

____

4. the product of 7 and 5

____

5. 3 times as old as 6 years old

____

6. 15 CDs more than 12 CDs

____

7. 32 carrots shared equally by 8 people

____

8. $20 paid from $50

____

There were 12 people on a bus. Write a numerical expression for the number of people after each action described. For each problem, start with 12 people.

9. 4 people leave the bus

____

10. 6 people get on the bus

____

11. half of the people leave the bus

____

12. twice as many people get on the bus

____

13. **Geometry** A figure has 3 more sides than a pentagon. Write an expression for the number of sides the new figure has.

____

14. Kim has 20 books on each of 4 shelves. Which number sentence shows how to find how many books in all?

A $20 + 4$ **C** $20 - 4$

B 4×20 **D** $20 \div 4$

Name ______________________

Geometric Patterns

Like number patterns, geometric patterns can have figures that grow. To extend geometric patterns follow the same steps as you would for number patterns.

Below is a pattern of squares.

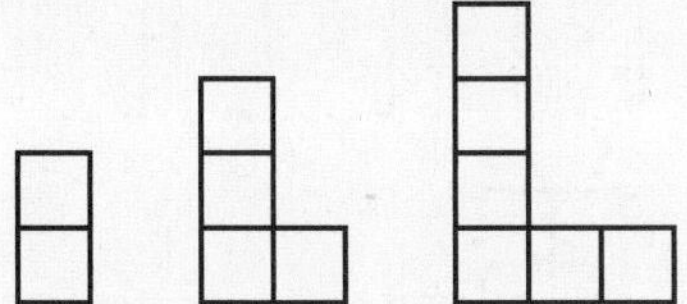

Number of Figure	1	2	3	4	5
Number of Squares	2	4	6		

Step 1

Look at the pattern. See how the figure has changed.

Each figure grows by 1 square in height and 1 square in width.

Each figure grows by 2 squares.

Step 2

Make the next two figures.

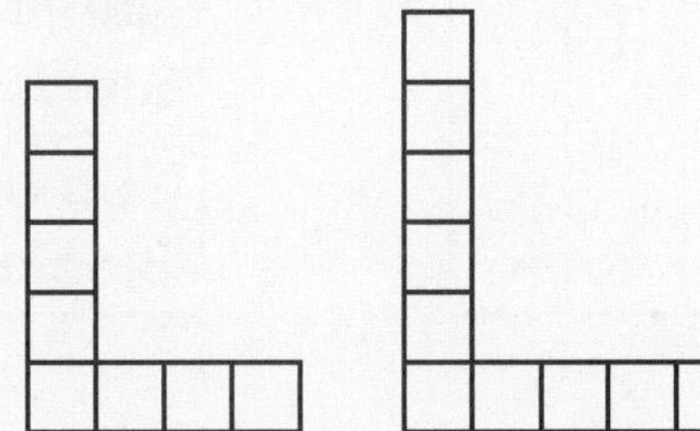

Step 3

Fill in the table.

Number of Figure	1	2	3	4	5
Number of Squares	2	4	6	8	10

Draw the next two towers in the pattern. Use grid paper. Find the missing numbers in each table.

1.

Number of Stories	1	2	3	4	5
Number of Blocks	4	8	12		

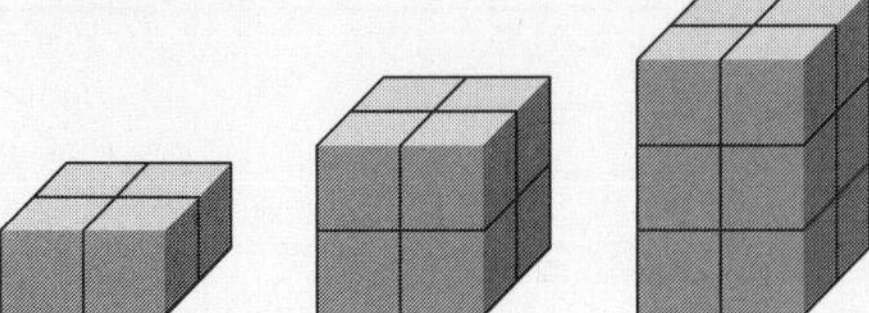

____

2.

Length of Sides	1	2	3	4	5
Sum of All Sides	5	10	15		

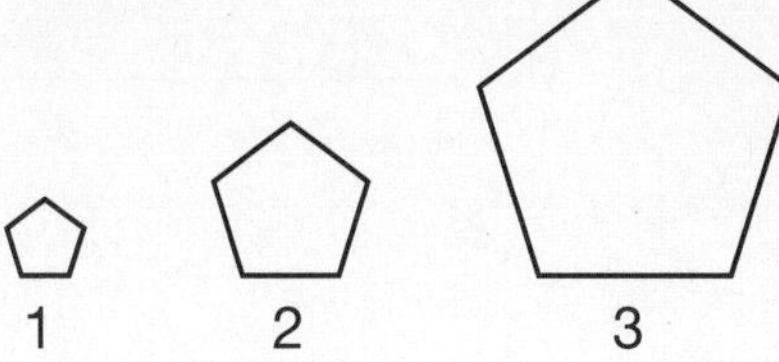

____

3. **Number Sense** If there were 10 stories in Exercise 1, how many blocks would there be? Explain.

____

Name ______________________________

Practice
9-6

Geometric Patterns

Draw the next two figures in the pattern.
Find the missing numbers in each table.

1.

Number of Stories	1	2	3	4	5
Number of Blocks	5	10	15		

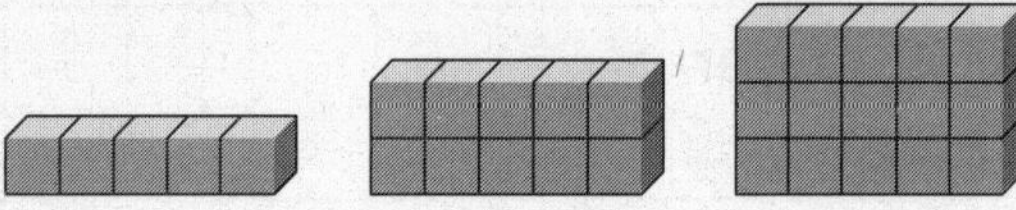

____

2.

Number of Stories	1	2	3	4	5
Number of Blocks	2	4	6		

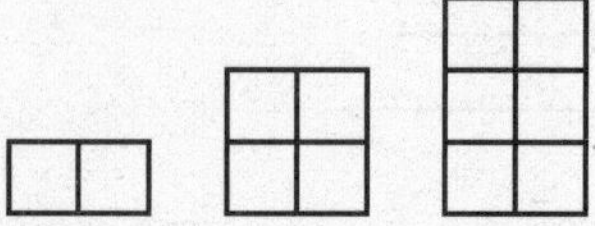

____

3.

Length of Each Side	1	2	3	4	5
Sum of All Sides	3	6	9		

1 2 3

____

4.

Number of Stories	1	2	3	4	5
Number of Blocks	6	12	18		

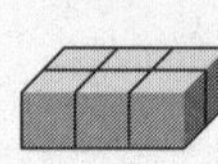
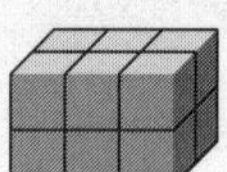
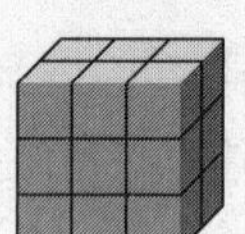

____

5. **Explain It** Use Exercise 4. How could you find how many blocks there were in 20 stories? How many blocks would there be?

____

____

____

____

6. Which is a rule for the table below?

In	3	9	4	7
Out	7	13	8	11

A Add 4

B Multiply 2

C Multiply 4

D Add 5

Practice **9-6**

Name ______________________

Reteaching
9-7

Equal or Unequal

An equation is a number sentence that says two expressions are equal. For example, $6 + 3 = 9$ is an equation because both sides are equal.

An inequality is a number sentence that says two expressions are not equal. Inequalities use the symbols $>$ (is greater than) and $<$ (is less than). For example, $7 + 3 > 9$ and $5 + 3 < 9$.

To find which symbol to use to compare the expressions, add or subtract on each side.

9 − 2 ◯ 8 + 1

7 ◯ 9

$7 < 9$

Sometimes you will need to find an unknown number. For an equation, there will be one correct answer. For an inequality, there will be a set of numbers.

3 + ☐ = 8	3 + ☐ > 8	3 + ☐ < 8
$3 + 5 = 8$	Any number greater than 5 makes the inequality true.	Any number less than 5 makes the inequality true.

Compare. Write $<$, $>$, or $=$ for each ◯.

1. 13 + 7 ◯ 20

2. 14 + 22 ◯ 21 + 13

3. 42 − 18 ◯ 27 + 6

4. 28 − 14 ◯ 7 + 9

Write a number that makes each number sentence true.

5. 5 + ☐ < 15

6. 19 − ☐ < 12

7. 8 + ☐ = 16

8. 13 + ☐ > 18

9. Write a Problem Write your own inequality and write the numbers that make your inequality true.

____

____

Reteaching **9-7**

Name ______________________

Practice 9-7

Equal or Unequal

Compare. Write <, >, or = for each ◯.

1. 8 + 17 ◯ 24

2. 22 + 29 ◯ 36 + 17

3. 44 + 12 ◯ 62 − 6

4. 38 + 27 ◯ 79 − 12

Write a number that makes each number sentence true.

5. 6 + ☐ = 15

6. 23 − ☐ < 14

7. 8 + ☐ > 14

8. 12 − ☐ > 6

9. Mr. King's and Ms. Rodney's classes are competing in field day. Mr. King's class has 12 boys and 13 girls. Ms. Rodney's class has 14 boys and 12 girls. Write a number sentence to compare the number of students.

____

10. Strategy Practice Adam has 24 U.S. stamps. Sara has 17 U.S. stamps. Adam gives Sarah 4 U.S. stamps. Write a number sentence to compare the number of U.S. stamps each has now.

____

11. Estimation Keisha has a shelf that has 38 books and another shelf that has 29 books. About how many books are on the two shelves in all?

____

12. Which symbol goes in the ◯ to compare the expressions correctly?

31 − 15 ◯ 9 + 6

A +

B >

C <

D =

Practice 9-7

Name ______________________

Reteaching
9-8

Problem Solving: Act It Out and Use Reasoning

Izzie has 12 coins. Four of the coins are quarters. He has 2 more dimes than nickels. How many of each coin does he have?

You can use logical reasoning to find the answer. You may be able to determine information that is not told.

What do I know?	What do I need to find out?	What can I determine from the information?
Izzie has 12 coins. 4 of the coins are quarters. Izzie has 2 more dimes than nickels.	How many dimes does Izzie have? How many nickels does Izzie have?	If 4 of the 12 coins are quarters, Izzie has a total of 8 dimes and nickels.

You can act it out to find how many dimes and nickels Izzie has.

Take 8 two-color counters. Find combinations so that one color will have 2 more than the other. If you try 4 and 4, the difference is 0, so try 5 and 3. It works.

      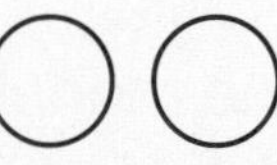

So, Izzie has 4 quarters, 5 dimes, and 3 nickels.

Solve. Find the number of each kind of object in the collection.

1. **Kim's Music Video Collection**

   13 videos in all
   4 concert videos
   3 more rap videos than pop videos

   Concert videos = ☐

   Rap videos = ☐

   Pop videos = ☐

2. **Molly's Art Collection**

   5 paintings
   3 more sculptures than mosaics
   16 pieces in all

   Paintings = ☐

   Sculptures = ☐

   Mosaics = ☐

Reteaching 9-8

Name ______________________________

Problem Solving: Act It Out and Use Reasoning

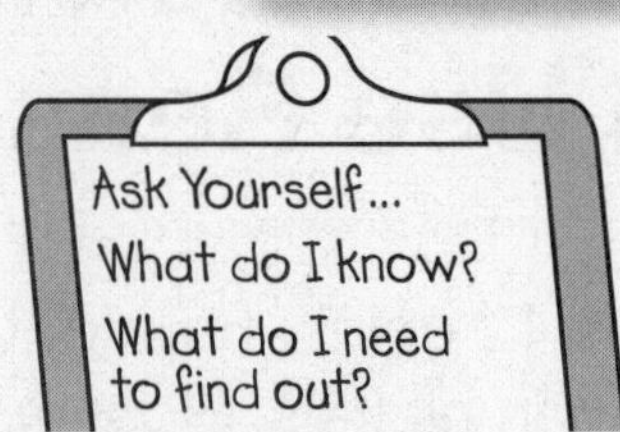

Solve. Find the number of each kind of object in the collection.

1. **Sue's Card Collection**

   8 packs of baseball cards
   3 fewer packs of hockey cards than football cards
   17 packs in all

   Baseball cards = ☐

   Hockey cards = ☐

   Football cards = ☐

2. **Drew's DVD Collection**

   7 comedy DVDs
   4 more drama DVDs than horror DVDs
   15 DVDs in all

   Comedy DVDs = ☐

   Drama DVDs = ☐

   Horror DVDs = ☐

3. **Strategy Practice** Mike is 8 years older than Kyle. Kyle is 6 years old. The sum of Mike's, Kyle's, and Jamal's ages is 23. How many years old is Jamal?

   ____

4. Miranda has 24 CDs in her collection. Of those CDs, 10 are pop CDs. She has 6 more country CDs than jazz CDs. How many country CDs does Miranda have?

   ____

5. Curt has 12 models in all. Three of the models are airplanes. Curt has 5 more models of cars than boats. How many models of cars does Curt have?

   ____

6. Stevie, Lindsey, and Christine are the lead singers in a band. They will sing 18 songs. Lindsey will sing 8 songs. Christine will sing 6 fewer songs than Stevie. How many songs will Stevie sing?

   A 2 **B** 4 **C** 6 **D** 8

Name ________________________________

Solid Figures

Three-dimensional objects are called solid figures. Solid figures are found in the world in many shapes and sizes.

The battery is an example of a cylinder. A **solid figure** is named according to its features.

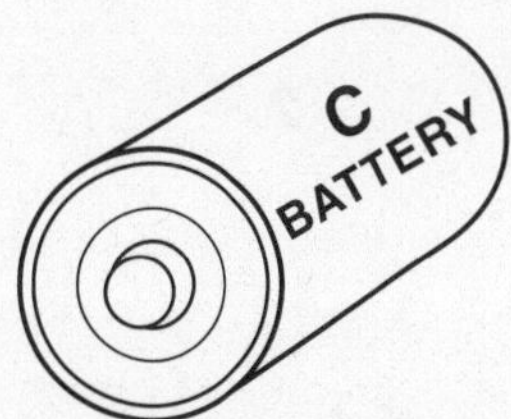

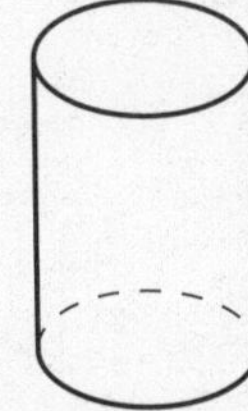

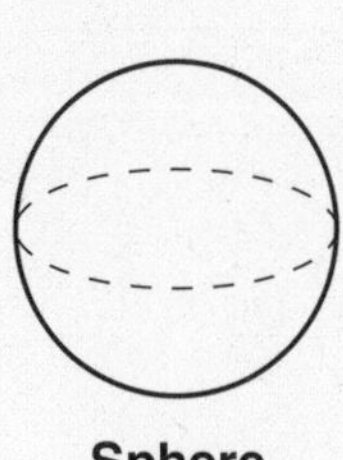

Sphere

Cone

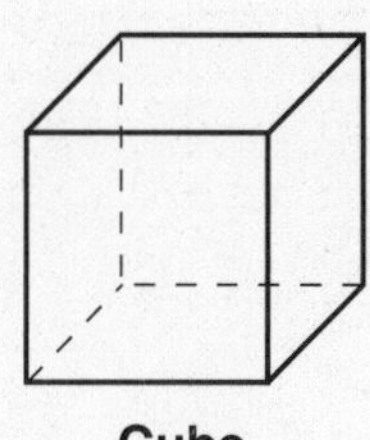

Cube

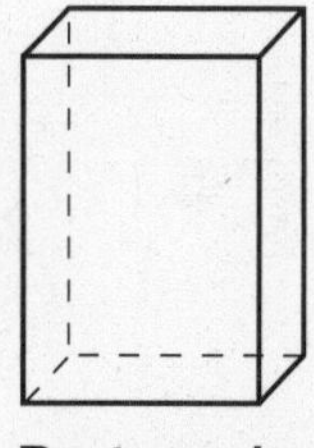

Rectangular Prism

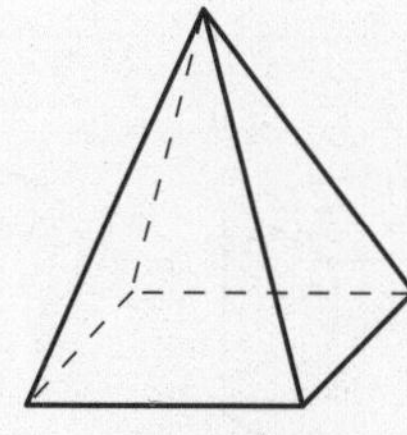

Pyramid

Name the solid figure that each object looks like.

1.

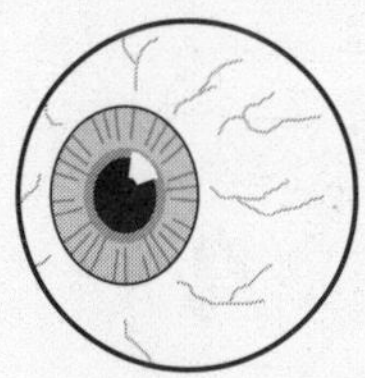

____

2.

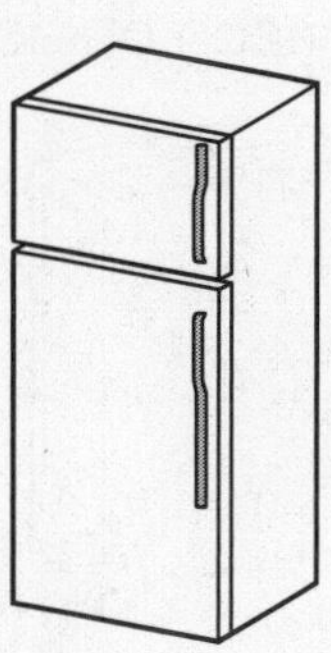

____

3.

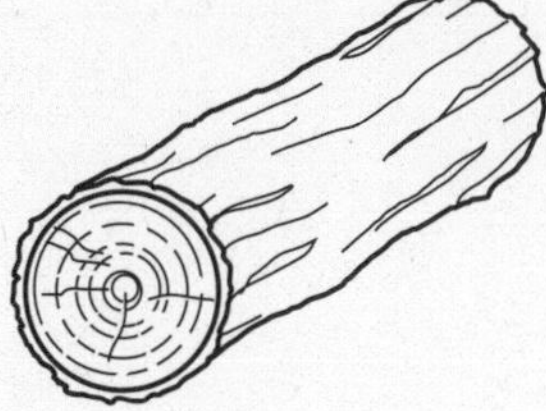

____

4.

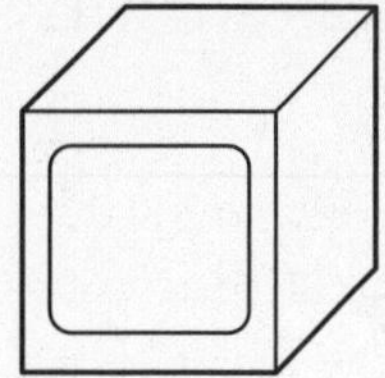

____

5. Mike put a pyramid and a sphere on a table. Which is most likely going to fall off the table if pushed? Explain.

____

Name ______________________

Solid Figures

Name the solid figure.

1. 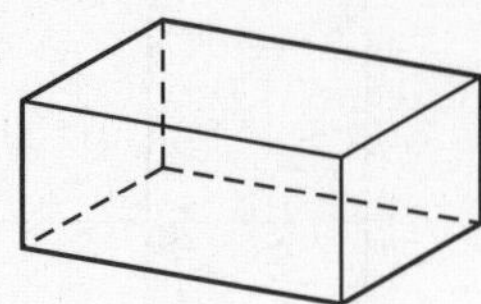
2. 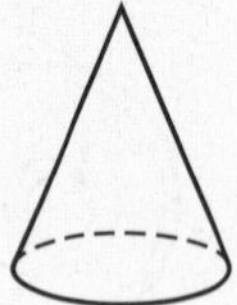
3. 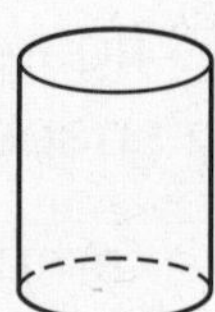

______ ______ ______

4. 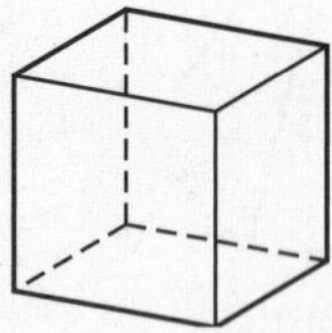
5. 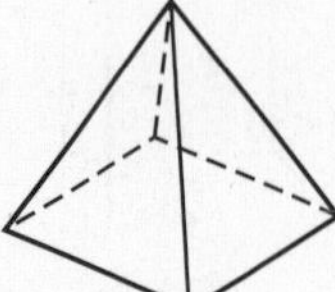
6. 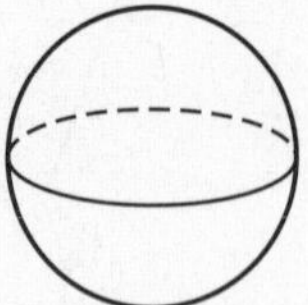

______ ______ ______

Name the solid figure that each object looks like.

7. 
8. 

9. 

10. 

______ ______ ______ ______

11. **Reasoning** What solid figures would you get if you cut a cube as shown? ______

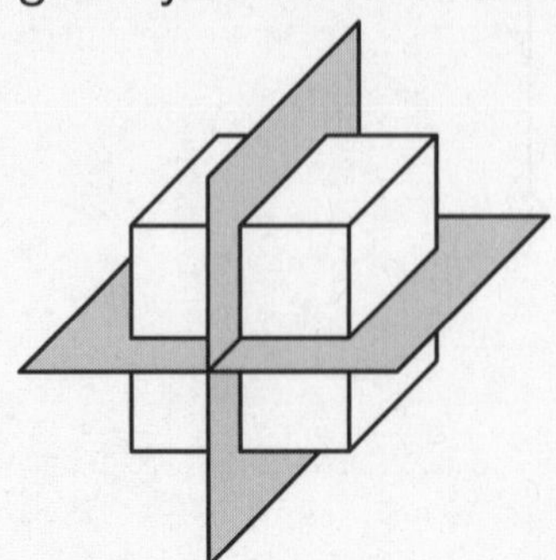

12. What solid figure does this figure most resemble?

A Cylinder **B** Cone **C** Pyramid **D** Sphere

Name ______________________

Relating Solids and Shapes

Some solid figures have faces, edges, and vertices. Below is an example of the faces, edges, and vertices of a cube.

A face is a flat surface on a solid figure. There are 6 faces on a cube.

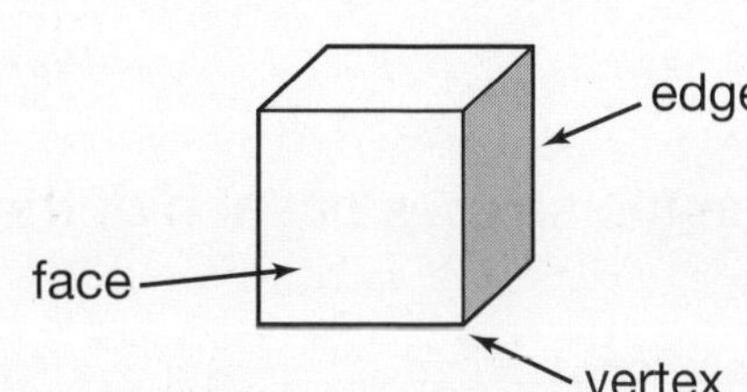

An edge is where two faces meet. There are 12 edges on a cube.

A vertex is where 3 or more edges meet. There are 8 vertices on a cube.

Some figures do not have edges or vertices.

Look at the solid figures below.

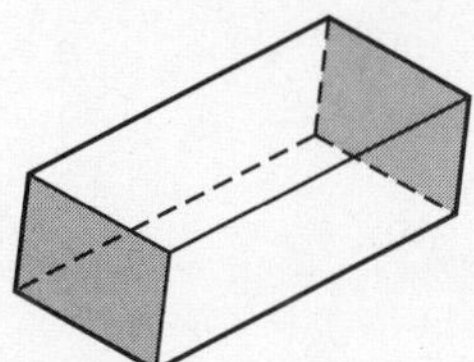 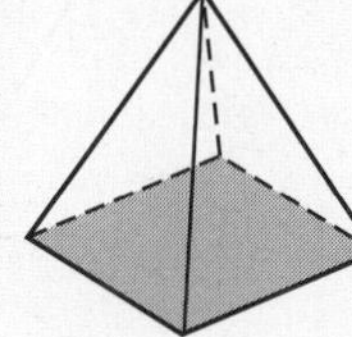 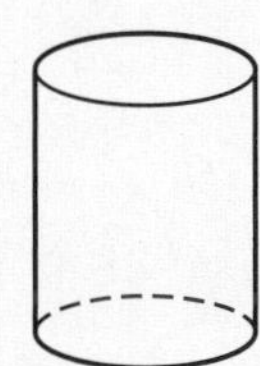 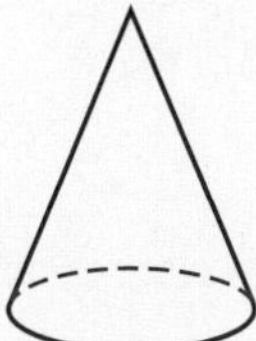 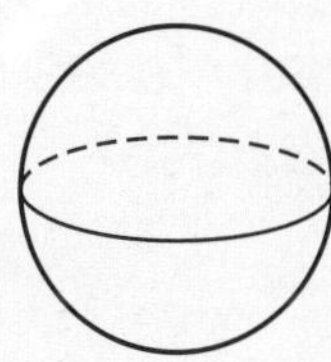

1. Which solid figure has the same number of faces, edges, and vertices as a cube?

   ____

2. Which solid figure has 4 triangular faces?

   ____

3. Which solid figure has only 2 flat surfaces?

   ____

4. Which solid figures do not have any vertices?

   ____

5. **Reasoning** How are a cube and a rectangular prism alike? How are they different?

   ____

   ____

   ____

   ____

Name ______________________________

Practice **10-2**

Relating Solids and Shapes

For **1** through **4**, use the rectangular prism pictured at the right.

1. How many faces does this rectangular prism have?

______

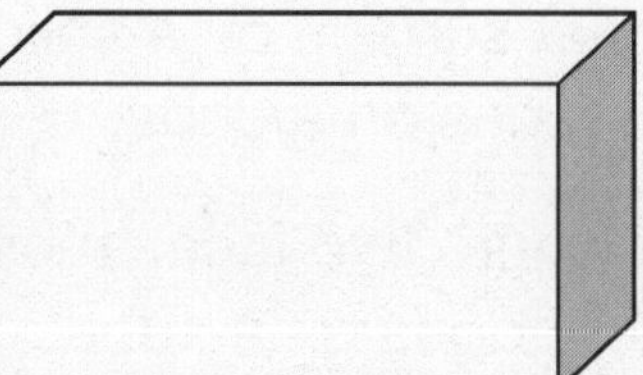

2. What are the shapes of each of the faces?

____

3. How many edges does this rectangular prism have?

______

4. How many vertices does this rectangular prism have?

______

For **5** through **8**, use the pyramid pictured at the right.

5. How many faces does this pyramid have?

______

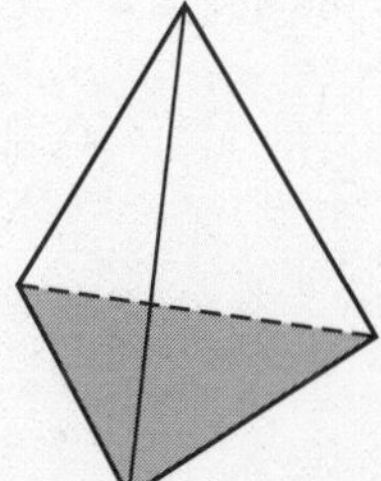

6. What are the shapes of each of the faces?

____

7. How many edges does this pyramid have?

______

8. How many vertices does this pyramid have?

______

9. Explain It How could you describe a cylinder to someone who has never seen one?

____

____

____

10. Which two figures have the same number of faces, edges, and vertices?

A Cylinder and pyramid

B Rectangular prism and sphere

C Pyramid and cube

D Rectangular prism and cube

Practice **10-2**

Name ____________________

Lines and Line Segments

You can find lines and parts of lines in shapes and objects.

•	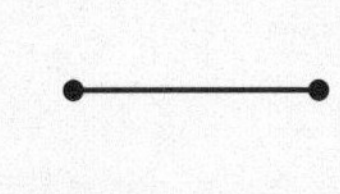	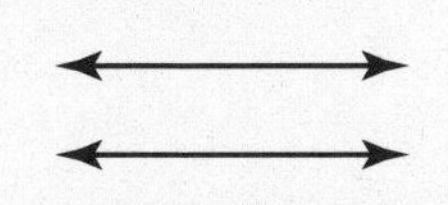	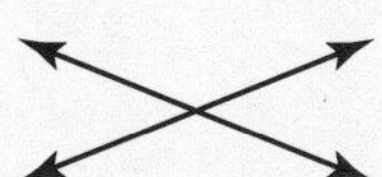	
A point is an exact location in space	A line is a set of points that goes forever in both directions.	A line segment is part of a line with two endpoints.	Parallel lines never meet or cross and remain the same distance apart.	Intersecting lines meet or cross.

Write the name for each.

1. 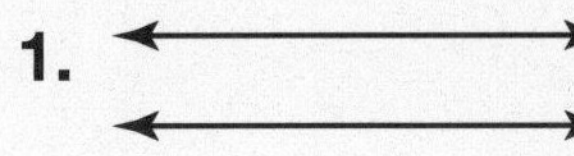

   ____

2. 

   ____

3. 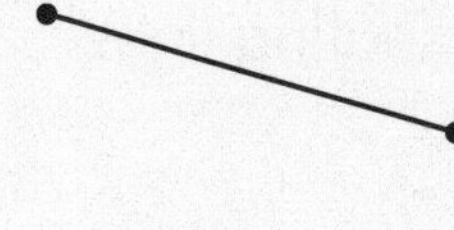

   ____

4. 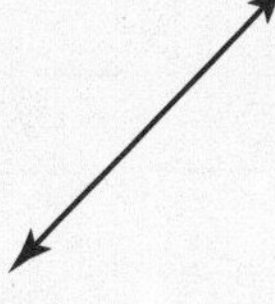

   ____

5. •

   ____

6. 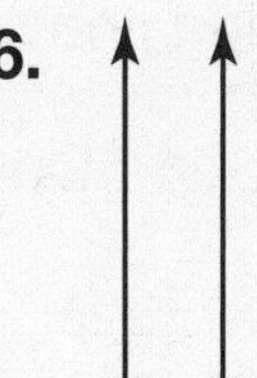

   ____

7. **Reasoning** Leo said that a line is part of a line segment.
   Carol said that a line segment is a part of a line.
   Who is correct? Explain.

   ____

   ____

   ____

Name ______________________

Practice
10-3

Lines and Line Segments

Write the name for each.

1. 

2. ●———●

3. 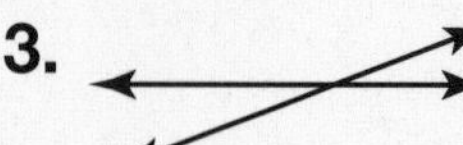

4. ⟷ ⟷

______ ______ ______ ______

Draw and label a picture of each.

5. Parallel lines

6. Line segment

7. Intersecting lines

8. Line

Practice **10-3**

For **9** and **10**, use the map at the right. Tell if the trails named look like intersecting lines or parallel lines.

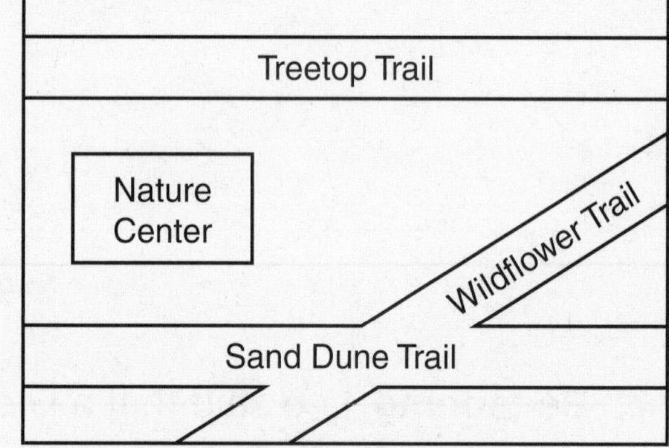

9. Treetop and Sand Dune

____

10. Sand Dune and Wildflower

____

11. **Explain It** What is the difference between a line and a line segment?

____

____

____

12. How many times does a pair of intersecting lines cross?

A Never **B** 1 time **C** 2 times **D** 3 times

Name ______________________

Reteaching

10-4

Angles

Angles are formed by two rays that share a vertex. Three types of angles are right angles, acute angles, and obtuse angles.

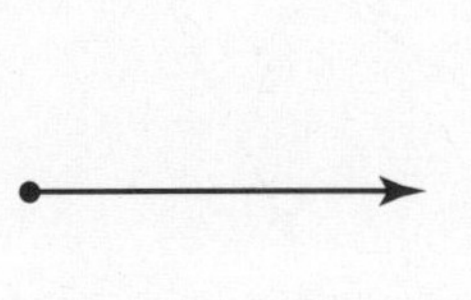

A ray is part of a line that has one endpoint and goes forever in one direction.

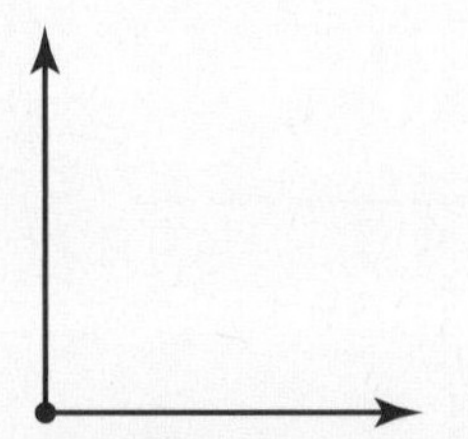

A right angle forms a square corner.

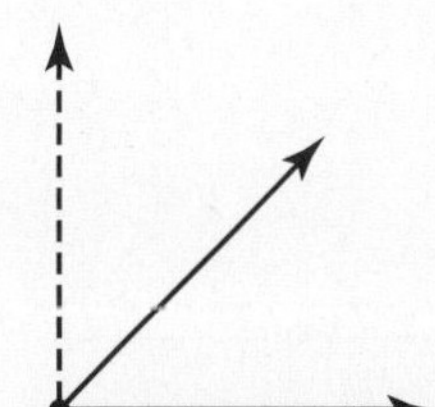

An acute angle is less than a right angle.

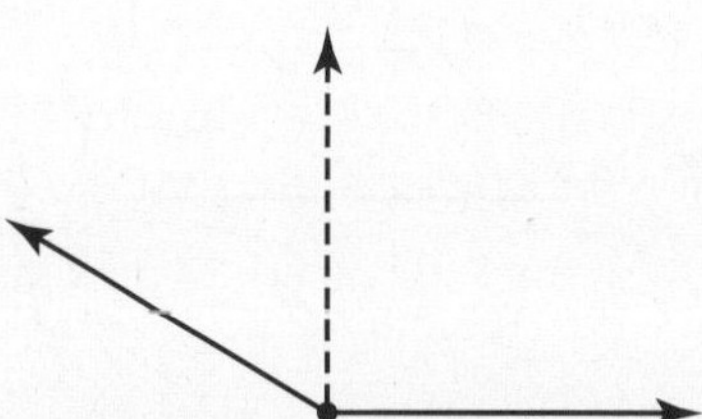

An obtuse angle is greater than a right angle.

Lines that meet or cross at a right angle are perpendicular lines.

Tell if each angle is right, acute, or obtuse.

1.

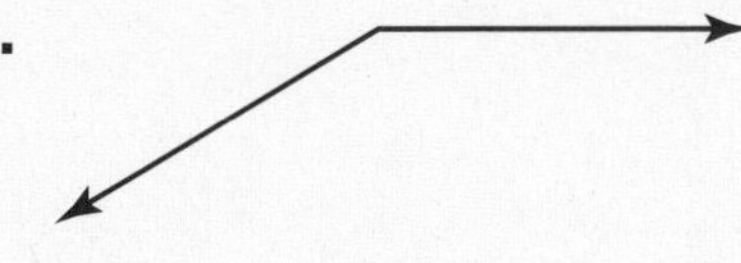

____

2.

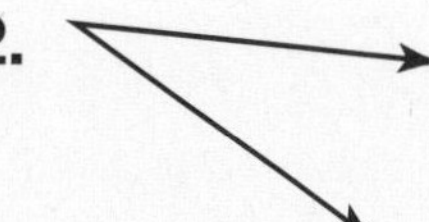

____

3.

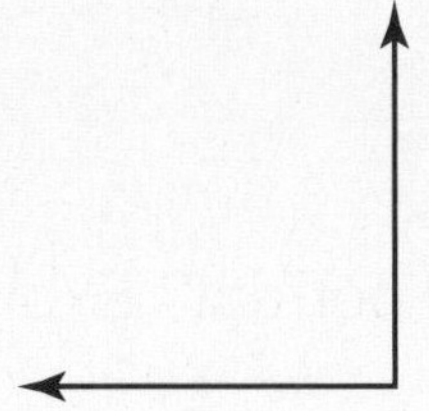

____

4.

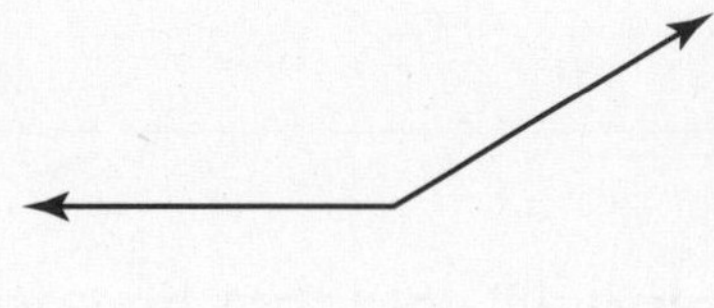

____

5. Explain It How can you use a right angle to determine the classification of another angle?

____

____

____

Name ______________________

Angles

Tell if each angle is right, acute, or obtuse.

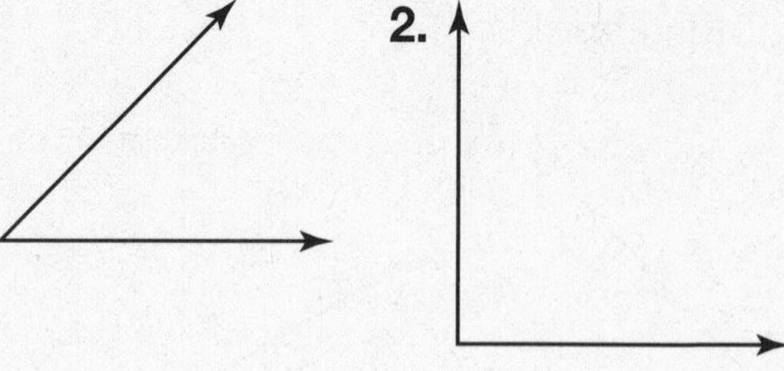

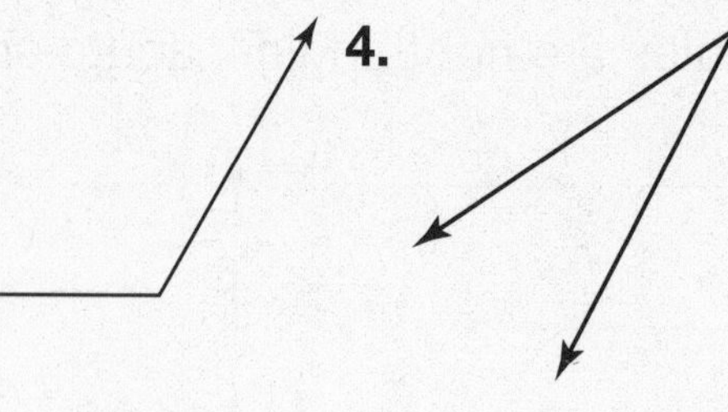

______ ______ ______ ______

Draw and label a picture of each.

5. Acute angle

6. Ray

7. Right angle

8. Obtuse angle

9. **Explain It** How are perpendicular lines similar to intersecting lines? How are they different?

____

____

10. **Reasoning** Jill said that an angle is made of two rays. Is she correct? Explain.

____

____

11. Can parallel rays form an angle? Explain.

____

12. At what time do the hands of a clock form an acute angle?

A 2:00 **B** 4:00 **C** 6:00 **D** 8:00

Name ______________________

Polygons

Polygons are closed figures that are made up of straight line segments.

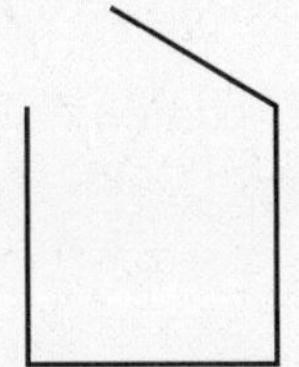

Not a polygon
Not a closed figure

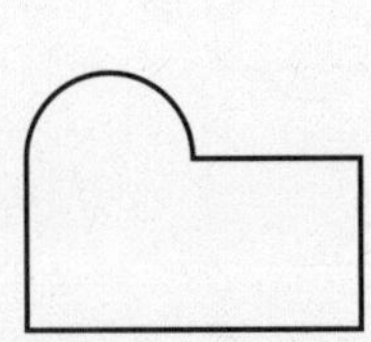

Not a polygon
Not all straight lines

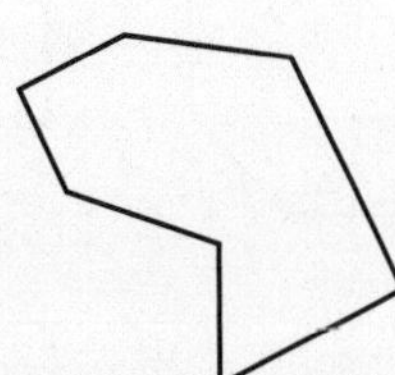

Polygon
Closed figure
All straight lines

The number of sides in a polygon gives the polygon its name.

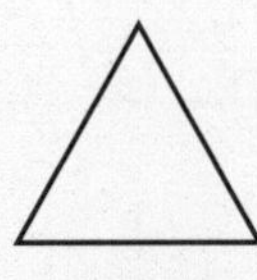

Triangle
3 sides

Quadrilateral
4 sides

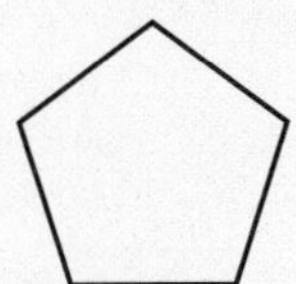

Pentagon
5 sides

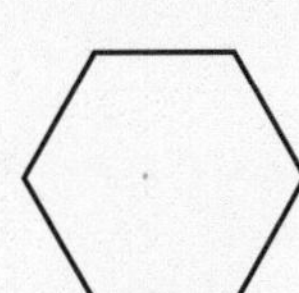

Hexagon
6 sides

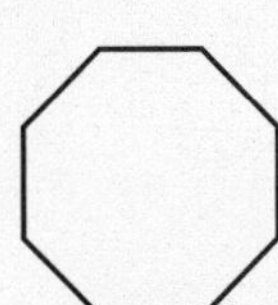

Octagon
8 sides

Is each figure a polygon? If it is a polygon, give its name. If not, explain why.

1. 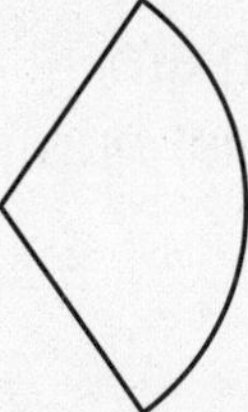

____

____

2. 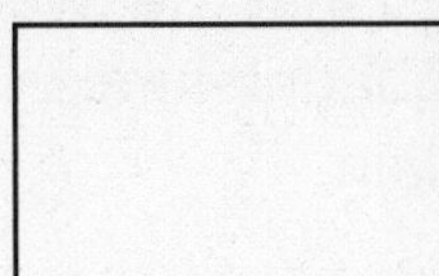

____

____

3. 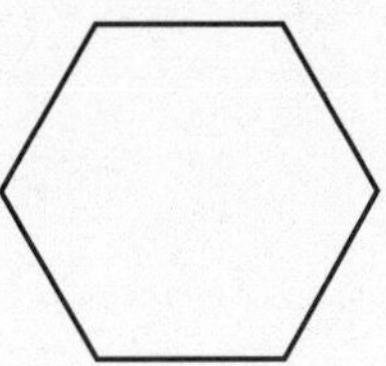

____

____

4.  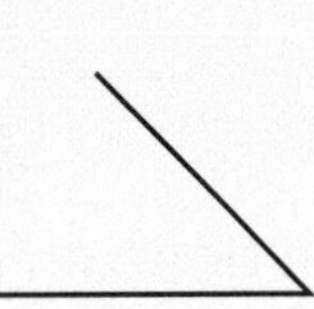

____

____

Name ______________________

Practice
10-5

Polygons

Name the polygon.

1. 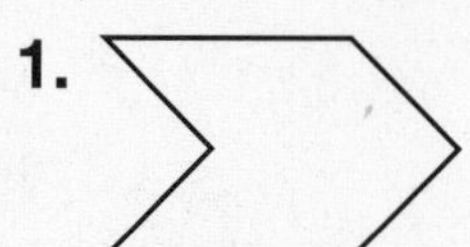
2. 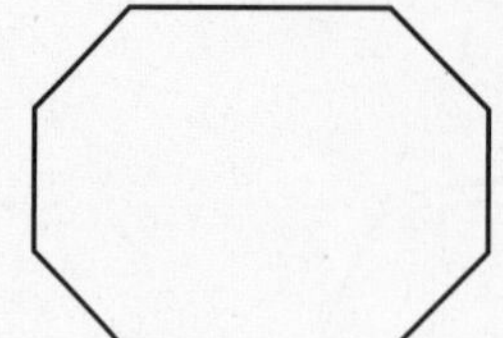
3. 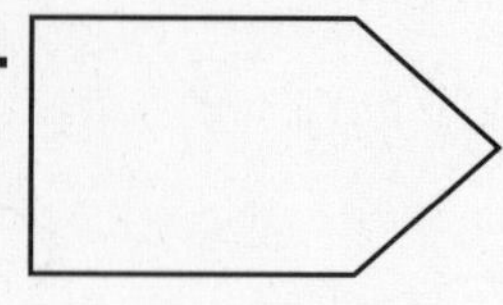
4. 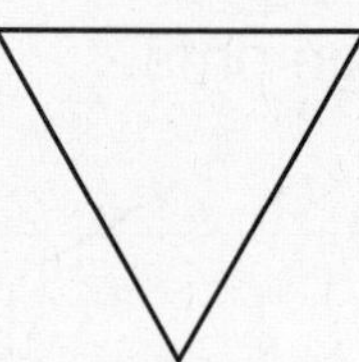

Is each figure a polygon? If it is not, explain why.

5. 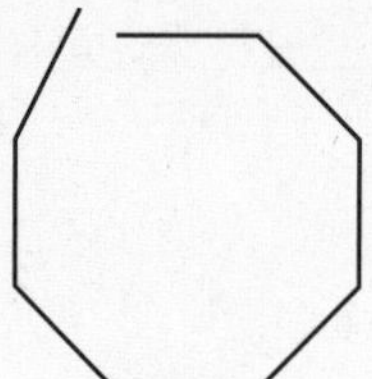
6. 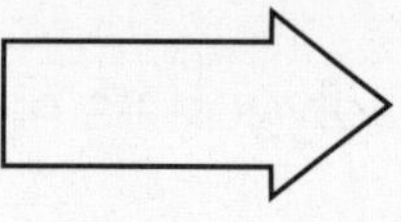
7. 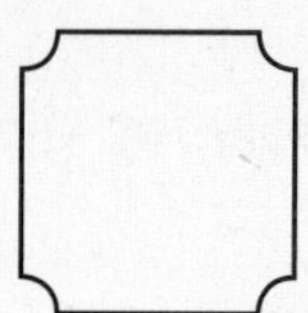
8. 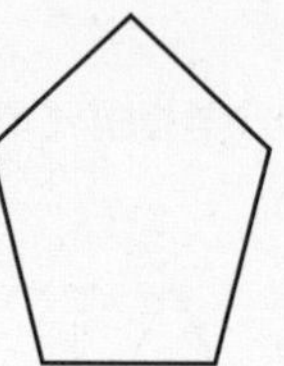

Practice 10-5

9. **Explain It** Juan said that the two figures below are quadrilaterals. Is he correct? Explain.

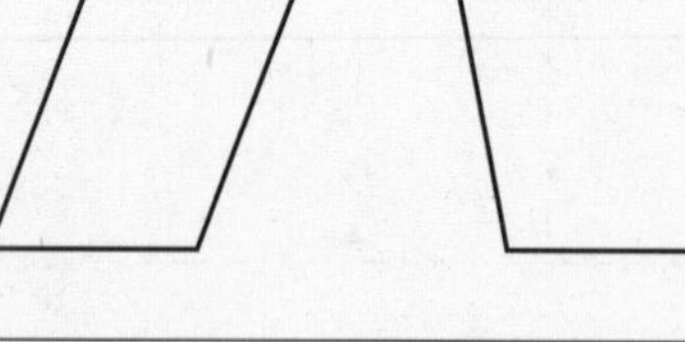

10. **Reasoning** If two of the line segments of a polygon are parallel, what is the least number of sides it could have?

11. How many more sides does an octagon have than a pentagon?

A 1 **B** 2 **C** 3 **D** 4

Name ______________________________

Triangles

Triangles are polygons with three sides.

Triangles can be named by the lengths of their sides.

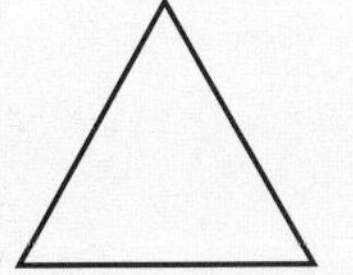

Equilateral Triangle
All sides are the same length.

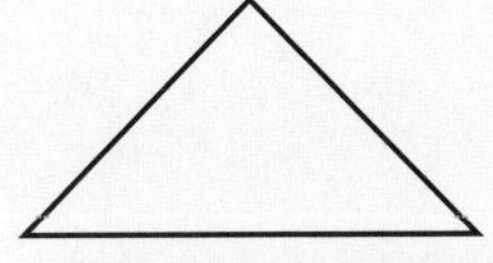

Isosceles Triangle
At least two sides are the same length.

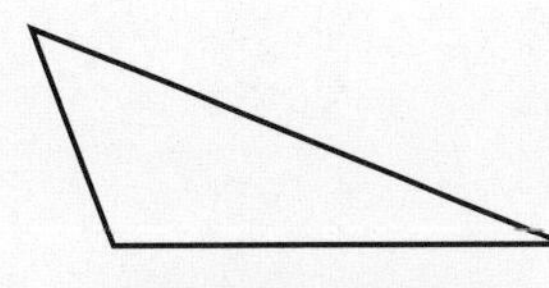

Scalene Triangle
No sides are the same length.

Triangles can also be described by their angles.

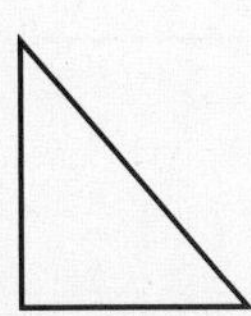

Right Triangle
One angle is a right angle.

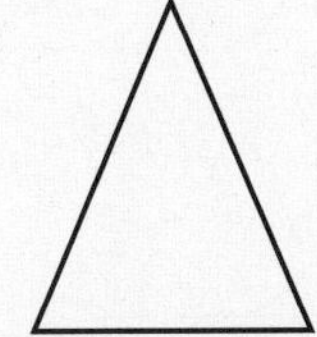

Acute Triangle
All three angles are acute angles.

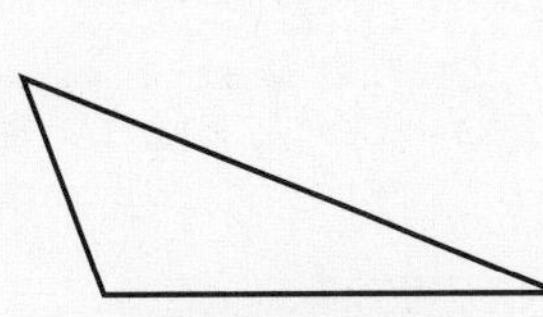

Obtuse Triangle
One angle is an obtuse angle.

Tell if the triangle is equilateral, isosceles, or scalene.

1. 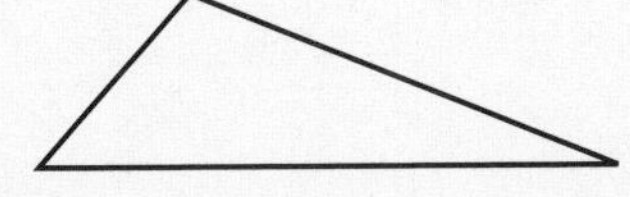

____

2. 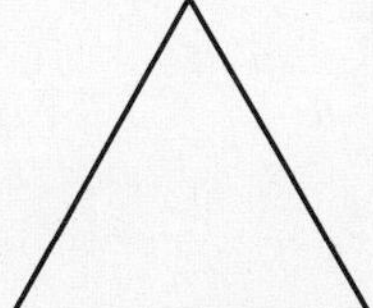

____

3. 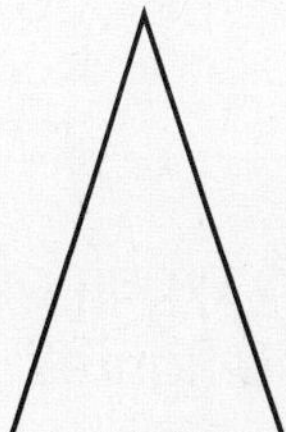

____

Tell if the triangle is right, acute, or obtuse.

4. 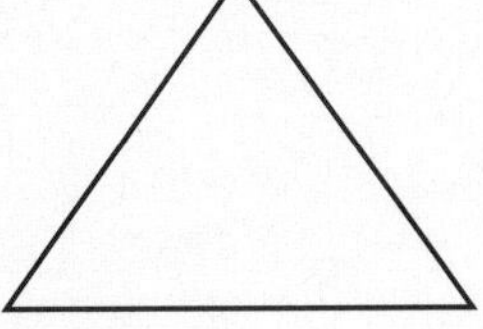

____

5. 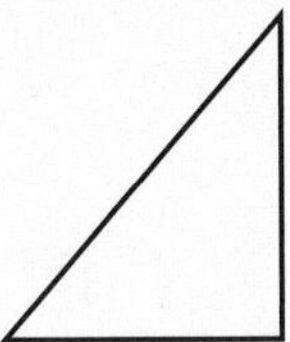

____

6. 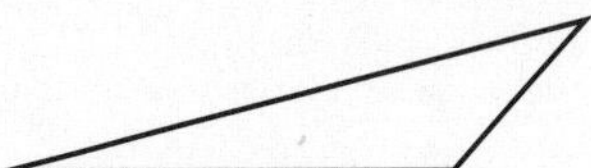

____

Name ______________________

Practice **10-6**

Triangles

Tell if each triangle is equilateral, isosceles, or scalene.

1.  ____________

2.  ____________

3. 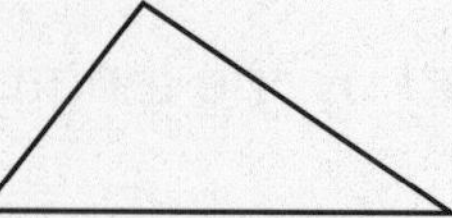 ____________

4. 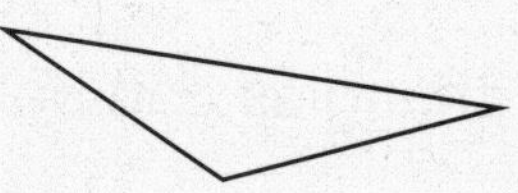 ____________

Tell if each triangle is right, acute, or obtuse.

5. 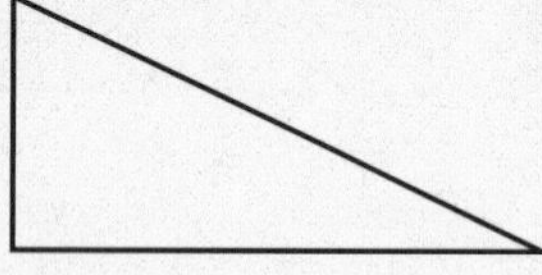 ____________

6.  ____________

7.  ____________

8. 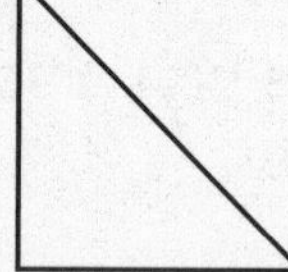 ____________

9. Explain It Can a triangle have 2 right angles? Explain.

____

____

____

10. Reasoning What is the least number of acute angles that a triangle can have?

____

11. Which two types of triangles identify the figure?

A Equilateral triangle, acute triangle

B Equilateral triangle, right triangle

C Scalene triangle, acute triangle

D Isosceles triangle, obtuse triangle

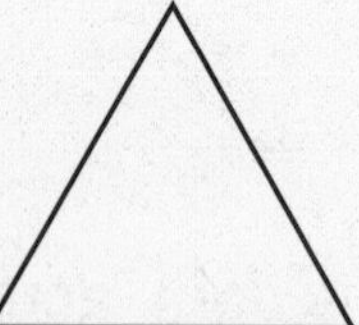

Practice 10-6

Name ______________________________

Quadrilaterals

Quadrilaterals are polygons with four sides. Some quadrilaterals have special names because of their sides. Some have special names because of their angles. Here are some examples.

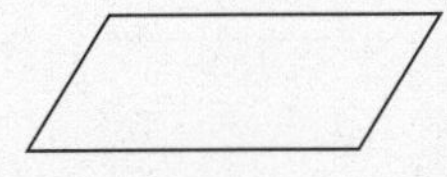	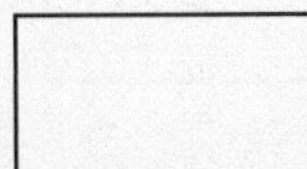	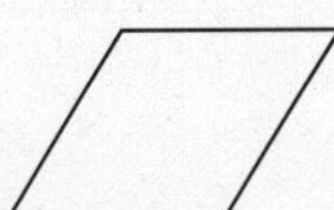		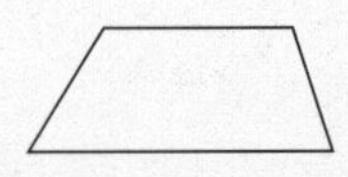
Parallelogram Opposite sides are equal and parallel.	**Rectangle** Parallelogram with 4 right angles	**Rhombus** Parallelogram with 4 equal sides	**Square** A rhombus with 4 right angles	**Trapezoid** Exactly one pair of parallel sides

Write as many names as possible for each quadrilateral.

1. 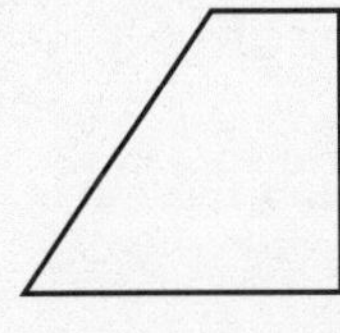

____

____

2. 

____

____

3. 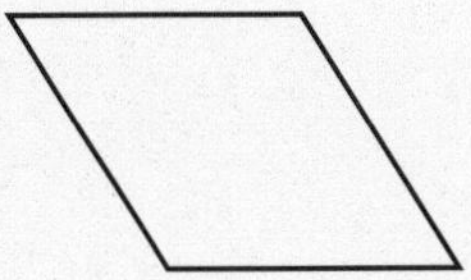

____

____

4. 

____

____

5. Reasoning Is a trapezoid also a parallelogram? Explain why or why not.

____

____

____

Name ____________________

Practice **10-7**

Quadrilaterals

Write as many names as possible for each quadrilateral.

1.  **2.** **3.** 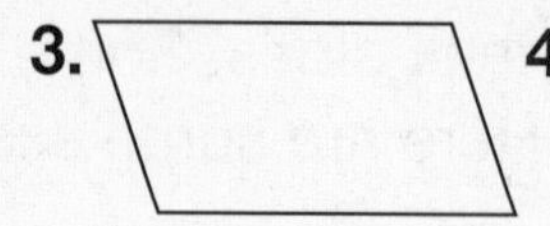 **4.** **5.** 

In **6** through **9**, write the name that best describes the quadrilateral.

6. A parallelogram with 4 equal sides, but no right angles.

7. A rectangle with 4 right angles and all sides the same length.

8. A figure that is not a parallelogram, with one pair of parallel sides.

9. A parallelogram with 4 right angles and with sides different in length and width.

10. Explain It Can a rectangle also be a rhombus?

11. Which of the following correctly names the figure?

A Rhombus

B Trapezoid

C Parallelogram

D Rectangle

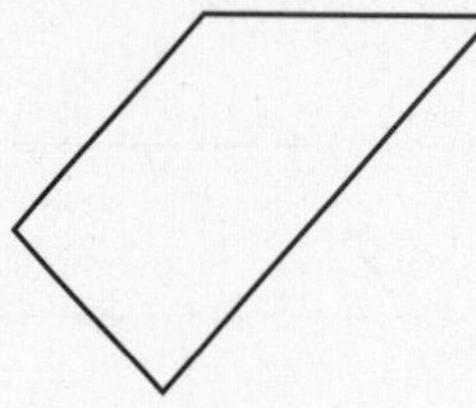

Practice 10-7

Name ______________________

Problem Solving: Make and Test Generalizations

A generalization is a statement that has drawn a conclusion about something. For example, look at these three figures.

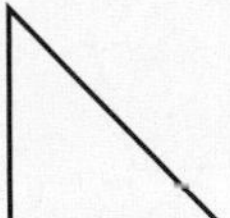
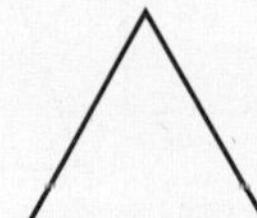
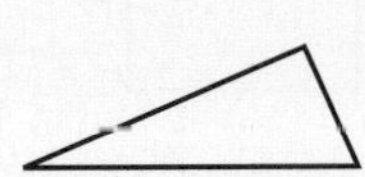

Make a generalization: The figures are all acute triangles.
The triangle on the left has a right angle, making it a right triangle.
This generalization is not true.

Try another generalization: The figures are all triangles.
Each of the figures is a polygon with 3 sides. This generalization is correct.

Make and test a generalization for each set of polygons.

1. 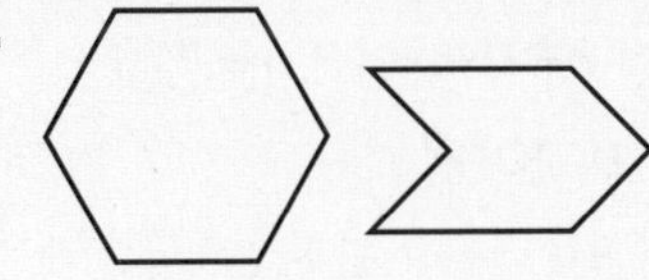

____

____

2. 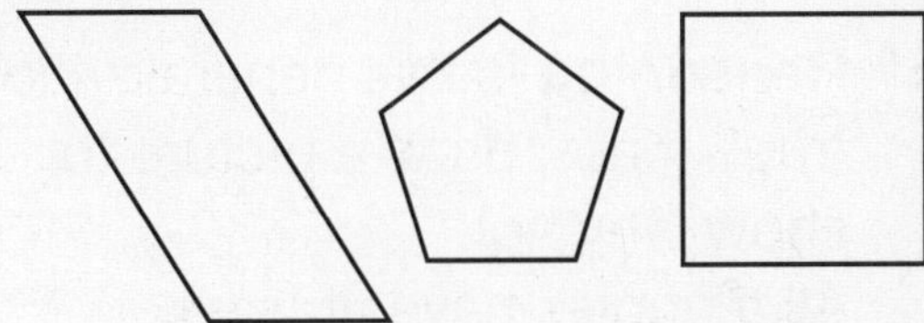

____

____

3. 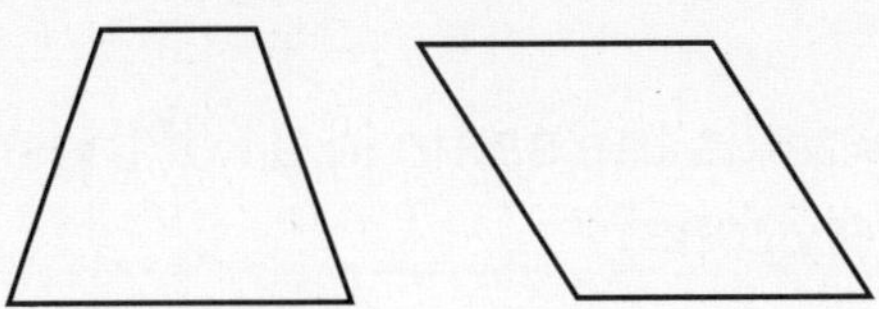

____

____

4. 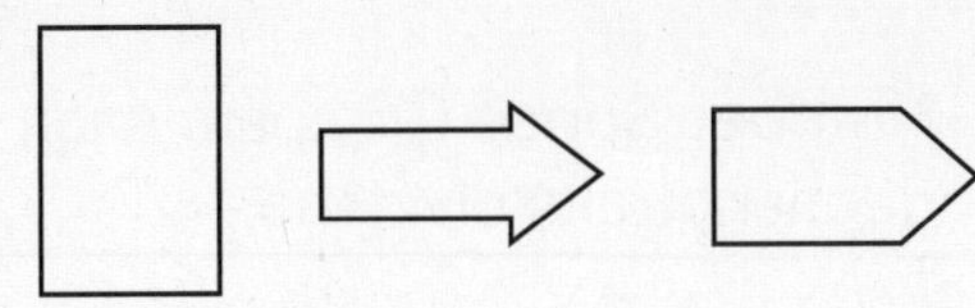

____

____

Name ______________________________

Practice 10-8

Problem Solving: Make and Test Generalizations

In **1** through **4**, make a generalization for each set of polygons.

1. 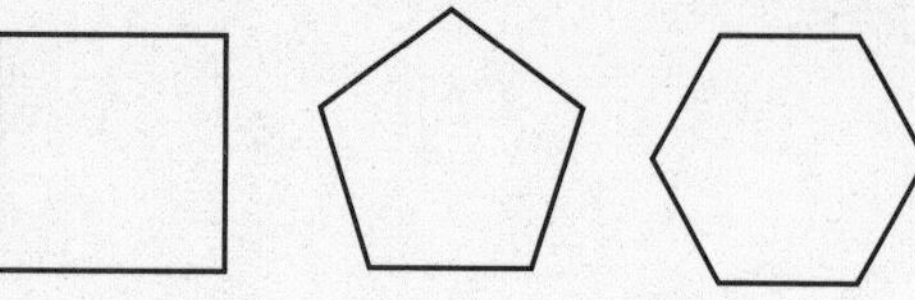

____

2. 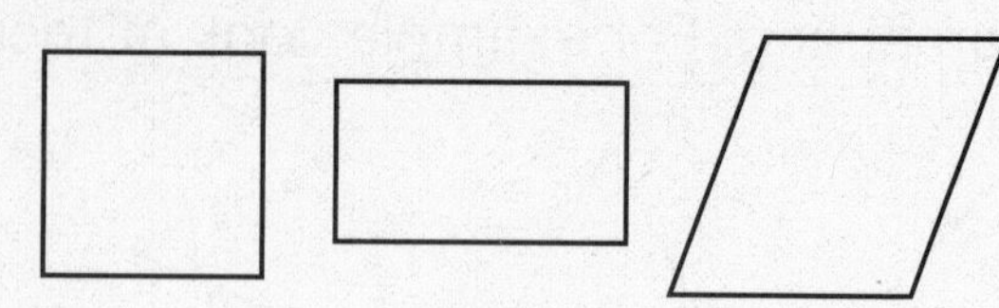

____

3. 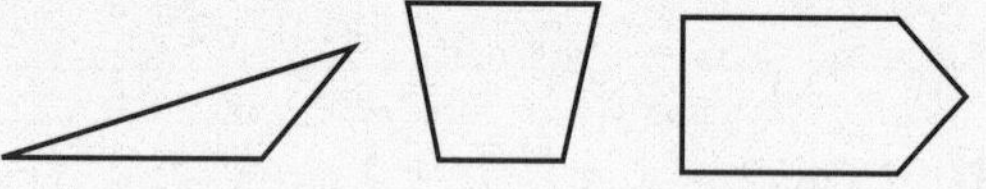

____

4. 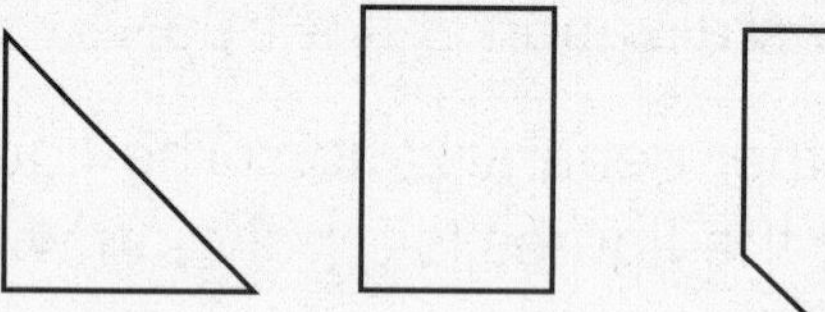

____

5. Reasoning Is this generalization true? If not, draw a picture to show why not.
All triangles have at least 2 acute angles.

____

6. What do all of these numbers have in common?

3, 5, 7, 11, 13

____

____

____

7. Number Sense Compare each quotient to its dividend.

$42 \div 6 = 7$
$8 \div 1 = 8$
$12 \div 12 = 1$

Make a generalization about dividends and quotients for whole numbers.

____

8. What is the same in all of these polygons?

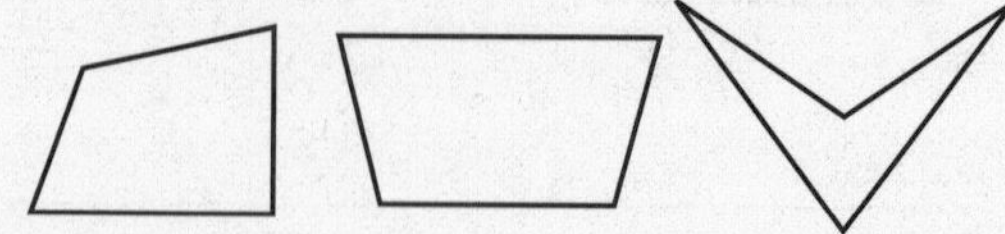

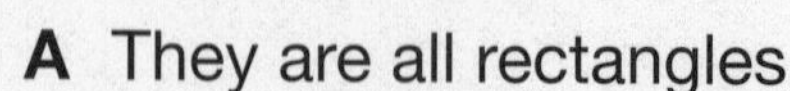

A They are all rectangles.
B They are all rhombuses.
C They are all quadrilaterals.
D They all have right angles.

Practice 10-8

Name ______________________________

Congruent Figures and Motion

Reteaching
11-1

Congruent figures are figures that have the same size and the same shape.

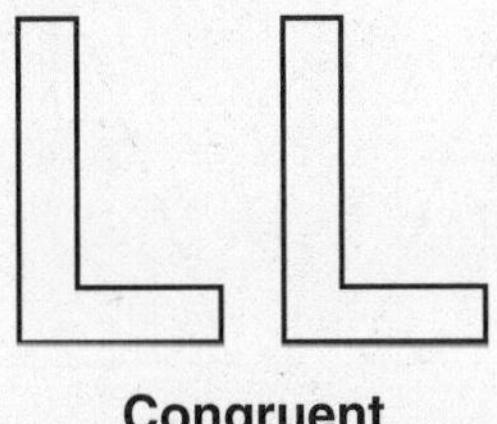

Congruent
Same size and shape

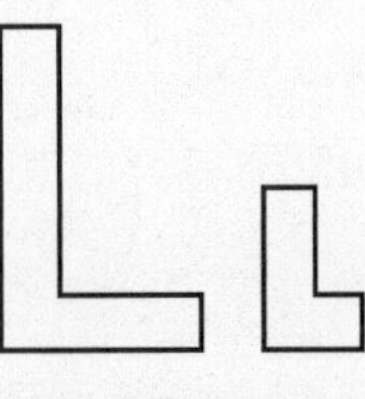

Not Congruent
Different shape

Not Congruent
Different size

Figures can be moved in a number of ways. You can slide, turn, or flip a figure without changing its size or shape.

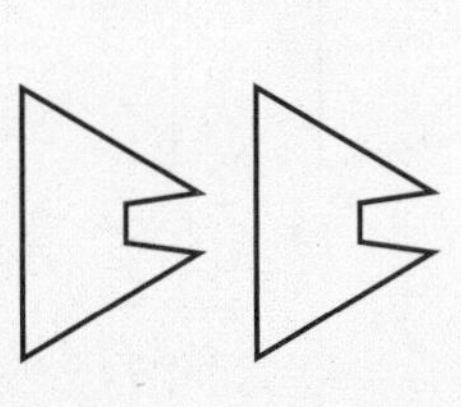

Slide or **Translation**

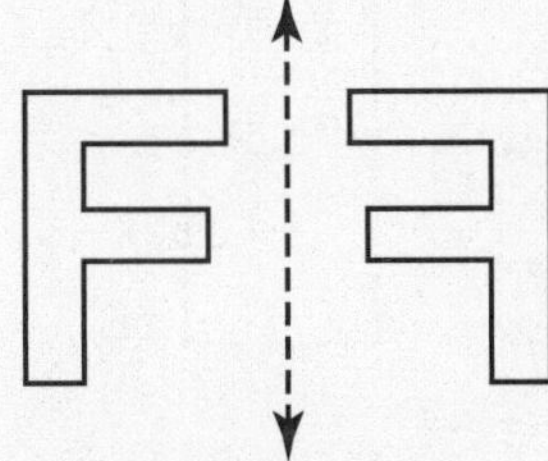

Flip or **Reflection**

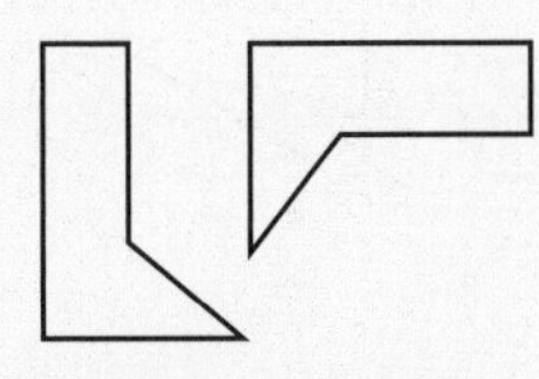

Turn or **Rotation**

In each case, the original figure has been moved to form a new figure that is congruent to the original.

Are the figures congruent? Write *yes* or *no*.

1. 

____

2. 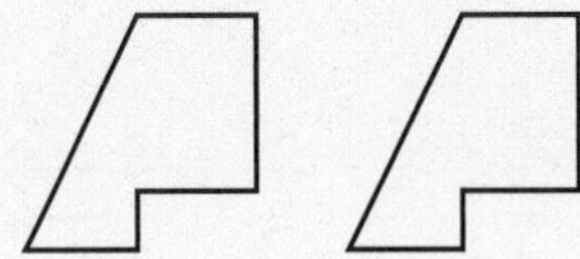

____

Write *flip*, *slide*, or *turn* for each.

3. 

____

4. 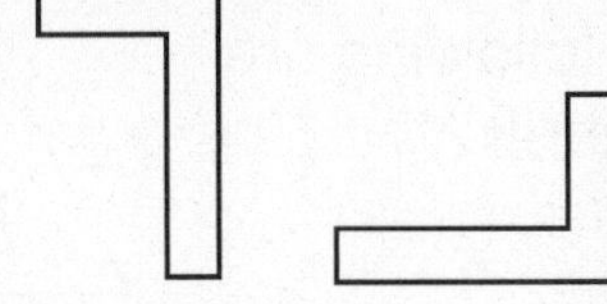

____

Reteaching **11-1**

Name ______________________________

Practice
11-1

Congruent Figures and Motion

Write *translation, reflection,* or *rotation* for each pair of congruent figures.

1. 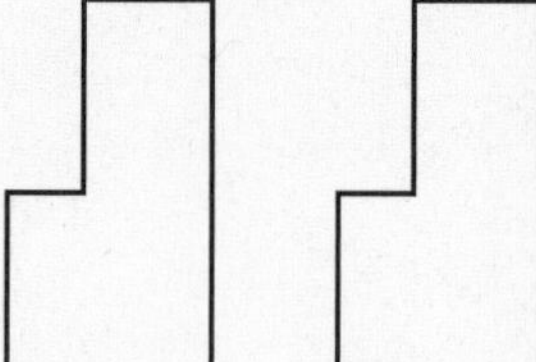
____

2. 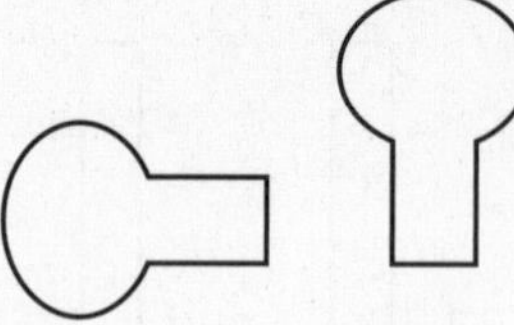
____

3. 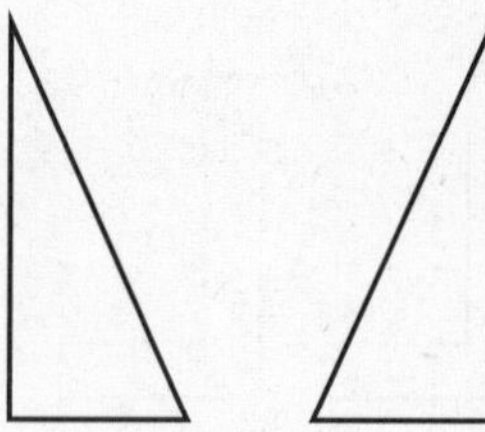
____

Are the figures congruent? Write *yes* or *no*. You may trace to decide.

4. 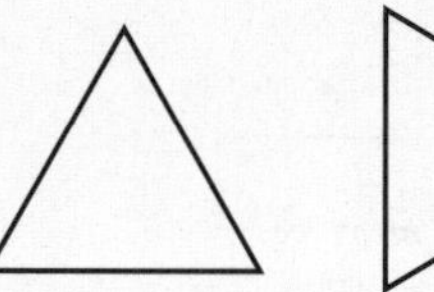
____

5. 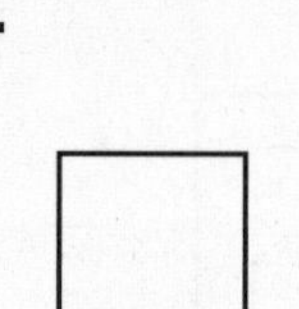 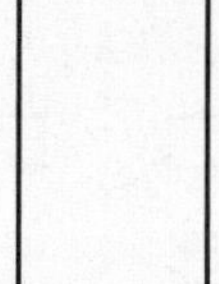
____

6. 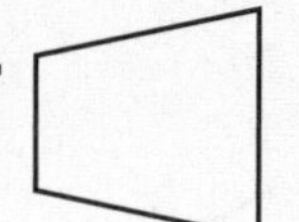 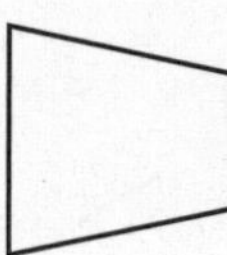
____

7. Reasoning Are all squares congruent? Explain.

____

8. Explain It Could a triangle and a rectangle ever be congruent? Explain.

____

9. Which of the following are congruent figures?

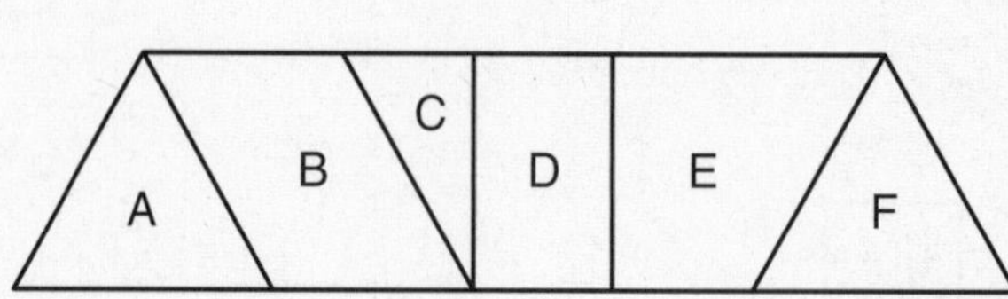

A A and E **B** B and D **C** C and F **D** A and F

Practice 11-1

Name ______________________________

Line Symmetry

Figures are **symmetric** if you can divide them in half and both halves match exactly.

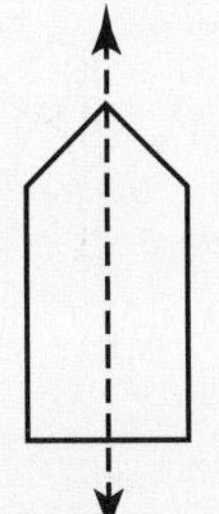

The figure is symmetric. The halves match.

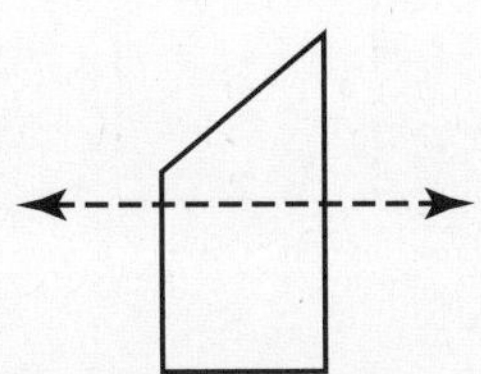

The figure is not symmetric. The halves do not match.

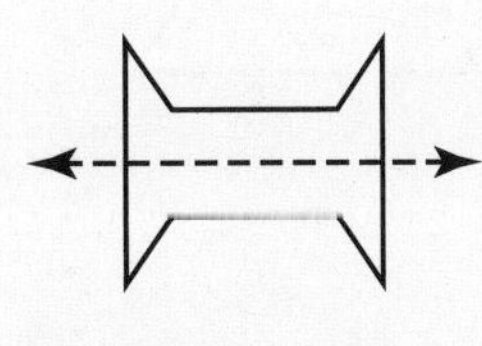

The figure is symmetric. The halves match.

A line that divides a figure into congruent halves is called a **line of symmetry**. Some figures have more than one line of symmetry.

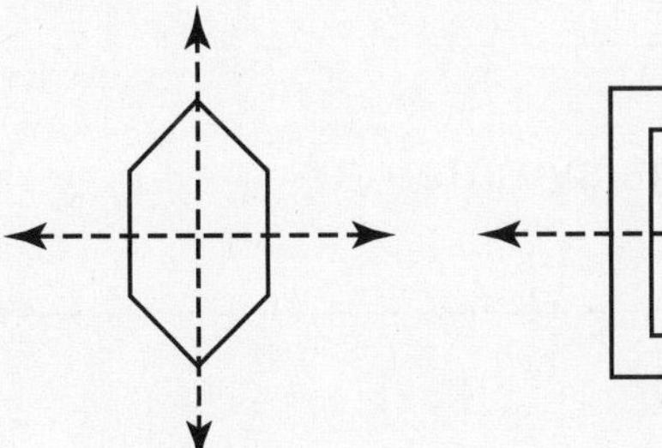

The figure has two lines of symmetry.

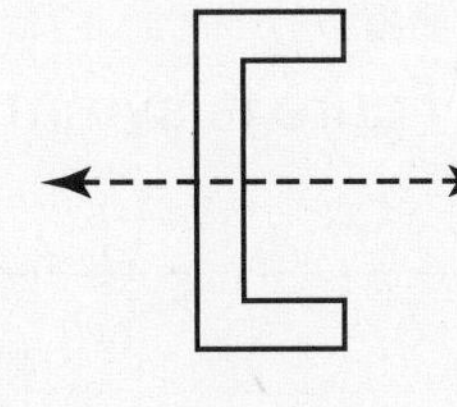

The figure has one line of symmetry.

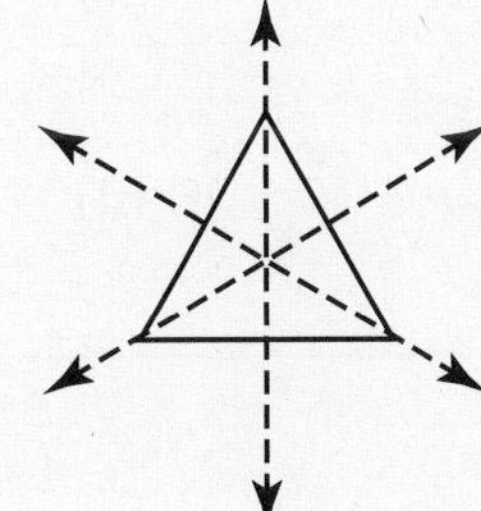

The figure has three lines of symmetry.

Tell whether each figure is symmetric. Write *yes* or *no*.

1. 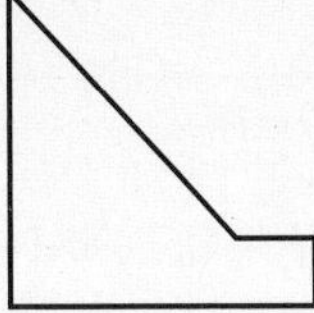

____

2. 

____

3. 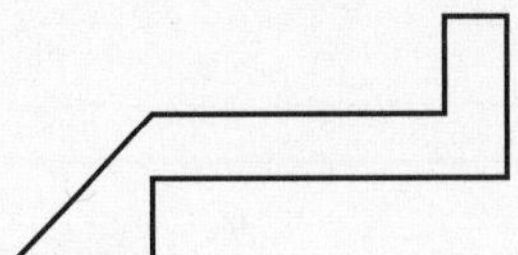

____

4. 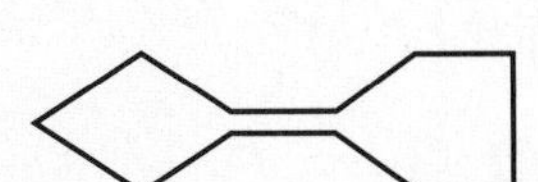

____

5. 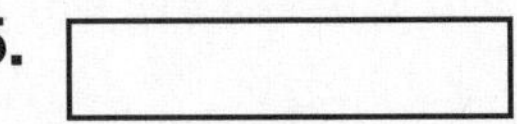

____

6. 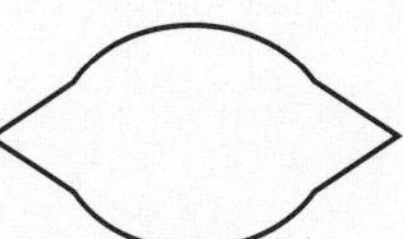

____

Name ______________________

Line Symmetry

Is the figure symmetric? Write *yes* or *no*. You may trace to decide.

1. 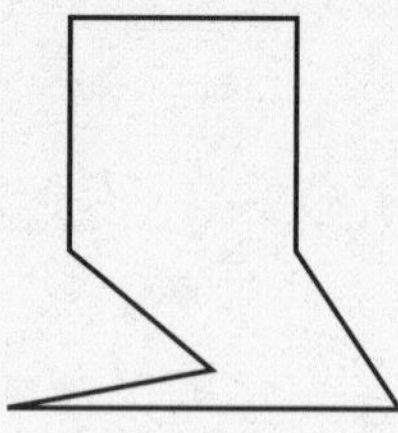
______

2. 
______

3. 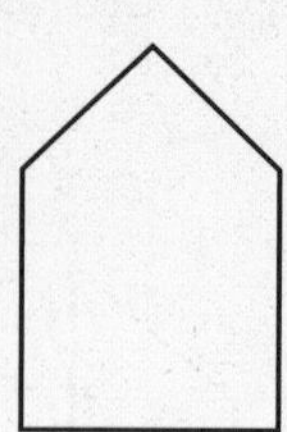
______

4. 
______

5. 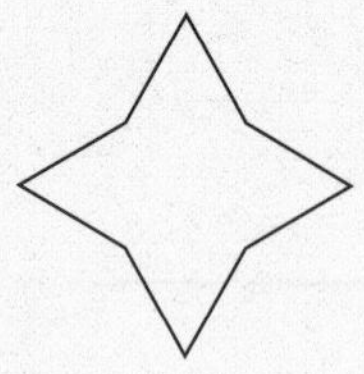
______

6. 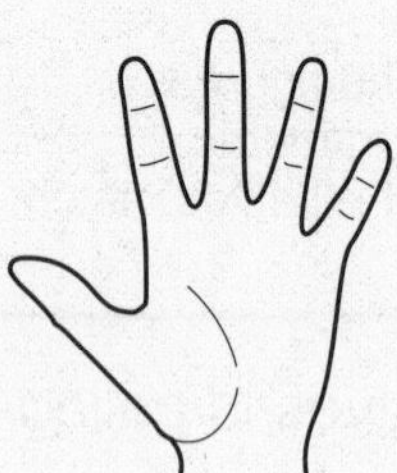
______

7. 
______

8. 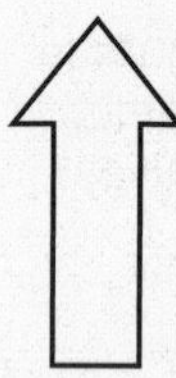
______

9. **Writing to Explain** How do you know if a figure is symmetric?

______

10. **Reasoning** One of the figures in 1–4 above has more than 1 line of symmetry. Which figure? Explain.

______

11. How many lines of symmetry does the rhombus to the right have?

A 0 **B** 1 **C** 2 **D** 3

12. Which figures always have the same number of lines of symmetry?

A Triangles **B** Trapezoids **C** Squares **D** Pentagons

Name ________________________________

Drawing Shapes with Lines of Symmetry

A figure has a line of symmetry if the two halves match exactly when you fold along that line. To the right is half of a figure.

You can draw the other half of the figure. Draw an exact match of what is already there. The dashed line is the line of symmetry.

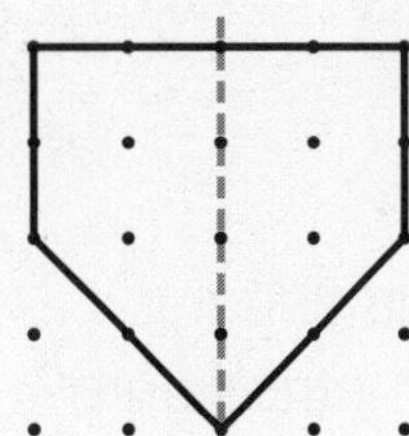

The figure is a pentagon. This pentagon has one line of symmetry.

Complete the figure so the dashed line segment is part of a line of symmetry.

1. 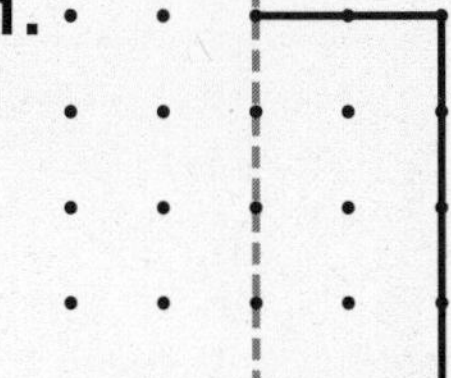

2. 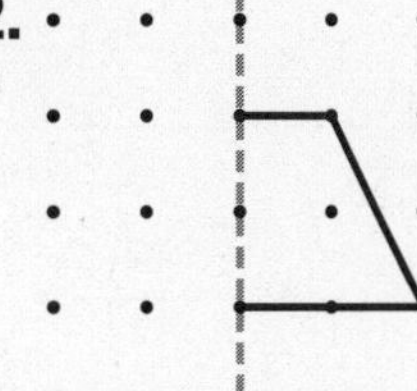

3. 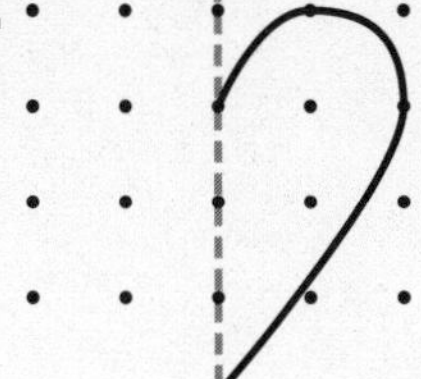

4. 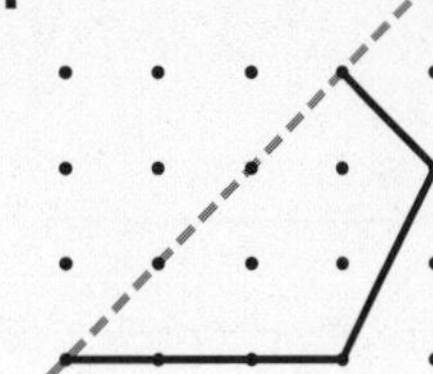

Name ___________________________

Drawing Shapes with Lines of Symmetry

Complete the figure so the dashed line segment is part of a line of symmetry.

1. 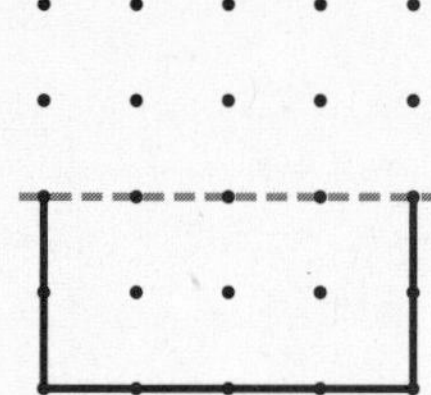

2. 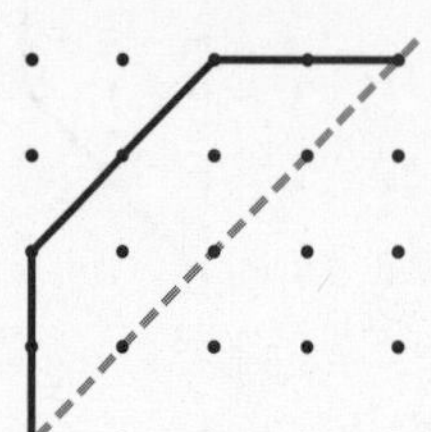

3. 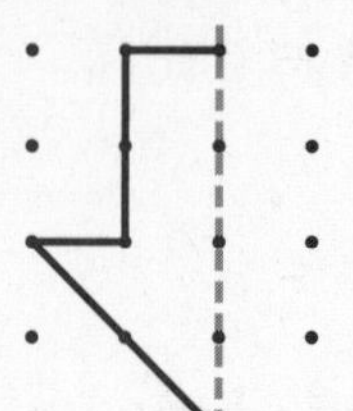

4. 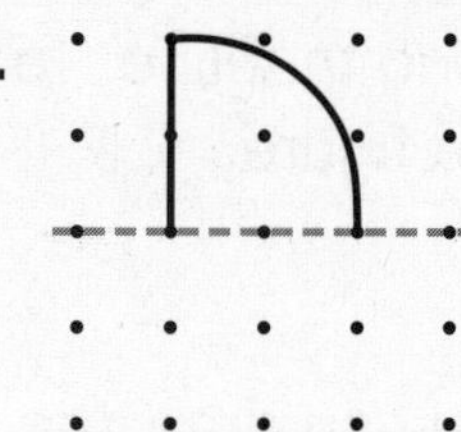

5. **Explain It** How can you use this shape to make a symmetric figure? Classify the shape created.

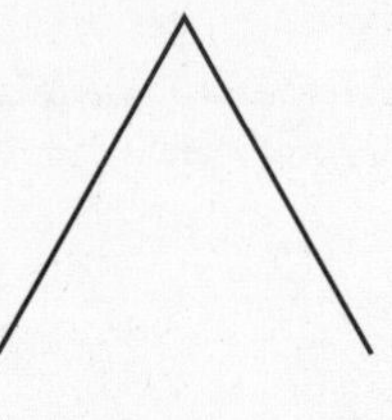

6. The dashed line is part of a line of symmetry. Which picture completes the figure?

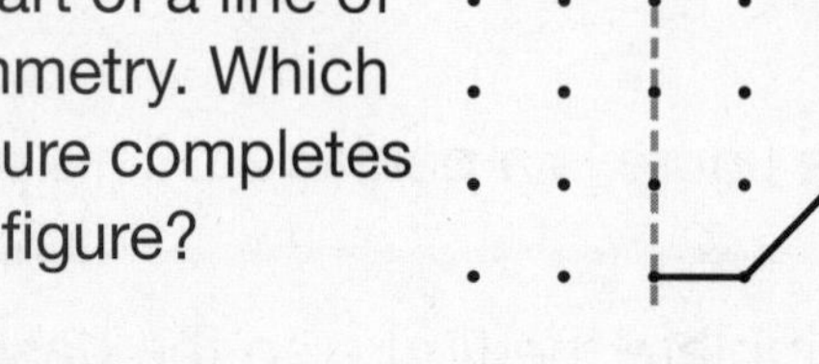

A 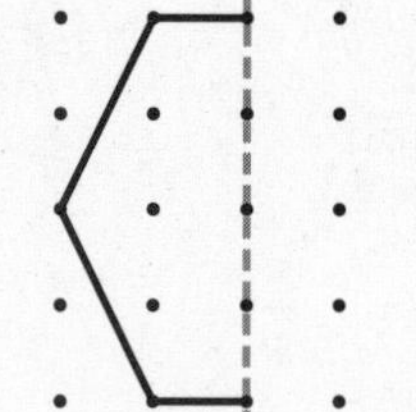

B 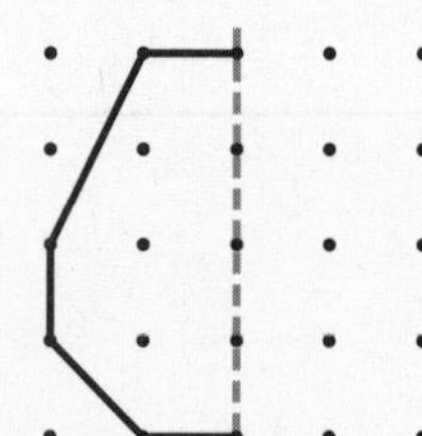

C 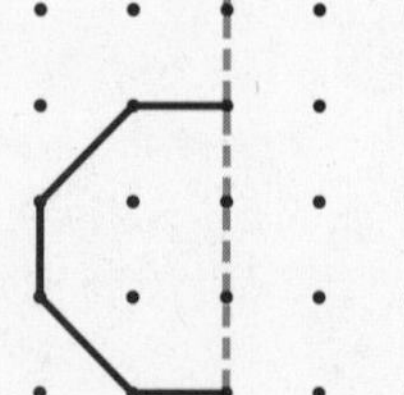

D 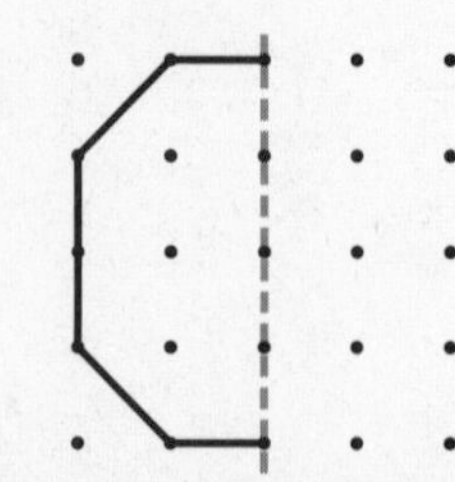

Name ___________________________

Reteaching
11-4

Problem Solving: Use Objects

A tangram is a square that is made of seven smaller shapes.

You can make different shapes from parts of the tangram. Some examples are shown below.

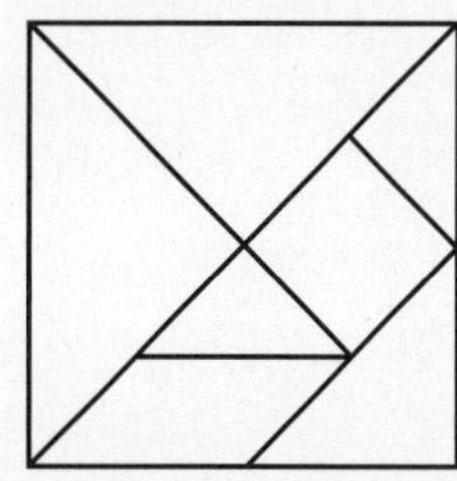

Use 2 pieces to create a figure with at least 1 line of symmetry.

Use 3 pieces to create a figure with at least 1 line of symmetry.

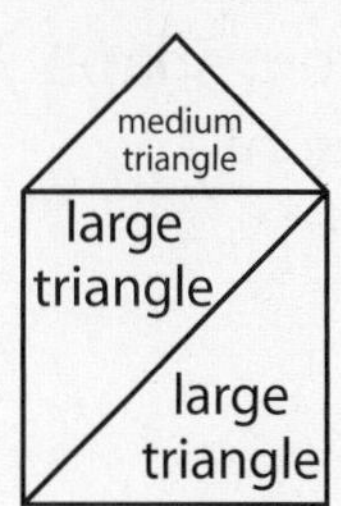

Use the tangram to make the shape. Draw what you made.

1. Make a rectangle from two small triangles and a medium triangle.

2. Use a medium triangle, a parallelogram, and a small triangle. Make a pentagon with one line of symmetry.

3. **Writing to Explain** How do you know if a shape made with tangram pieces has a line of symmetry?

____

____

____

Reteaching **11-4**

Name ______________________________

Problem Solving: Use Objects

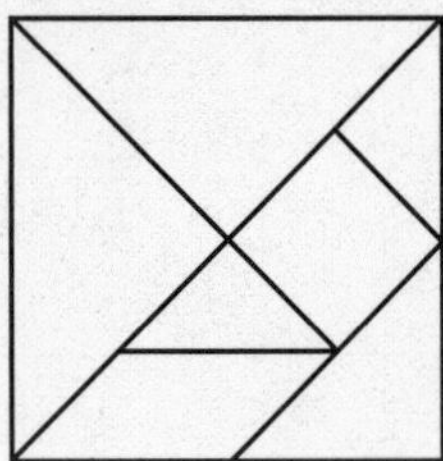

Use the tangram to make the shape. Draw the shape you made.

1. Use the medium triangle and the two small triangles. Make a shape that has at least two lines of symmetry.

2. Use the square and the two small triangles. Make a shape that has at least two lines of symmetry.

3. **Draw a Picture** Use the two large triangles and the medium triangle to make a 5-sided figure with one line of symmetry.

4. Use any five pieces from the tangram set. Make at least three different shapes. Draw all of the shapes you made.

Name ____________________

Dividing Regions into Equal Parts

A whole can be divided into equal parts in different ways.

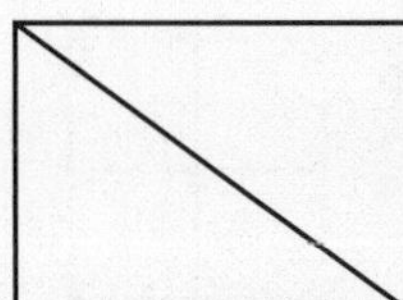

2 equal parts
halves

3 equal parts
thirds

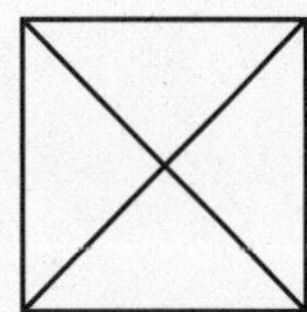

4 equal parts
fourths

5 equal parts
fifths

6 equal parts
sixths

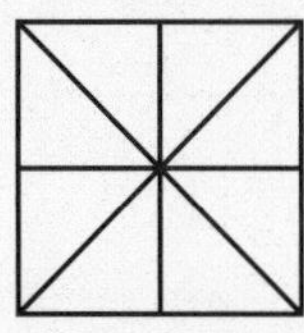

8 equal parts
eighths

10 equal parts
tenths

12 equal parts
twelfths

Tell if each shows equal parts or unequal parts.
If the parts are equal, name them.

1. ____________________

2. 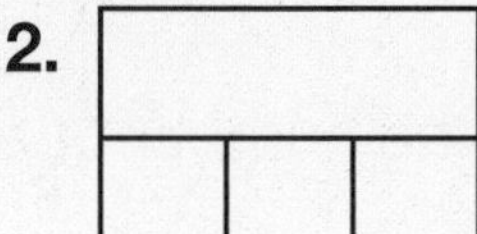

____

3. 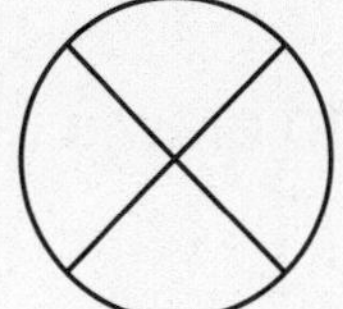

____

Name the equal parts of the whole.

4. 

____

5. 

____

6. 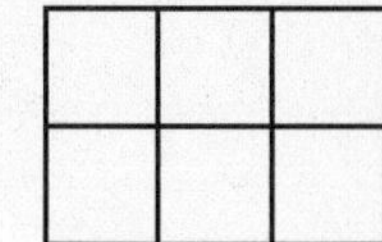

____

7. Using grid paper, draw a picture of a whole that is divided into thirds.

8. **Reasoning** How many equal parts are there when you divide a figure into fifths? ____________________

Name ______________________________

Dividing Regions into Equal Parts

Tell if each shows equal or unequal parts.
If the parts are equal, name them.

1. 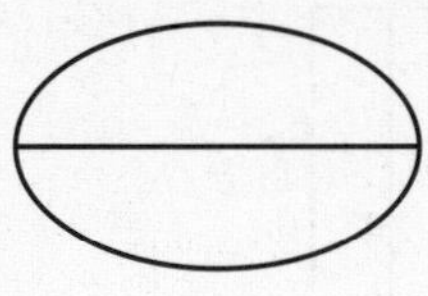

2. 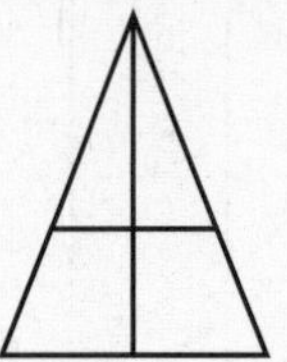

3. 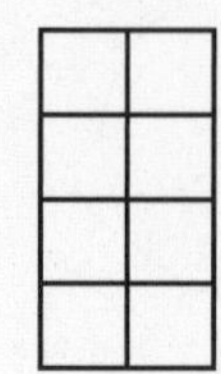

4. 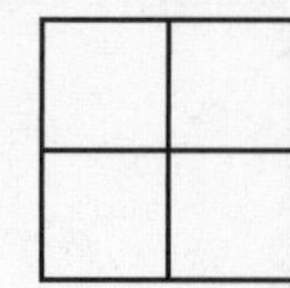

Name the equal parts of the whole.

5. 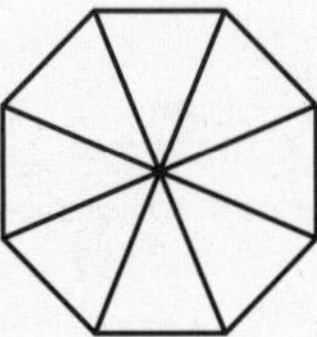

6. 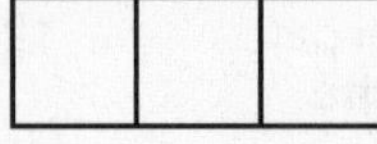

7. 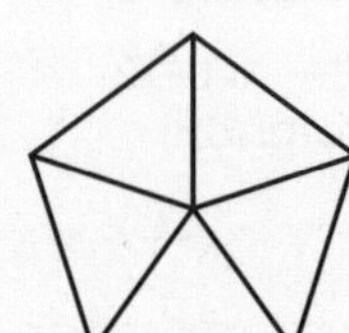

8. 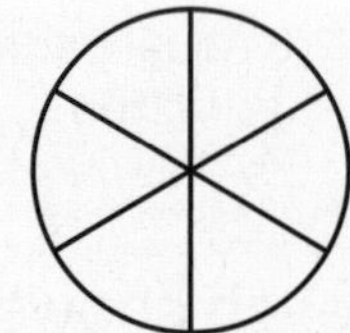

Use the grid to draw a region showing the number of equal parts named.

9. tenths

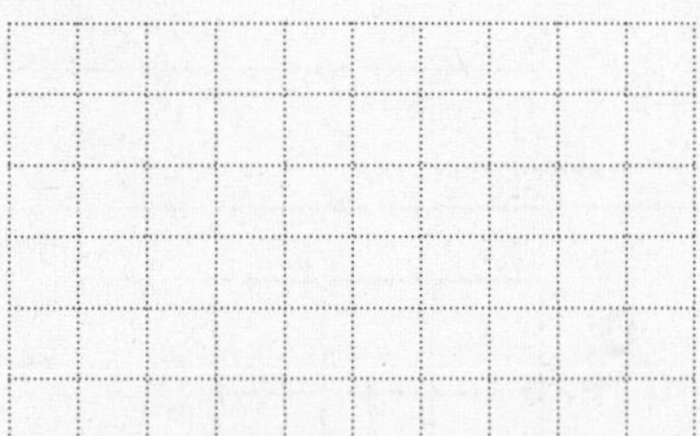

10. sixths

11. **Geometry** How many equal parts does this figure have?

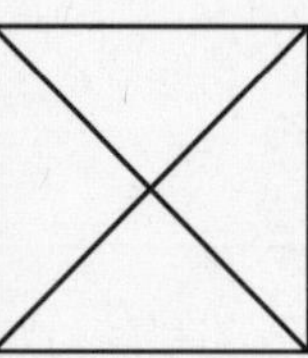

12. Which is the name of 12 equal parts of a whole?

A halves **B** sixths **C** tenths **D** twelfths

Name ___________________________

Fractions and Regions

A fraction can be used to name part of a whole.

The denominator names the number of equal parts.

The numerator names the number of parts being considered.

number of parts shaded ⟶ 1 ⟵ Numerator
number of equal parts ⟶ 5 ⟵ Denominator

One fifth of the rectangle is shaded.

Here are some other fractions to represent parts of a whole.

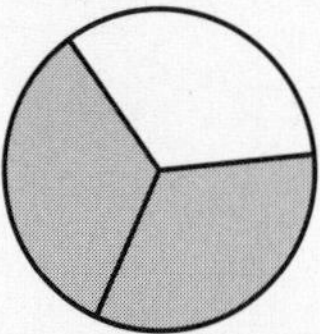

$\frac{2}{3}$ of the circle is shaded.

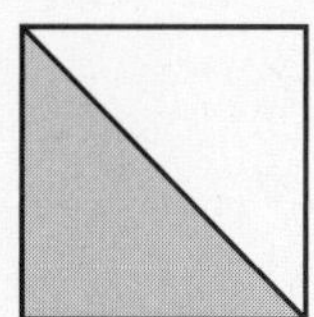

$\frac{1}{2}$ of the square is shaded.

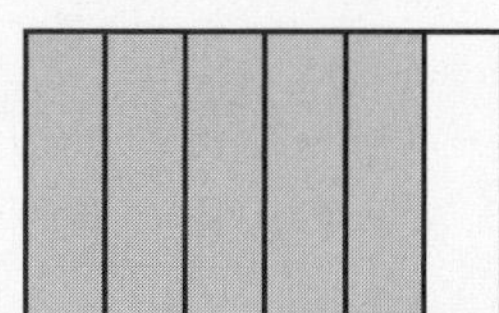

$\frac{5}{6}$ of the rectangle is shaded.

Write the fraction of each figure that is shaded.

1. 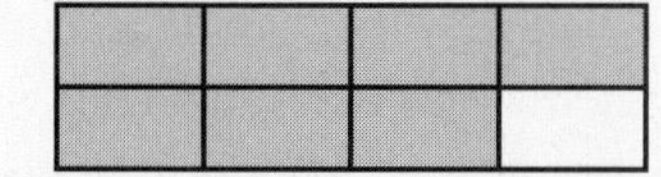 ________

2. 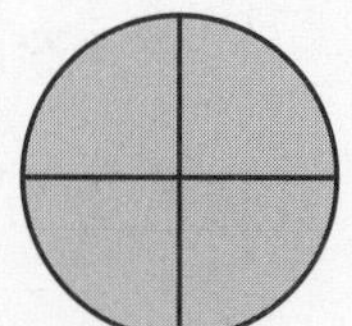 ________

3. 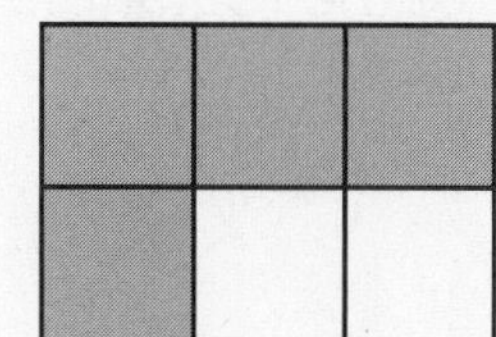 ________

4. 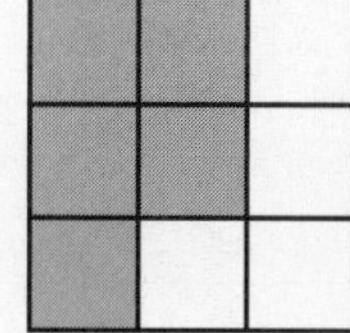 ________

Draw a figure to show each fraction.

5. $\frac{1}{3}$

6. $\frac{5}{12}$

7. $\frac{3}{5}$

8. **Reasoning** A shape is $\frac{1}{7}$ shaded. What fraction is not shaded?

____

Name ____________________

Practice
12-2

Fractions and Regions

Write the fraction of each figure that is shaded.

1. 
______

2. ______

3. 
______

4. 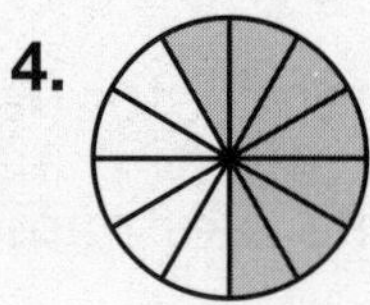
______

Draw a picture to show each fraction.

5. $\frac{3}{8}$

6. $\frac{1}{4}$

7. $\frac{4}{5}$

Practice 12-2

In **8** and **9**, use the information below.

Three parts of a rectangle are red. Two parts are blue.

8. What fraction of the rectangle is red?

______

9. **Reasoning** What fraction of the rectangle is blue?

______

10. **Draw a Picture** A banner is made of 8 equal parts. Five of the parts contain stars. Three of the parts contain hearts. Draw the banner.

11. How can you write the fraction $\frac{4}{6}$ in word form?

A fourth sixth **B** four sixes **C** four sixths **D** fourth six

Name ______________________

Fractions and Sets

A fraction can name part of a group.

What fraction of the marbles are black?

3 ⟵ Number of black marbles
8 ⟵ Total number of marbles

$\frac{3}{8}$ of the marbles are black.

1. What fraction of the toys are balls? ______

2. What fraction of the fruits are oranges? ______

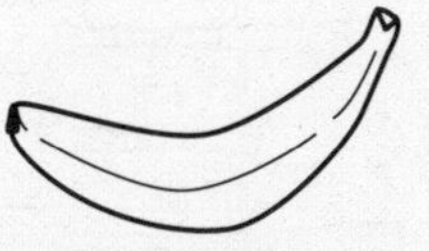
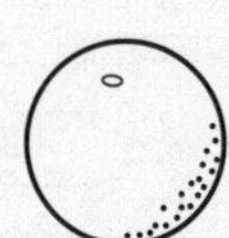
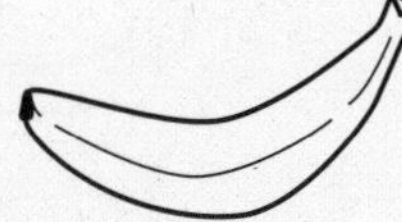

3. What fraction of the blocks have letters on them? ______

4. What fraction of the days of the week begin with the letter *T*? ______

For **5** and **6** draw a picture to show each fraction of a set.

5. $\frac{3}{5}$ of the squares are shaded.

6. $\frac{2}{3}$ of the balls are footballs.

7. **Reasoning** Out of 6 cats, 2 are tan. What fraction of cats are **NOT** tan? ______

Name ______________________

Practice 12-3

Fractions and Sets

In **1** through **3**, write the fraction of the counters that are shaded.

1. 

______

2. 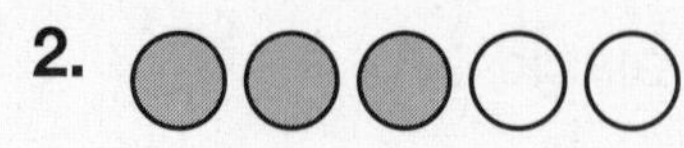

______

3. 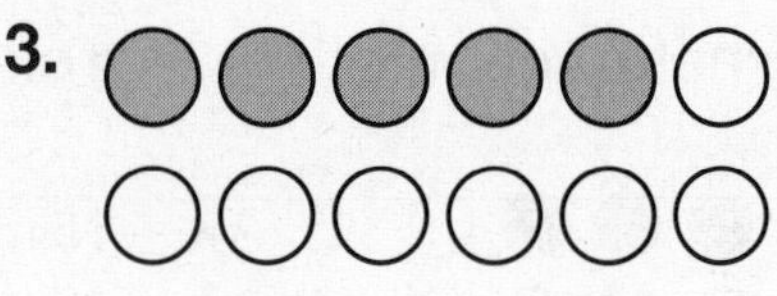

______

Draw a picture of the set described.

4. 4 shapes, $\frac{3}{4}$ of the shapes are squares

5. 6 shapes, $\frac{1}{6}$ of the shapes are circles

6. 10 shapes, $\frac{7}{10}$ of the shapes are triangles

In **7** and **8**, use the utensils to answer the questions.

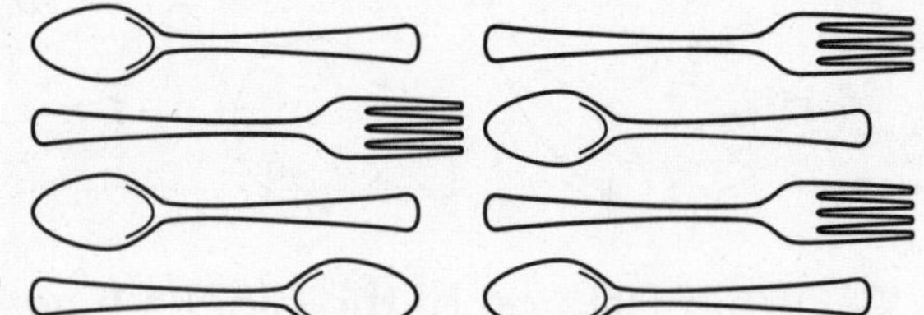

7. What fraction of the utensils are forks?

______

8. What fraction of the utensils are spoons?

______

9. **Number Sense** Johnny bought 5 movie tickets and spent $44. Of the tickets he bought, $\frac{3}{5}$ were children's tickets that cost $8 each. The other tickets were adult tickets. How much does one adult ticket cost?

______

10. Pamela has 4 pink ribbons, 3 green ribbons, and 2 blue ribbons. What fraction of Pamela's ribbons are green?

A $\frac{3}{9}$ **B** $\frac{3}{6}$ **C** $\frac{3}{5}$ **D** $\frac{3}{4}$

Practice 12-3

Name ______________________

Benchmark Fractions

You can use benchmark fractions to help you estimate parts. Benchmark fractions are $\frac{1}{4}$, $\frac{1}{3}$, $\frac{1}{2}$, $\frac{2}{3}$, and $\frac{3}{4}$.

One way to think of benchmark fractions is to think of part of a clock.

$\frac{1}{2}$ shaded

$\frac{1}{3}$ shaded

$\frac{2}{3}$ shaded

$\frac{1}{4}$ shaded

$\frac{3}{4}$ shaded

Estimate the fractional part that is shaded.

1. ______________________

2. ______________________

3. ______________________

4. ______________________

5. Number Sense About how much of the casserole is left over?

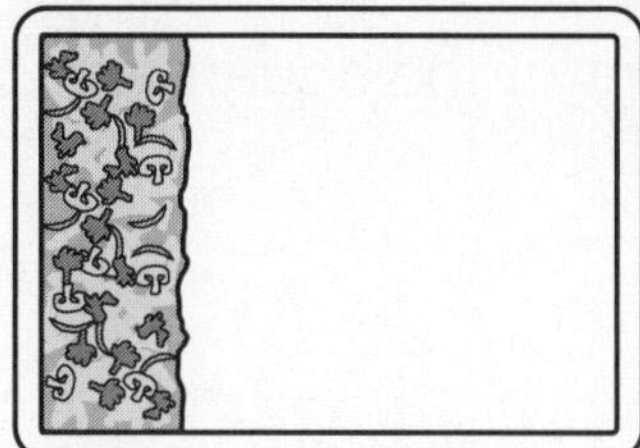

____

Name ____________________

Benchmark Fractions

Estimate the fractional part of each that is shaded.

1. ____________________

2. ____________________

3. ____________________

4. ____________________

What benchmark fraction is closest to each point? Choose from the benchmark fractions $\frac{1}{2}$, $\frac{1}{3}$, $\frac{2}{3}$, $\frac{1}{4}$, and $\frac{3}{4}$.

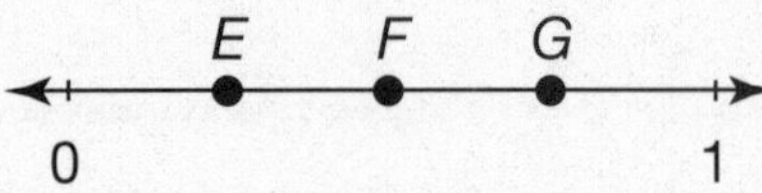

5. *E* __________ **6.** *F* __________ **7.** *G* __________

Estimate the amount that is left.

8.

____

9.

____

10.

____

11. Draw a Picture Draw a circle and shade it to show about $\frac{1}{3}$ shaded.

12. Which is the best estimate for the amount of the square that is shaded?

A $\frac{1}{4}$

B $\frac{1}{3}$

C $\frac{1}{2}$

D $\frac{2}{3}$

Name ______________________________

Finding Equivalent Fractions

Equivalent fractions are fractions that name the same amount. Equivalent fractions have different numerators and denominators, but their values are equal.

You can find equivalent fractions by using fraction strips.

$$\frac{1}{4} = \frac{■}{8}$$

Find how many $\frac{1}{8}$s are equal to $\frac{1}{4}$. The denominator is 8 so use $\frac{1}{8}$ strips.

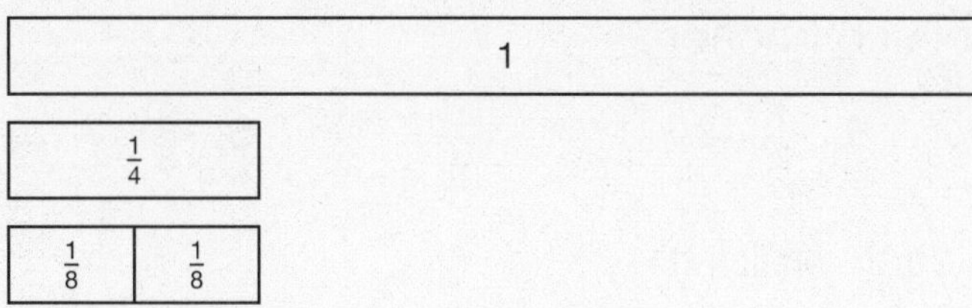

So, two $\frac{1}{8}$ strips are equal to $\frac{1}{4}$.

$$\frac{1}{4} = \frac{2}{8}$$

Another name for $\frac{1}{4}$ is $\frac{2}{8}$.

Complete each number sentence.

1. 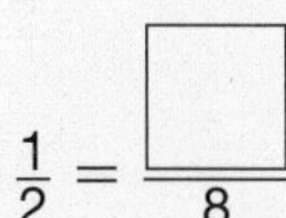

$\frac{1}{2} = \frac{\square}{8}$

2. 1 | $\frac{1}{3}$ $\frac{1}{3}$ | $\frac{1}{12}$ $\frac{1}{12}$ $\frac{1}{12}$ $\frac{1}{12}$ $\frac{1}{12}$ $\frac{1}{12}$ $\frac{1}{12}$ $\frac{1}{12}$

$\frac{2}{3} = \frac{\square}{12}$

3. 1 | $\frac{1}{5}$ $\frac{1}{5}$ $\frac{1}{5}$ $\frac{1}{5}$ | $\frac{1}{10}$ $\frac{1}{10}$ $\frac{1}{10}$ $\frac{1}{10}$ $\frac{1}{10}$ $\frac{1}{10}$ $\frac{1}{10}$ $\frac{1}{10}$

$\frac{4}{5} = \frac{\square}{10}$

4. Name two fractions that are equivalent to $\frac{3}{4}$.

____

5. **Reasoning** Larry and Willa are each reading the same book. Larry has read $\frac{2}{3}$ of the book. Willa said that she has read $\frac{4}{6}$ of the book, so she read more. Is Willa correct? Explain.

____

____

____

Name ______________________

Practice
12-5

Finding Equivalent Fractions

Complete each number sentence.

1. 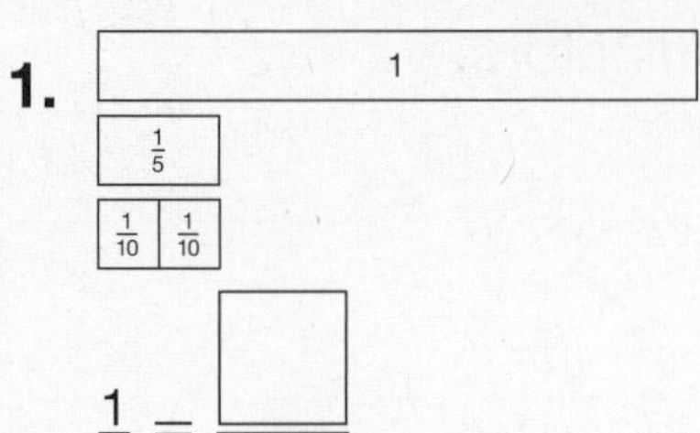

$\frac{1}{5} = \frac{\square}{10}$

2.

1											
$\frac{1}{4}$			$\frac{1}{4}$			$\frac{1}{4}$					
$\frac{1}{12}$	$\frac{1}{12}$	$\frac{1}{12}$	$\frac{1}{12}$	$\frac{1}{12}$	$\frac{1}{12}$	$\frac{1}{12}$	$\frac{1}{12}$	$\frac{1}{12}$			

$\frac{3}{4} = \frac{\square}{12}$

3. 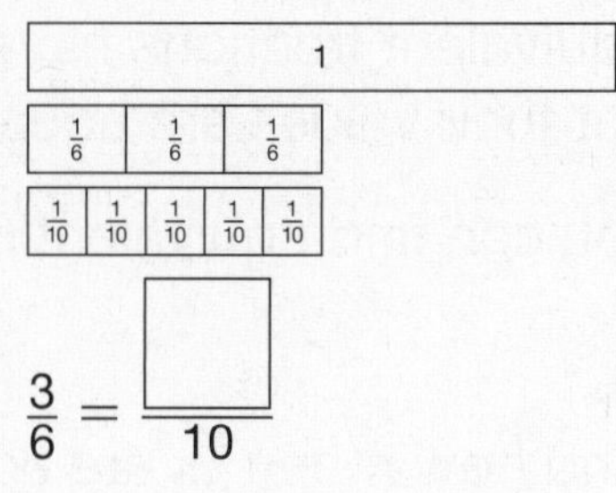

$\frac{3}{6} = \frac{\square}{10}$

Find the simplest form of each fraction.

4. $\frac{3}{12}$ __________

5. $\frac{8}{10}$ __________

6. $\frac{3}{8}$ __________

Name a fraction to solve each problem.

7. Rob colored $\frac{1}{4}$ of a rectangle. What is another way to name $\frac{1}{4}$?

____

8. Three fifths of the cast in a musical have to sing. What fraction of the cast does not have to sing?

____

Complete each pattern.

9. $\frac{1}{3}, \frac{2}{6}, \frac{3}{9}, \frac{4}{\square}$

10. $\frac{1}{2}, \frac{2}{4}, \frac{3}{6}, \frac{4}{8}, \frac{5}{\square}, \frac{6}{\square}$

11. **Explain It** When using fraction strips, how do you know that two fractions are equivalent?

____

____

____

____

____

12. Samuel has read $\frac{5}{6}$ of his assignment. Judy has read $\frac{10}{12}$ of her assignment. Their assignments were the same size. Which sentence is true?

A Samuel read more than Judy.

B Judy read more than Samuel.

C They read the same amount.

D They will both finish the assignment at the same time.

Practice 12-5

Name ______________________

Use Models to Compare Fractions

You can compare fractions by using fraction strips.

Linda and Patti have the same number of raffle tickets to sell. Linda has sold $\frac{3}{5}$ of her raffle tickets. Patti has sold $\frac{2}{3}$ of her raffle tickets. Who sold more of her raffle tickets: Linda or Patti?

Use fraction strips to represent each fraction.

Line up the fraction strips on the left.

Linda	$\frac{1}{5}$	$\frac{1}{5}$	$\frac{1}{5}$
Patti	$\frac{1}{3}$	$\frac{1}{3}$	

The fraction strip that ends farther to the right shows the greater amount. If the right side lines up, the fractions are equal.

So, $\frac{3}{5} < \frac{2}{3}$. Patti sold more of her raffle tickets than Linda sold of hers.

Compare. Write >, <, or =.

1.

$\frac{1}{2}$		
$\frac{1}{4}$	$\frac{1}{4}$	$\frac{1}{4}$

$\frac{1}{2}$ ◯ $\frac{3}{4}$

2.

$\frac{1}{5}$	$\frac{1}{5}$
$\frac{1}{3}$	

$\frac{2}{5}$ ◯ $\frac{1}{3}$

3.

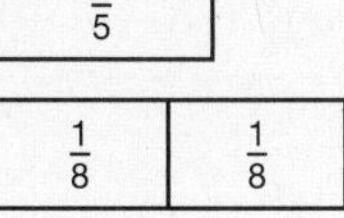

$\frac{2}{8}$ ◯ $\frac{1}{5}$

4.

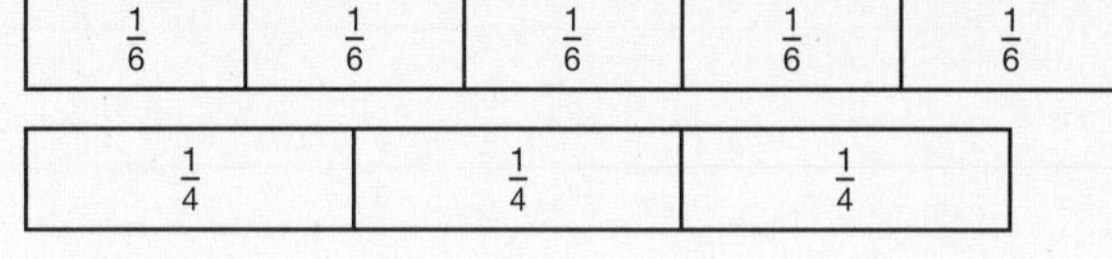

$\frac{5}{6}$ ◯ $\frac{3}{4}$

5. Writing to Explain Why is it important to line up the fraction strips on the left?

____

____

Reteaching 12-6

Name ____________________

Practice
12-6

Use Models to Compare Fractions

Compare. Write >, <, or =.

1. 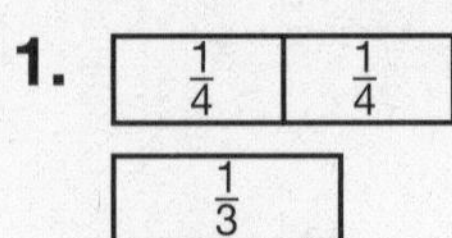

$\frac{2}{4}$ ◯ $\frac{1}{3}$

2. $\frac{1}{8}$ $\frac{1}{8}$ $\frac{1}{8}$

$\frac{1}{2}$

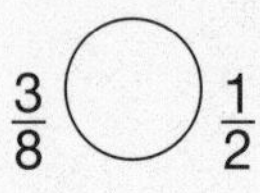

$\frac{3}{8}$ ◯ $\frac{1}{2}$

3. $\frac{1}{4}$ $\frac{1}{4}$ $\frac{1}{4}$

$\frac{1}{8}$ $\frac{1}{8}$ $\frac{1}{8}$ $\frac{1}{8}$ $\frac{1}{8}$ $\frac{1}{8}$

$\frac{3}{4}$ ◯ $\frac{6}{8}$

4. 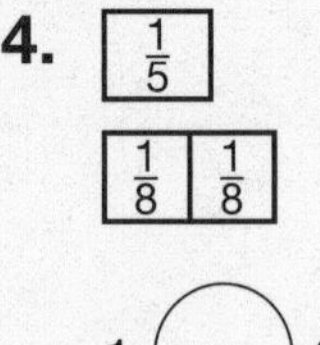

$\frac{1}{5}$ ◯ $\frac{2}{8}$

5. 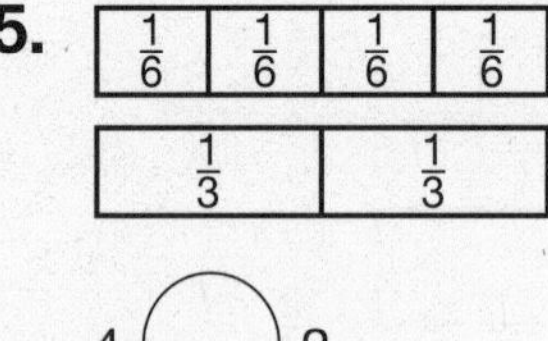

$\frac{4}{6}$ ◯ $\frac{2}{3}$

6. 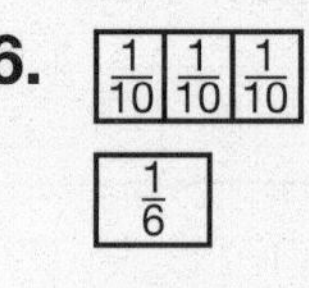

$\frac{3}{10}$ ◯ $\frac{1}{6}$

7. Number Sense Your body consists of $\frac{7}{10}$ water. Is more than $\frac{1}{2}$ your body water? Explain.

____

____

____

____

8. Two fractions have the same numerator, but different denominators. Is the fraction with the greater denominator greater than or less than the fraction with the lesser denominator?

____

____

____

____

9. Draw a Picture Draw a figure that is less than $\frac{1}{6}$.

10. Which fraction is greater than $\frac{1}{2}$?

A $\frac{1}{4}$

B $\frac{2}{6}$

C $\frac{3}{8}$

D $\frac{3}{4}$

Nombre_______________________________

Reteaching
12-7

Fractions on the Number Line

A number line can be used to represent fractions and mixed numbers. Mixed numbers are numbers that have a whole number part and a fraction part.

To read a number line, find what each mark represents. The number line will follow a pattern. In the number line below, each mark represents $\frac{1}{4}$.

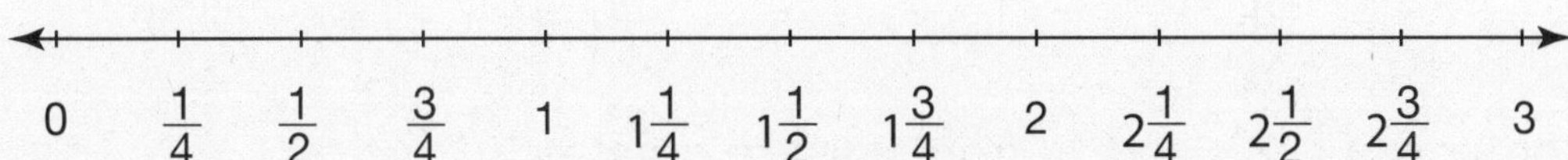

You can use a number line to compare fractions and mixed numbers. The number that is farther to the right is the greater number.

$1\frac{1}{2} \bigcirc 1\frac{3}{4}$

Since $1\frac{3}{4}$ is to the right of $1\frac{1}{2}$,

$1\frac{1}{2} < 1\frac{3}{4}$

1. Write the missing fractions or mixed numbers on the number line.

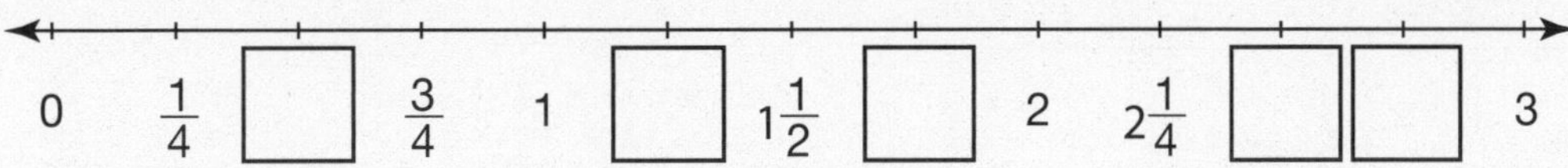

2. Write the missing numbers in order from greatest to least.

____

Compare. Write <, >, or =. Use the number line above to help.

3. $\frac{1}{2} \bigcirc \frac{3}{4}$ 4. $1 \bigcirc \frac{1}{2}$ 5. $2\frac{1}{4} \bigcirc 1\frac{3}{4}$

6. **Reasoning** Is a mixed number always greater than a whole number? Explain.

____

____

____

Reteaching **12-7**

Name ______________________

Fractions on the Number Line

1. Complete the number line by writing the missing fractions and mixed numbers.

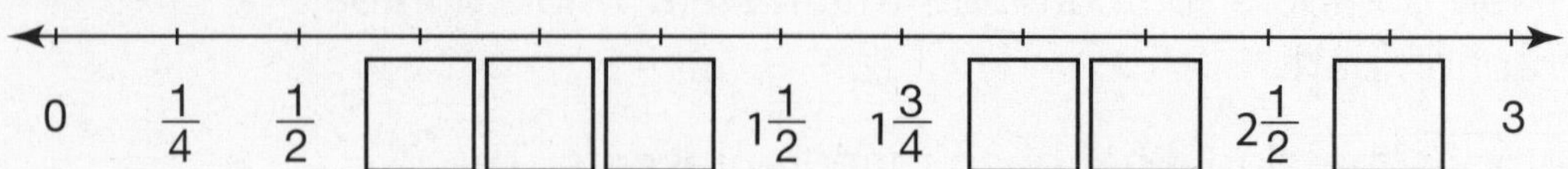

Compare. Write <, >, or =. Use the number line above to help.

2. $\frac{3}{4} \bigcirc \frac{1}{2}$ **3.** $1\frac{2}{4} \bigcirc 1\frac{1}{2}$ **4.** $1\frac{3}{4} \bigcirc 2\frac{1}{4}$

5. What is the order of $1\frac{1}{4}$, $2\frac{1}{2}$, and $1\frac{3}{4}$ from least to greatest?

____

Use the number line for **6** and **7**.

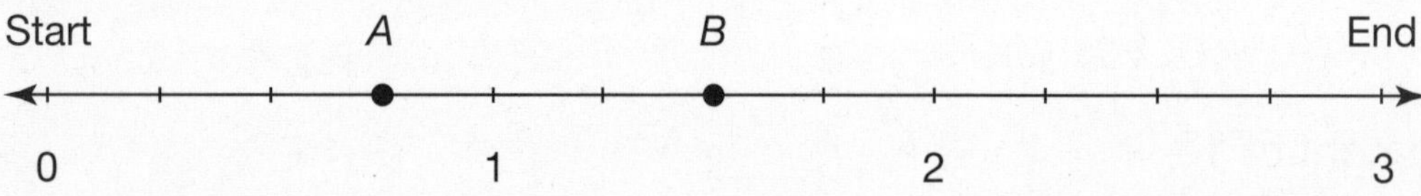

6. Lorne is running a 3-mile race. He stops at Water Stop A. How far did Lorne run?

____

7. How far is Water Stop B from the end of the race?

____

8. Explain It How can you compare two fractions by using a number line?

9. Geometry What fraction of the angles in this parallelogram are acute angles?

A $\frac{1}{4}$

B $\frac{1}{2}$

C $\frac{2}{3}$

D $\frac{3}{4}$

Name ____________________

Reteaching
12-8

Using Models to Add Fractions

You can use fraction strips to add fractions.

Add $\frac{3}{10} + \frac{2}{10}$.

Step 1

Place three $\frac{1}{10}$ fraction strips to the left of two $\frac{1}{10}$ fraction strips.

$\frac{1}{10}$	$\frac{1}{10}$	$\frac{1}{10}$

$\frac{1}{10}$	$\frac{1}{10}$

How many $\frac{1}{10}$ fraction strips? 5

So, $\frac{3}{10} + \frac{2}{10} = \frac{5}{10}$

Step 2

Write the sum in simplest form.

$\frac{1}{10}$	$\frac{1}{10}$	$\frac{1}{10}$	$\frac{1}{10}$	$\frac{1}{10}$

$\frac{1}{2}$

$\frac{5}{10} = \frac{1}{2}$

So, $\frac{3}{10} + \frac{2}{10} = \frac{1}{2}$

Write the sum in simplest form. You may use fraction strips or draw a picture to help.

1. $\frac{3}{6} + \frac{1}{6}$

$\frac{1}{6}$	$\frac{1}{6}$	$\frac{1}{6}$

$\frac{1}{6}$

____

2. $\frac{5}{8} + \frac{1}{8}$

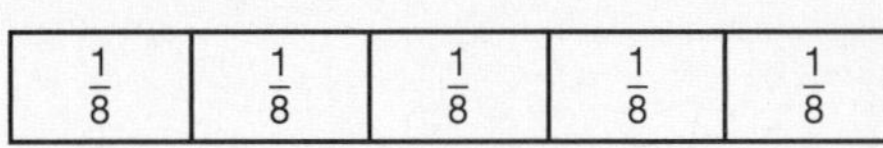

$\frac{1}{8}$

____

3. $\frac{2}{5} + \frac{2}{5}$ __________

4. $\frac{3}{12} + \frac{5}{12}$ __________

5. $\frac{3}{8} + \frac{1}{8}$ __________

6. $\frac{4}{10} + \frac{2}{10}$ __________

7. Explain It How do you know whether you have to write a sum in simplest form?

____

Name ___________________________________

Practice

12-8

Using Models to Add Fractions

Add. Write the sum in simplest form. You may draw a picture to help.

1. $\frac{3}{8} + \frac{4}{8}$ ________

2. $\frac{2}{6} + \frac{2}{6}$ ________

3. $\frac{3}{10} + \frac{4}{10}$ ________

4. $\frac{2}{4} + \frac{1}{4}$ ________

5. $\frac{1}{8} + \frac{5}{8}$ ________

6. $\frac{2}{5} + \frac{2}{5}$ ________

7. Marlon and Ricky ate a pizza that was divided into eighths. Marlon ate $\frac{2}{8}$ and Ricky ate $\frac{2}{8}$ of the pizza. How much of the pizza did they eat in all? Write your sum in simplest form.

____

8. Buddy has 8 CDs in his CD book. Six of the CDs are classic rock. The rest are country CDs. In simplest form, what fraction of the CDs are country CDs?

____

9. Write a Problem Write an addition problem that has $\frac{9}{10}$ as the sum.

____

____

____

____

10. Madison read $\frac{4}{10}$ of the chapters of a book Saturday and another $\frac{2}{10}$ Sunday. In simplest form, what fraction of the book did Madison read?

$\frac{1}{10}$	$\frac{1}{10}$	$\frac{1}{10}$	$\frac{1}{10}$

$\frac{1}{10}$	$\frac{1}{10}$

A $\frac{3}{4}$

B $\frac{3}{5}$

C $\frac{7}{10}$

D $\frac{1}{2}$

11. Of Tami's pets $\frac{2}{6}$ are dogs and $\frac{3}{6}$ are cats. What fraction of Tami's pets are dogs or cats?

____

Practice 12-8

Name ______________________________

Reteaching
12-9

Using Models to Subtract Fractions

You can use fraction strips to subtract fractions.

Subtract $\frac{7}{8} - \frac{3}{8}$.

Step 1

Use seven $\frac{1}{8}$ fraction strips. Cross out three of the $\frac{1}{8}$ fraction strips.

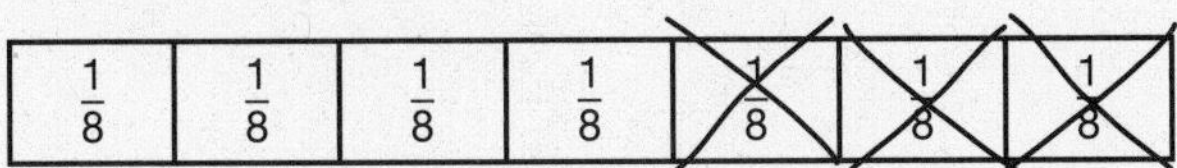

How many $\frac{1}{8}$ fraction strips are left? 4

So, $\frac{7}{8} - \frac{3}{8} = \frac{4}{8}$

Step 2

Write the difference in simplest form.

$\frac{1}{8}$	$\frac{1}{8}$	$\frac{1}{8}$	$\frac{1}{8}$
$\frac{1}{2}$			

$\frac{4}{8} = \frac{1}{2}$

So, $\frac{7}{8} - \frac{3}{8} = \frac{1}{2}$

Subtract. Write the difference in simplest form. You may use fraction strips or draw a picture to help.

1. $\frac{5}{6} - \frac{3}{6}$

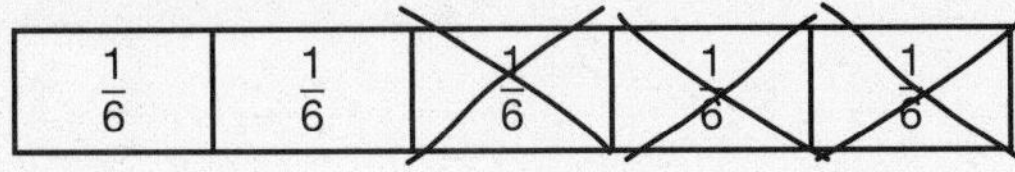

____

2. $\frac{7}{10} - \frac{1}{10}$

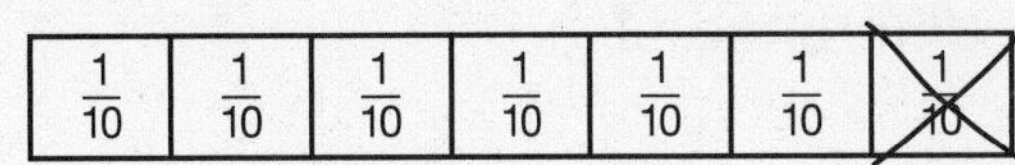

____

3. $\frac{5}{8} - \frac{2}{8}$ ______________

4. $\frac{8}{9} - \frac{5}{9}$ ______________

5. $\frac{11}{12} - \frac{2}{12}$ ______________

6. $\frac{3}{8} - \frac{1}{8}$ ______________

7. **Reasoning** Judy left $\frac{4}{5}$ of a pot of stew for Dan. Dan ate $\frac{2}{5}$ of what she left. What fraction of the pot of stew was left after Dan ate?

____

Reteaching 12-9

Name ______________________

Practice
12-9

Using Models to Subtract Fractions

Subtract. Write the difference in simplest form. You may draw a picture to help.

1. $\frac{7}{12} - \frac{5}{12}$

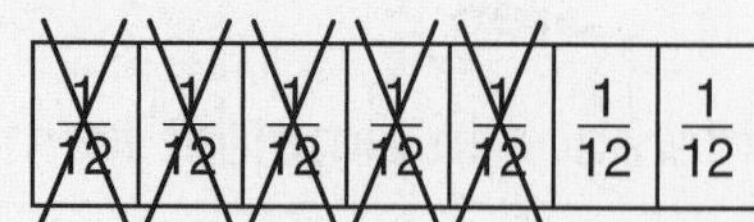

______

2. $\frac{5}{8} - \frac{2}{8}$

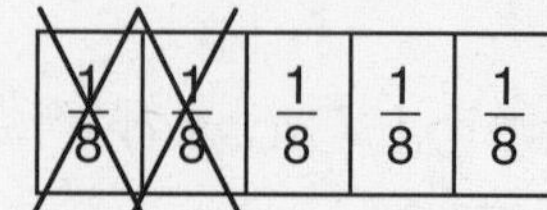

______

3. $\frac{9}{10} - \frac{4}{10}$ ______

4. $\frac{3}{6} - \frac{1}{6}$ ______

5. $\frac{7}{9} - \frac{4}{9}$ ______

6. $\frac{8}{10} - \frac{6}{10}$ ______

7. Patricia is responsible for washing $\frac{6}{8}$ of the desks in her classroom. She has already washed $\frac{4}{8}$ of the desks. What fraction of the desks does she still have to wash? Write your difference in simplest form. ______

8. Write a Problem Write a subtraction problem that has a difference of $\frac{1}{6}$.

______

9. Of the pets sold this week at a pet store, $\frac{5}{10}$ were dogs and $\frac{3}{10}$ were cats. What fraction describes how many more dogs were sold than cats? Write your difference in simplest form.

______

10. Reasoning Colin said that $\frac{7}{10} - \frac{2}{10} = \frac{5}{10}$. Louisa said that $\frac{7}{10} - \frac{2}{10} = \frac{1}{2}$. Who is correct?

______

______

11. Of the license plates that Sue saw, $\frac{5}{8}$ were from California and $\frac{1}{8}$ were from Oregon. In simplest form, what fraction of the plates were from other states?

______

12. What is $\frac{8}{9} - \frac{4}{9}$?

A $\frac{2}{3}$

B $\frac{4}{9}$

C $\frac{5}{9}$

D $\frac{1}{3}$

Practice 12-9

Name ______________________________________

Reteaching

12-10

Problem Solving: Make a Table and Look for a Pattern

Unger Soda hired 20 testers to try their new celery soda. Seven of the testers did not like the taste of the new soda. Suppose that pattern continues. If 100 people were hired in all, how many would **NOT** like the taste of the soda?

Make a table. Then write the information that you know. Find a pattern to extend the table until you find the results for 100 testers.

Doesn't Like	7	14	21	28	35	Increases by 7.
Total Testers	20	40	60	80	100	Increases by 20.

So, 35 people out of 100 will not like the taste of the Unger's celery soda.

Complete each table to solve.

1. Ms. Lee is buying bags of mixed dumplings. There are 40 dumplings in each bag. In each bag are 10 pork dumplings. If Ms. Lee buys 200 dumplings, how many will be pork dumplings?

Pork Dumplings	10				
Total Dumplings	40				

2. Packages of mixed socks contain 12 pairs of socks. In each package, there are 5 pairs of white socks. How many pairs of white socks would there be in 60 pairs of socks?

Pairs of White Socks	5				
Total Pairs of Socks	12				

3. Explain It Look back at Exercise 2. What pattern do you see?

____

____

____

____

4. Write a Problem Write a problem that can be solved by making a table and using a pattern. Then solve the problem.

____

____

____

Reteaching **12-10**

Name ______________________

Practice
12-10

Problem Solving: Make a Table and Look for a Pattern

Complete each table to solve.

1. Roses at a flower shop are sold in packages of 12. Each package contains 4 red roses. How many red roses will you get if you buy 60 roses?

Red Roses	4				
Total Roses	12				

2. There are 20 lollipops in each package of Yum's Lollipops. Each package contains 4 grape lollipops. How many grape lollipops will you get if you buy 100 lollipops?

Grape Lollipops	4				
Total Lollipops	20				

3. There are 9 bottles of salsa in a gift pack of Pedro's Salsa. In each gift pack, 2 of the bottles are extra spicy. Suppose someone buys 45 bottles. How many of the bottles will be extra spicy?

Extra Spicy Bottles	2				
Total Bottles	9				

4. Reasoning Look back at Exercise 3. Suppose Jackie bought 27 bottles.

a. How many of the bottles would not be extra spicy?

____

b. How many more bottles are not extra spicy than are extra spicy?

____

5. In a package of 25 colored pencils, 8 are red. If you bought 125 pencils, how many would be red?

Red Pencils	8				
Total Pencils	25				

6. Write a Problem Write a problem that can be solved by making a table and using a pattern. Then solve the problem.

____

____

____

Practice 12-10

Name ______________________

Fractions and Decimals

Tenths show 10 equal parts of a whole. Hundredths show 100 equal parts of the whole. Fractions and decimals can be used to write tenths and hundredths.

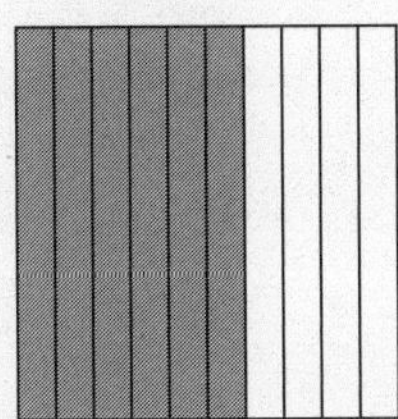

Word form: six tenths

Fraction: $\frac{6}{10}$

Decimal: 0.6

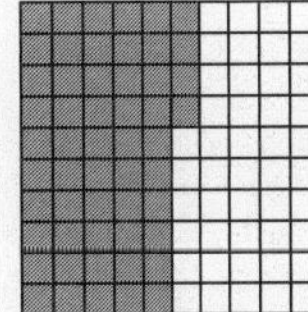

Word form: fifty-four hundredths

Fraction: $\frac{54}{100}$

Decimal: 0.54

Write a fraction and a decimal for each shaded part.

1. 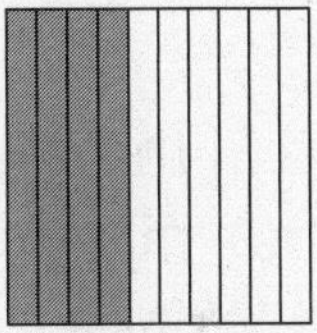

____

2. 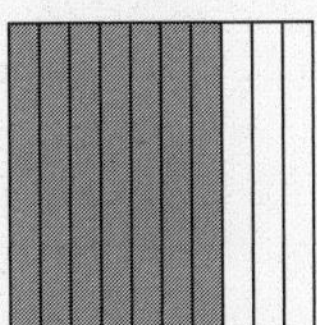

____

3. 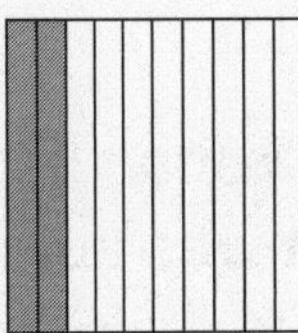

____

4. 

____

5. 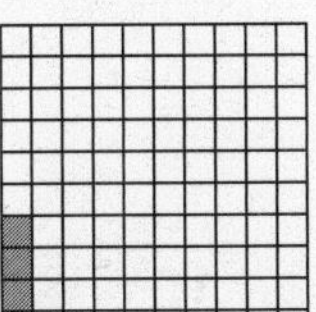

____

6. 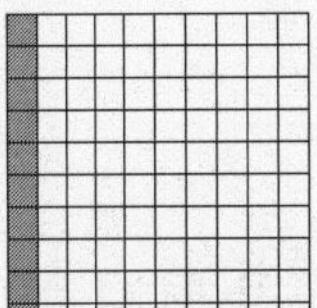

____

7. **Number Sense** How do you write $\frac{5}{10}$ as a decimal?

____

Name ______________________

Practice
13-1

Fractions and Decimals

Write a fraction and a decimal for each shaded part.

1. 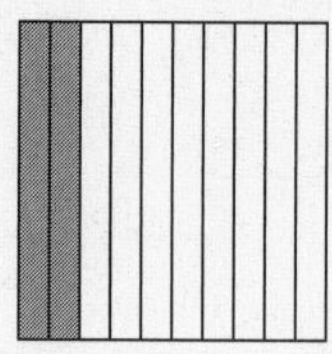

____

2. 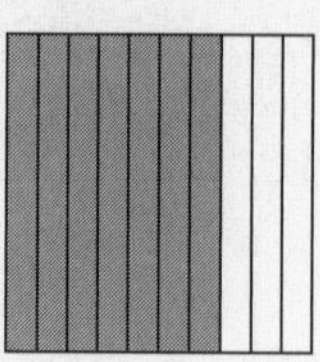

____

3. 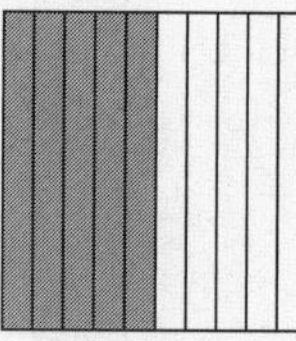

____

4. 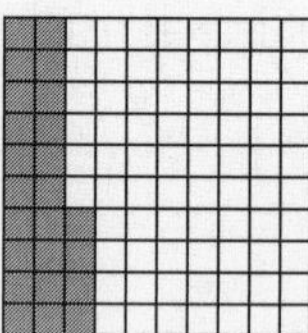

____

5. 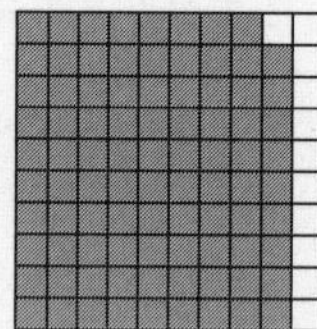

____

6. 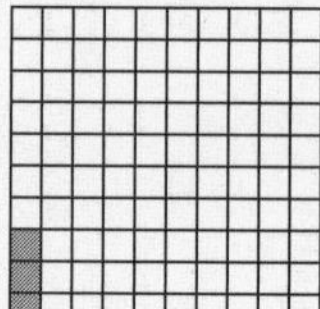

____

7. **Number Sense** Len bought a pizza that was cut into 10 slices. He ate 4 of the slices. What decimal represents the part of the pizza that remains?

____

8. There are 100 players in the soccer league. Of those players, 15 are on the Sharks. Write a fraction and a decimal to show what part of the league's players are on the Sharks.

____

9. What fraction is equal to 0.8?

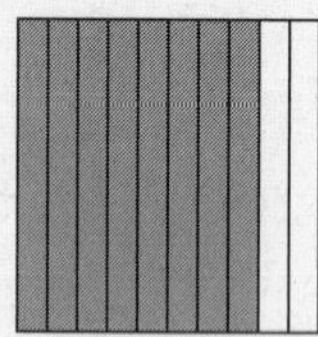

____

10. Which decimal is equivalent to $\frac{30}{100}$?

A 30.0

B 3.0

C 0.3

D 0.03

Practice 13-1

Name ____________________

Using Money to Understand Decimals

You can use money to help you to understand decimals.
Coins are part of a dollar.

$0.01 $0.05 $0.10 $0.25 $0.50 $1.00

    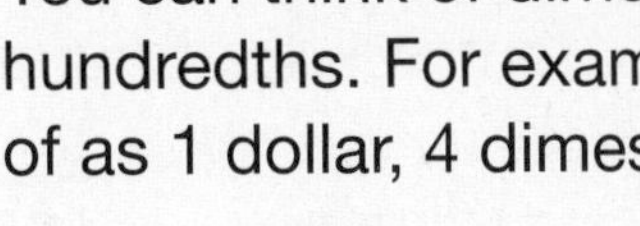

You can think of dimes as tenths and pennies as hundredths. For example, $1.45 can be thought of as 1 dollar, 4 dimes, and 5 pennies.

Complete.

1. $7.42 = ☐ dollars + ☐ dimes + ☐ pennies

   7.42 = ☐ ones + ☐ tenths + ☐ hundredths

2. $5.04 = ☐ dollars + ☐ dimes + ☐ pennies

   5.04 = ☐ ones + ☐ tenths + ☐ hundredths

Write each number with a decimal point.

3. four and twenty-eight hundredths

   ____

4. six and seven hundredths

   ____

5. **Reasoning** Rob has $2.30 made up only of dollar bills and dimes. Leslie also has $2.30, but she does not have any quarters, dimes, or nickels. What bills and coins could each have?

   ____

   ____

Name ______________________

Practice
13-2

Using Money to Understand Decimals

Complete.

1. $5.38 = ☐ dollars + ☐ dimes + ☐ pennies

   5.38 = ☐ ones + ☐ tenths + ☐ hundredths

2. $9.15 = ☐ dollars + ☐ dimes + ☐ pennies

   9.15 = ☐ ones + ☐ tenths + ☐ hundredths

3. $6.09 = ☐ dollars + ☐ dimes + ☐ pennies

   6.09 = ☐ ones + ☐ tenths + ☐ hundredths

4. $3.82 = ☐ dollars + ☐ dimes + ☐ pennies

   3.82 = ☐ ones + ☐ tenths + ☐ hundredths

Practice 13-2

Write each number with a decimal point.

5. eight and twenty-six hundredths ______________

6. seven and nine hundredths ______________

7. two and thirty hundredths ______________

8. four and nineteen hundredths ______________

9. **Draw a Picture** Using rectangles for dollars and circles for coins, make a drawing to represent $2.65.

10. Which money amount represents 3 dollars, 4 quarters, 2 dimes, 3 nickels?

    A $3.95

    B $4.10

    C $4.25

    D $4.35

Name ______________________

Reteaching
13-3

Adding and Subtracting Money

You can add and subtract money as you would add and subtract whole numbers. The difference is that money has a dollar sign ($) and a decimal point. Line-up the decimal points in the numbers to be added or subtracted. Then compute from right to left.

Add $12.50 + $9.25.

```
    1
 $12.50
+  9.25
 $21.75
```

Subtract $15.85 − $8.79.

```
  0 15 7 15
 $15.85
−  8.79
  $7.06
```

1. $2.87 + 1.09

2. $15.21 − 2.27

3. $13.22 + 3.67

4. $10.07 − 0.88

5. $6.29 + 5.47

6. $20.00 − 9.52

7. $14.79 + 11.25

8. $17.21 − 12.33

9. $7.65 + $0.82 ________

10. $6.00 − $2.57 ________

11. $8.35 + $5.78 ________

12. $3.00 − $0.79 ________

13. $15.63 + $8.92 ________

14. $9.27 − $8.85 ________

15. **Estimation** George has a $10 bill. He buys a newspaper for $1.19 and a magazine for $3.67. Will George receive more or less than $5.00 in change? Explain.

____

____

Reteaching 13-3

Name ______________________________

Practice
13-3

Adding and Subtracting Money

Find each sum or difference.

1. $7.29 − 1.03

2. $3.50 + 2.91

3. $6.00 − 2.59

4. $17.99 − 13.86

5. $20.00 − 18.42

6. $12.04 + 3.16

7. $4.21 + 3.99

8. $6.18 − 3.19

9. $7.83 + $0.62 ________

10. $16.02 − $5.19 ________

11. $18.21 + $14.36 ________

12. $27.36 − $15.29 ________

13. $1.25 + $0.59 + $3.57 ________

14. $30.00 − $21.78 ________

15. Cindy bought a T-shirt for $17.59 and a baseball cap for $12.85. How much money did Cindy spend altogether?

____

16. Terrell bought a book for $15.97. He paid for the book with a $20 bill. How much change should Terrell receive back?

____

17. Explain It How is adding and subtracting with money like adding and subtracting whole numbers?

____

____

____

____

____

18. Sam paid for a notebook that costs $2.76 with a $10 bill. What was his change?

A $7.24

B $7.34

C $8.24

D $12.76

Practice 13-3

Name ______________________

Reteaching
13-4

Problem Solving: Draw a Picture and Write a Number Sentence

Fred read $\frac{2}{5}$ of a book Saturday and $\frac{1}{5}$ Sunday. How much of the book did he read in all? How much more of the book did he read Saturday than Sunday?

Let's answer the first question.

There will be 5 parts, so draw a figure with 5 equal parts. Shade 2 parts one way and 1 part another way. Count how many parts are shaded in all.

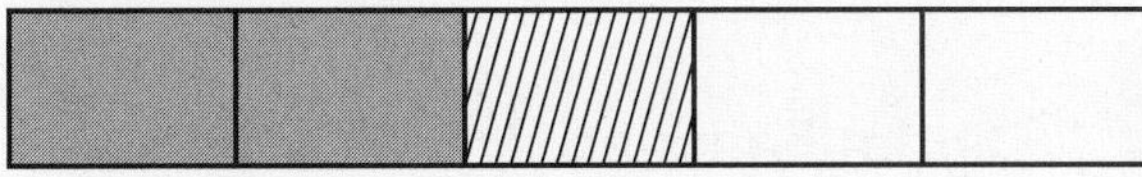

$\frac{2}{5} + \frac{1}{5} = \frac{3}{5}$

So Fred read $\frac{3}{5}$ of the book in all.

Let's answer the second question.

Make a drawing to show what you are comparing.

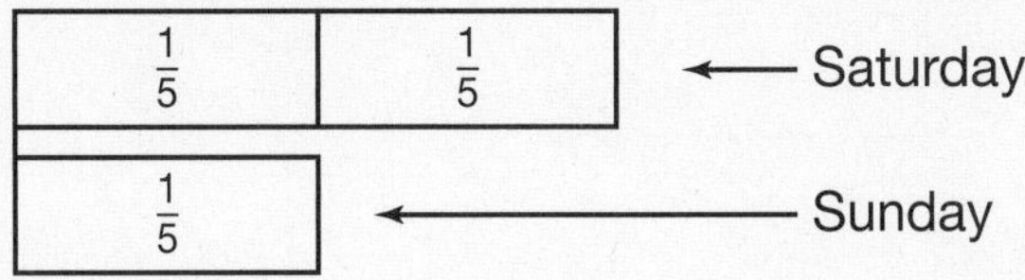

$\frac{2}{5} - \frac{1}{5} = \frac{1}{5}$

So, Fred read $\frac{1}{5}$ more of the book on Saturday than on Sunday.

1. Of Carlos's stamp collection, $\frac{5}{8}$ are from the United States and $\frac{2}{8}$ are from European countries. In simplest form, what fraction describes how many more of Carlos's stamps are from the United States than Europe?

   ____

2. Third-grade students make up $\frac{4}{10}$ of the swim team. Fourth-grade students make up $\frac{4}{10}$ of the team. In simplest form, what fraction of the team is from the third or fourth grades?

   ____

Reteaching **13-4**

Name ______________________

Practice 13-4

Problem Solving: Draw a Picture and Write a Number Sentence

Solve. Draw a picture and write a number sentence.

1. Candi and Randy each have a CD with the same number of songs. On Candi's CD, $\frac{5}{8}$ of the songs are ballads. On Randy's CD, $\frac{2}{8}$ of the songs are ballads. How much more of Candi's CD contains ballads than Randy's CD?

   ____

2. Jaime is painting his backyard fence. He paints $\frac{4}{10}$ of the slats red. Then he paints $\frac{2}{10}$ of the slats blue. In simplest form, what fraction of the fence did Jaime paint in all?

   ____

3. Troy completed $\frac{5}{12}$ of his book report before dinner. He completed another $\frac{3}{12}$ of the report after dinner. In simplest form, how much of the report did he finish in all?

   ____

4. Sandra has read $\frac{3}{4}$ of a comic book. Tricia has read $\frac{1}{4}$ of the same comic book. How much more of the comic book has Sandra read than Tricia?

   ____

5. **Write a Problem** Write a real-world problem with fractions that you can solve by drawing a picture and writing a number sentence.

   ____
   ____
   ____
   ____
   ____

6. **Reasoning** When you add or subtract fractions with the same denominator, what happens to the denominator in your answer?

   ____
   ____
   ____

Practice 13-4

Name ______________________________

Reteaching
13-5

Problem Solving: Missing or Extra Information

Henry is working to buy a new bicycle helmet. The helmet costs $22. Henry is earning $5 per hour helping his mother plant flowers. How much money has he made so far?

What do you know? The helmet costs $22. Henry earns $5 per hour.

What are you being asked to find? The amount of money Henry has earned.

What information do you need? The number of hours Henry has worked. It is not given.

You do not know how many hours Henry worked. Therefore, you cannot answer the question. This is missing information.

The cost of the helmet is extra information since it is not necessary to answer the question.

Decide if each problem has extra information or missing information. Solve if you have enough information.

1. Ralph has $55. He buys a sweatshirt for $17 and a pair of pants for $26. How much money did Ralph spend altogether?

____

____

2. Lisa bought 4 magazines for a total of $16. She also bought 3 books that each cost the same amount of money. How much money did Lisa spend in all?

____

____

3. Reasoning The cast for the school play has 24 actors. There are 12 third-grade students in the cast. The rest are either second-grade students or fourth-grade students. Mr. Kemp wants to know how many more third-grade students are in the cast than fourth-grade students. Can Mr. Kemp answer the question? Explain.

____

____

Name ______________________________

Problem Solving: Missing or Extra Information

For **1** and **2**, decide if the problem has extra or missing information. Solve if you have enough information.

1. Each time Kendra walks Mr. Karl's dog, he gives her $3. Kendra walks the dog for 30 minutes. If she walks the dog on Monday, Tuesday, and Thursday, how much money does Kendra make each week for walking Mr. Karl's dog?

____

____

____

____

2. Dylan trades baseball cards with his friends. He received all of his cards as a gift from his grandmother. If Dylan trades 58 baseball cards away and gets 62 back, how many cards does he have now?

____

____

____

____

3. **Write a Problem** Write a problem about Marie who has to do homework in math, reading, and social studies. Include extra information in your problem. Then solve it.

____

____

____

____

4. Tommy has 36 CDs and 24 DVDs. All of his CDs are either rock and roll or hip hop. He has 15 drama DVDs and 6 comedy DVDs. What information do you need to find how many hip hop CDs Tommy has?

A the number of rock and roll CDs

B the number of music DVDs

C the number of rap CDs

D the number of country CDs

Name ___________________________

Understanding Measurement

To measure lengths, it helps to line up the object with the 0 mark on the ruler.

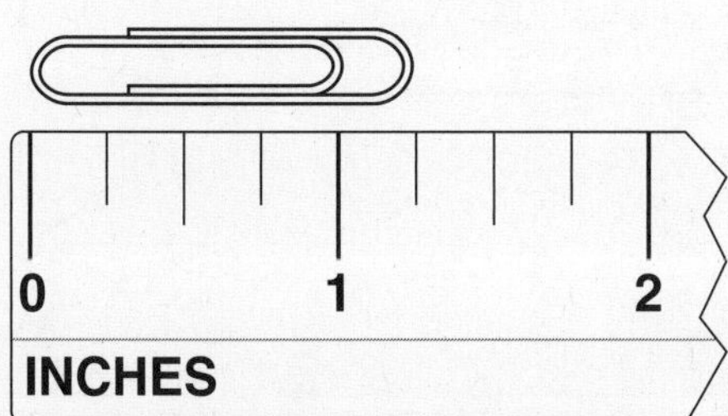

By lining the paper clip up with the zero, you can see that it is $1\frac{1}{4}$ inches long, which is 1 inch long to the nearest inch.

Estimate each length. Then measure it to the nearest inch.

1. 

____

2.

3. 

____

4. 

____

5. **Number Sense** Estimate the length of one of your index fingers. Then measure. Record the measurement to the nearest inch.

____

Name ____________________

Practice
14-1

Understanding Measurement

Estimate each length. Then measure to the nearest inch.

1. 

____

2. 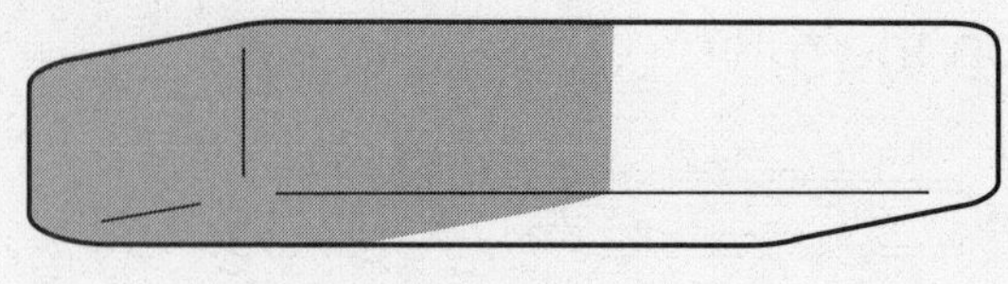

____

3. 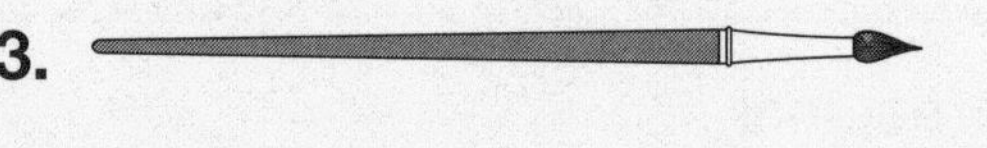

____

4. 

____

5. **Reasoning** To measure the length of a closet, Aaron used his foot and measured 6 foot-lengths. His father measured 4 foot-lengths. Could they be measuring the same closet? Explain.

____

____

6. Draw a line segment that is 2 inches long.

7. **Writing to Explain** Describe how to use a ruler to measure to the nearest inch.

____

____

8. Which paper clip is 1 inch long?

 **A** 

 **C** 

 **B** 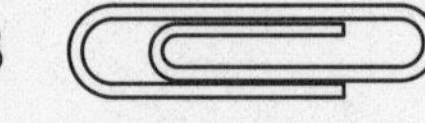

 **D** 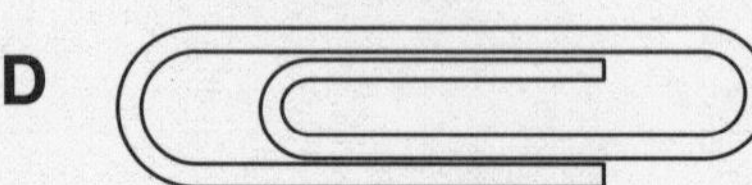

Practice **14-1**

Name ______________________

Reteaching
14-2

Fractions of an Inch

$\frac{1}{2}$ marks $\frac{1}{4}$ marks

0 1 2 3 4 5 6
INCHES

How long is the peanut to the nearest $\frac{1}{2}$ inch?

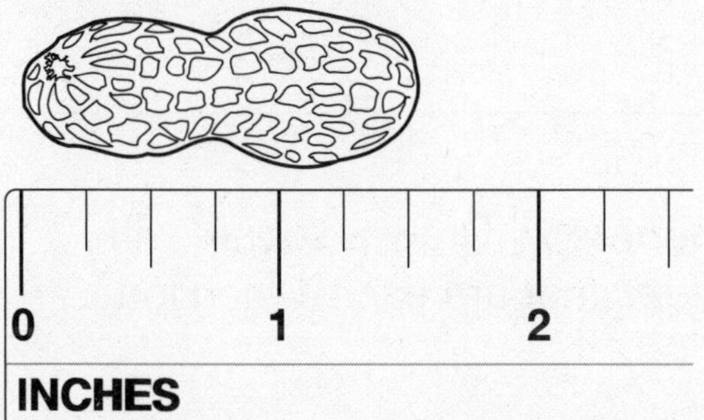

The peanut is $1\frac{1}{2}$ in. to the nearest $\frac{1}{2}$ inch.

How long is the chalk to the nearest $\frac{1}{4}$ inch?

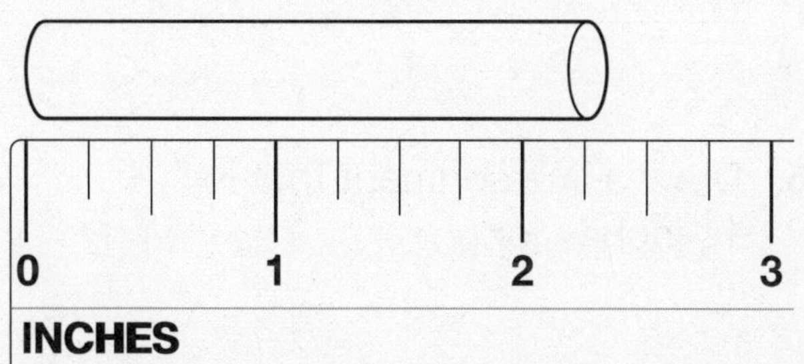

The chalk is $2\frac{1}{4}$ in. to the nearest $\frac{1}{4}$ inch.

Measure the length of each object to the nearest $\frac{1}{2}$ and $\frac{1}{4}$ inch.

1. 

____

2. 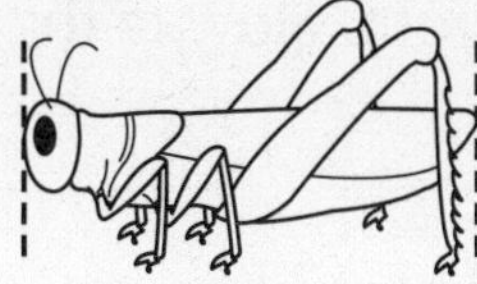

____

3. 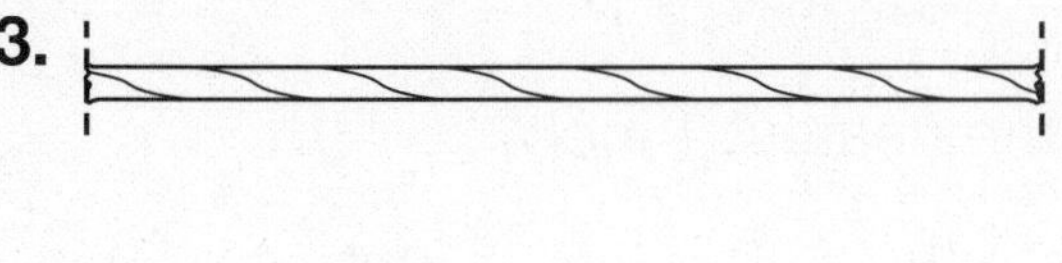

____

4. 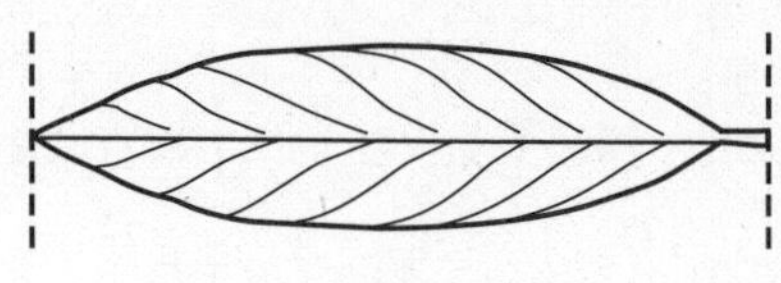

____

Reteaching **14-2**

Name ______________________

Practice 14-2

Fractions of an Inch

Measure the length of each object to the nearest $\frac{1}{2}$ inch and $\frac{1}{4}$ inch.

1. 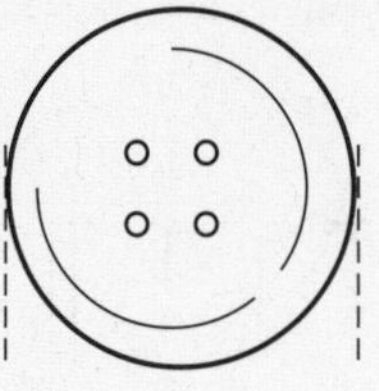

____

2. 

____

3. 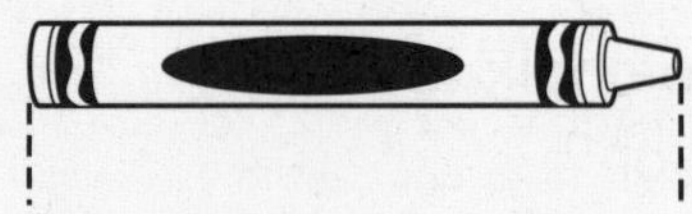

____

4. 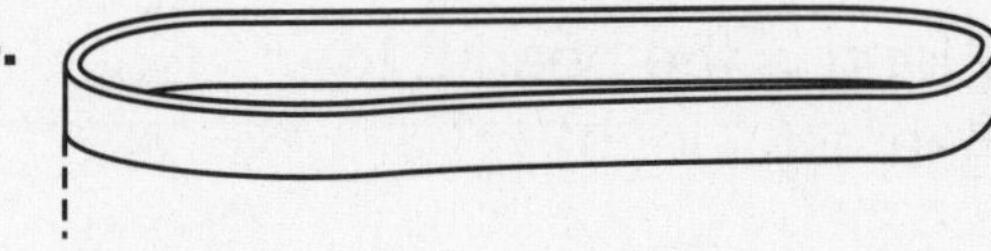

____

5. Draw a line segment that is $1\frac{1}{2}$ inches long.

6. **Geometry** Draw a square with sides that are each 1 inch long.

7. **Reasoning** Eric and Madison both measured the same trading card. Eric says the card is about 3 inches long. Madison says it is about $2\frac{3}{4}$ inches long. Their teacher says they are both correct. How is that possible?

____

____

____

8. Which can **NOT** be a length measured to the nearest $\frac{1}{4}$ inch?

A $\frac{1}{4}$ inch **B** $\frac{3}{8}$ inch **C** $\frac{1}{2}$ inch **D** $\frac{3}{4}$ inch

Name ______________________________

Reteaching
14-3

Using Inches, Feet, Yards, and Miles

The customary units of length are listed below.

Customary Units of Length		
12 inches (in.)	=	1 foot (ft)
3 feet	=	1 yard (yd)
36 inches	=	1 yard
5,280 feet	=	1 mile (mi)
1,760 yards	=	1 mile

To convert a larger unit to a smaller unit, multiply.

How many inches are in 4 feet?

Multiply: 4×12 in. $= 48$ in.

There are 48 inches in 4 feet.

Which is the best unit to use? Choose inches, feet, yards, or miles.

1. The height of a desk

____

2. The length of a soccer field

____

3. The length of a pair of scissors

____

In **4** through **7**, change the units.

4. How many feet are in 3 yards?

____

5. How many inches are in 2 feet?

____

6. How many inches are in 2 yards?

____

7. How many feet are in 6 yards?

____

8. Reasonableness Dexter said that 2 feet is equal to 6 yards. Is Dexter's statement reasonable? Explain.

____

____

Name ______________________

Practice

14-3

Using Inches, Feet, Yards, and Miles

In **1** through **8**, change the units.

1. 3 feet, 3 inches
1 foot = 12 inches
3 × 12 inches = 36 inches

36 inches + ☐ inches =
☐ inches

2. 2 yards, 1 foot
1 yard = 3 feet

2 × 3 feet = ☐ feet
☐ + 1 foot = ☐ feet

3. How many inches are in 2 yards?

______

4. How many feet are in 5 yards?

______

5. 2 feet 7 inches = ☐ inches

6. 5 feet 6 inches = ☐ inches

7. 4 feet 8 inches = ☐ inches

8. 3 yards 2 feet = ☐ feet

In **9** and **10**, choose the better estimate.

9. The depth of a swimming pool
10 feet or 10 miles

____

10. The length of your desk
2 inches or 2 feet

____

11. **Explain It** How do you convert feet to inches?

____

____

12. **Reasonableness** Would you measure the length between two cities in feet or miles?

____

____

13. Which measure is equal to 3 feet 7 inches?

A 37 inches **B** 43 inches **C** 44 inches **D** 55 inches

14. Which unit would be best to measure the length of your pinkie finger?

A Inches **B** Feet **C** Yards **D** Miles

Name ______________________

Reteaching

14-4

Customary Units of Capacity

Capacity is the amount of liquid a container can hold. The containers show the different units of customary capacity.

cup (c)

pint (pt)
1 pt = 2 c

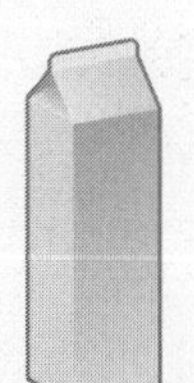

quart (qt)
1 qt = 2 pt

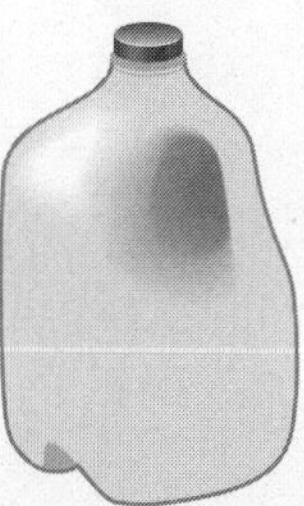

gallon (gal)
1 gal = 4 qt

Choose the better estimate for each.

1.

1 c or 1 gal ________

2.

1 qt or 1 gal ________

3.

1 c or 1 qt ________

4. small water bottle

1 pt or 1 gal ________

5. bucket

1 c or 1 gal ________

6. bathroom sink

2 c or 2 gal ________

7. **Reasoning** Suppose you want to fill a pot with 1 gallon of water. You can use a measuring cup the size of a cup or a quart. Which would be best to use? Explain your reasoning.

____

____

____

Reteaching **14-4**

Name ______________________________

Customary Units of Capacity

Choose the better estimate for each.

1. 
1 c or 1 gal
____

2. 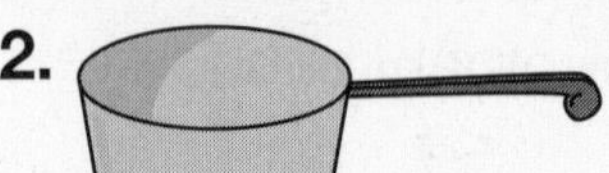
3 qt or 3 gal
____

3. 
1 pt or 1 gal
____

4. 
10 qt or 10 gal
____

5. coffee pot
1 c or 1 gal
____

6. bowl of soup
1 pt or 1 gal
____

7. thermos
1 qt or 1 gal
____

8. small milk carton
1 c or 1 gal
____

Choose the better unit to measure the capacity of each.

9. hot tub
qt or gal
____

10. shampoo bottle
pt or gal
____

11. bucket
c or gal
____

12. sports cooler
qt or gal
____

13. **Reasonableness** John has 4 cups filled with fruit juice. He said that he has a gallon of fruit juice. Is his statement reasonable? Explain why or why not.

____

____

____

14. **Estimation** Which measurement best describes the capacity of a kitchen sink?

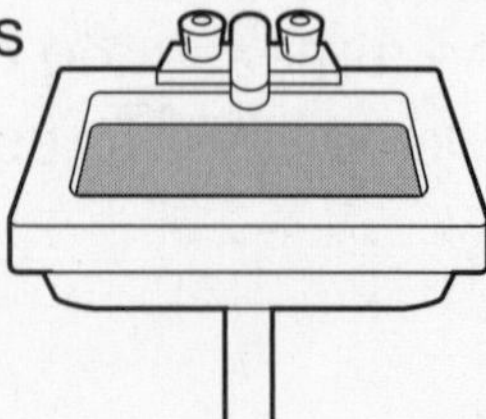

A 5 quarts **B** 5 pints **C** 5 cups **D** 5 gallons

Name ____________________

Units of Weight

Weight is the measure of how heavy an object is.
The units of weight are listed below.

1 pound (lb) = 16 ounces (oz)
1 ton (T) = 2,000 pounds

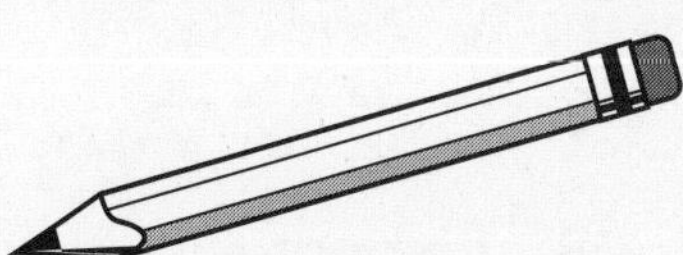

A pencil weighs about 1 ounce.

A telephone weighs about 1 pound.

A small car weighs about 1 ton.

Choose the better estimate for each.

1. 

   1 oz or 1 lb

   ____

2. 

   10 oz or 10 lb

   ____

3. 

   50 lb or 500 lb

   ____

4. paperback book
   1 oz or 1 lb

   ____

5. baseball
   5 oz or 5 lb

   ____

6. radio
   2 oz or 2 lb

   ____

7. **Number Sense** Mrs. Robertson wants to buy as big a package of chopped meat as possible. There is a 20-ounce package and a 1-pound package. She only wants to buy one package. Which should she buy?

   ____
   ____
   ____

Name ______________________

Practice 14-5

Units of Weight

Choose the better estimate for each.

1. 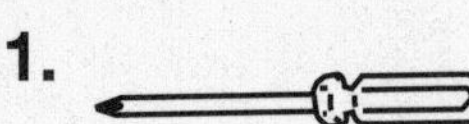

3 oz or 3 lb

______

2. 

30 oz or 30 lb

______

3. 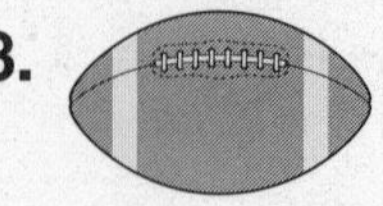

2 oz or 2 lb

______

4. 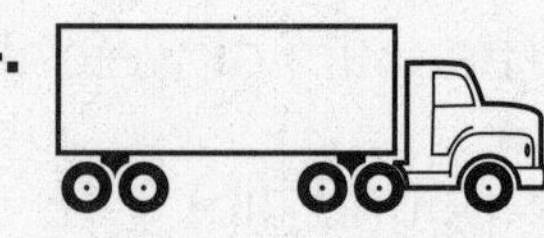

500 lb or 5 T

______

5. DVD
1 oz or 1 lb

______

6. chair
20 oz or 20 lb

______

7. cell phone
6 oz or 6 lb

______

8. computer
10 oz or 10 lb

______

Choose the better unit to measure the weight of each.

9. car
lb or T

______

10. strawberry
oz or lb

______

11. baseball
oz or lb

______

12. book
lb or T

______

13. **Explain It** Emily said the larger an object is, the more it weighs. Is Emily correct? Explain why or why not.

____

____

____

14. **Estimation** Which of the following objects can best be measured in ounces?

A pencil **B** couch **C** desk **D** doghouse

Name ______________________________

Problem Solving: Act It Out and Use Reasoning

You can view this figure in different ways.

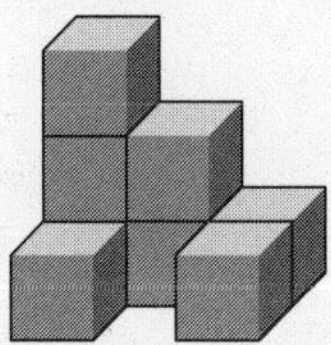

You can look at the figure from the front.

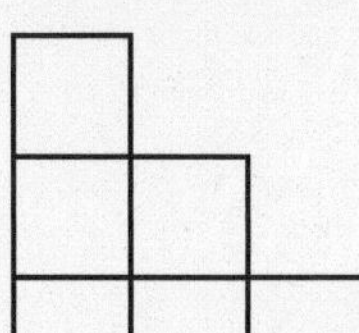

You can look at the figure from the right side.

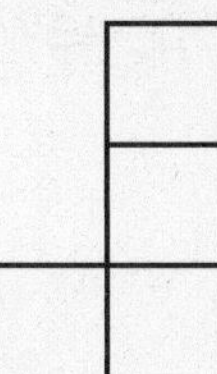

You can look at the figure from the top.

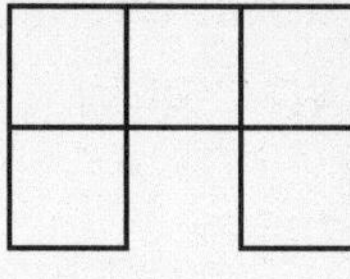

1. Use cubes to build the figure shown in these pictures.

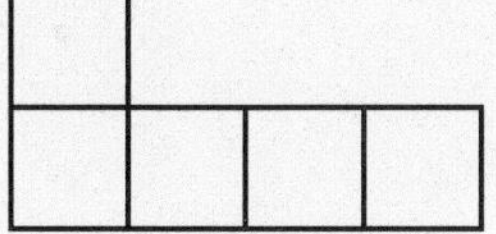

Front View

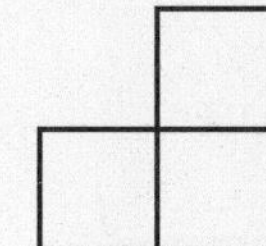

Right Side View

Top View

2. Draw the front, right side, and top views of this figure.

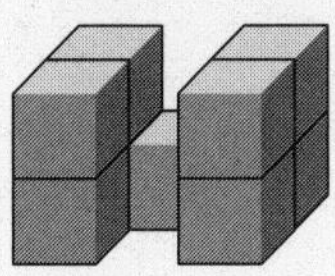

Front View Right Side View Top View

Name ______________________

Practice **14-6**

Problem Solving: Act It Out and Use Reasoning

1. Use grid paper. Draw the front, side, and top views of the figure shown below.

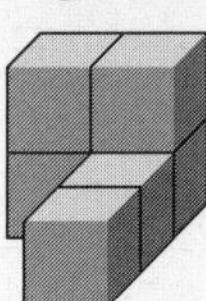

Front Right Side Top

2. Use grid paper. Draw the front, side, and top views of the figure shown below.

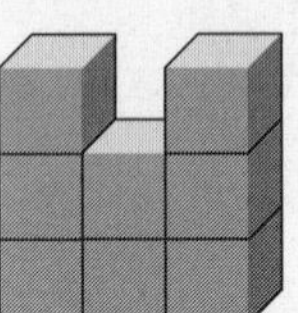

Front Right Side Top

3. Use cubes to build the figure shown in these pictures.

Front

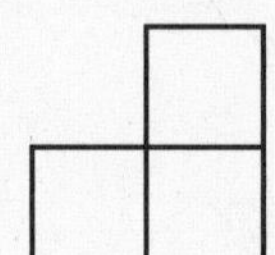

Right Side

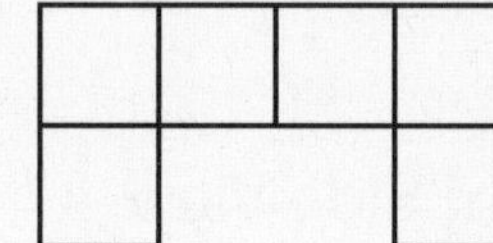

Top

4. **Reasoning** If the front, side, and top views are all the same, what type of figure are you looking at? Explain.

____

____

____

Name ______________________

Using Centimeters and Decimeters

A centimeter (cm) is a unit of measurement that is used to measure small objects. A decimeter (dm) is 10 cm long.

1 dm = 10 cm

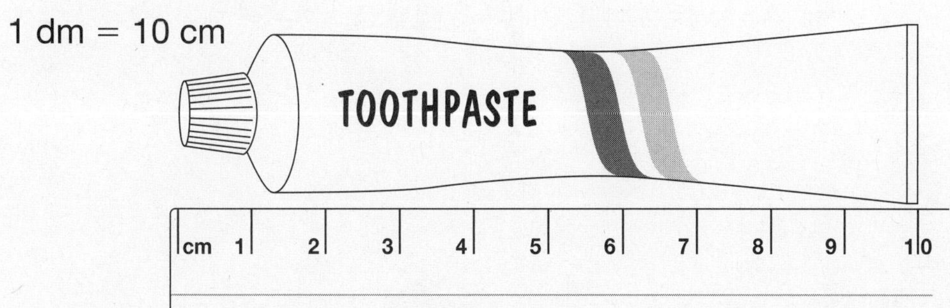

The tube of toothpaste is 10 cm long. We can also say that it is 1 dm long. The cap of the tube is about 1 cm long.

Estimate each length. Then measure to the nearest centimeter.

1.  ______________

2. 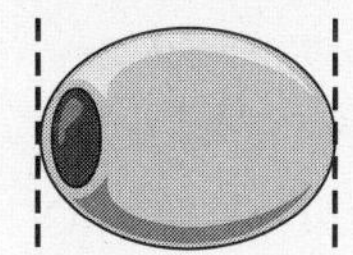 ______________

3.  ______________

4. 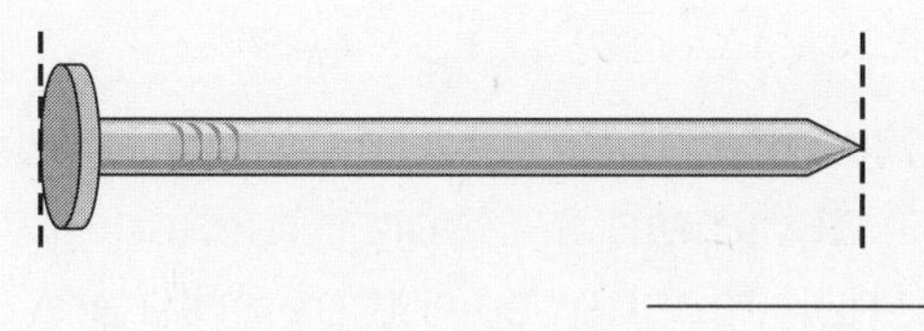 ______________

5. **Estimation** Estimate the length of your leg in centimeters. Then check your estimate.

____

6. **Reasonableness** Kent says that half of a decimeter is 3 cm. Do you agree? Explain.

____

Name ______________________

Using Centimeters and Decimeters

In **1** through **4**, estimate each length. Then measure to the nearest centimeter.

1. 

____

2. 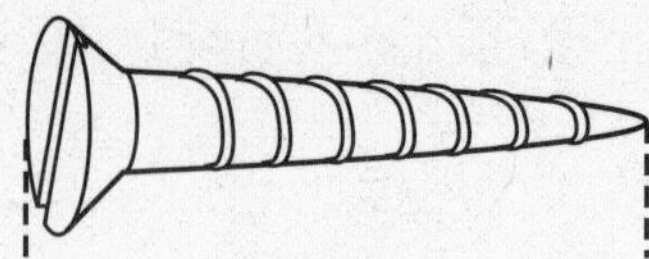

____

3. 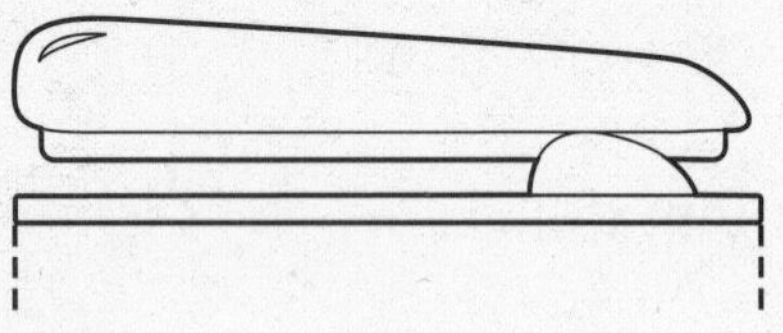

____

4. 

____

5. Draw a Diagram Draw a line segment that is 6 centimeters long.

6. Estimation Estimate the length of your desk in centimeters. Then measure the length of your desk.

____

7. Reasonableness Marian measured the length of a piece of paper as 7 decimeters. George measured the same length as 70 centimeters. Their teacher said they both are correct. Is that possible?

____

____

____

8. What is the length of the box of tape to the nearest centimeter?

A 2 centimeters **C** 4 centimeters

B 3 centimeters **D** 5 centimeters

Name ______________________

Using Meters and Kilometers

The units of metric length are listed below.

Metric Units of Length		
100 centimeters	=	1 meter (m)
1,000 meters	=	1 kilometer (km)

Meters are used to measure items like large pieces of lumber. They are also used to measure short distances, such as the distance from the house to the garage.

Kilometers are used to measure longer distances, such as the distance between two towns.

In **1** through **3**, tell if meter or kilometer is the better unit for each measurement.

1. The height of a ceiling

____

2. The length of a football field

____

3. The length of Lake Erie

____

In **4** and **5**, choose the better estimate.

4. The length of a car
5 meters or 5 kilometers

____

5. The length of a racecar track
3 meters or 3 kilometers

____

6. 7 meters = ■ centimeters

____

7. 5 kilometers = ■ meters

____

8. Explain It How do you convert 3 meters to centimeters?

____

____

Name ______________________

Practice
15-2

Using Meters and Kilometers

In **1** and **2**, convert the units. Complete.

1. How many centimeters are there in 3 meters 25 centimeters?

____

2. 5 meters = ■ centimeters

____

In **3** and **4**, choose the better estimate.

3. The length of a key
3 centimeters or 3 meters

____

4. The length of bike path
2 meters or 2 kilometers

____

5. Complete the table.

km	1	2	3	4
m	1,000	2,000		

6. Estimation Is the length of a pencil greater than or less than 1 meter? Explain.

____

____

____

7. Reasonableness Andy lives 6 kilometers from the mall. He said he lives 600 meters away from the mall. Is Andy's statement reasonable? Explain.

____

____

____

8. Which is the best estimate for the length of a calculator?

A 1 meter **B** 1 centimeter **C** 10 meters **D** 10 centimeters

Name ____________________

Metric Units of Capacity

Two units of capacity in the metric system are milliliters (mL) and liters (L).

1 liter = 1,000 milliliters

Milliliters are used to measure very small amounts of liquid.

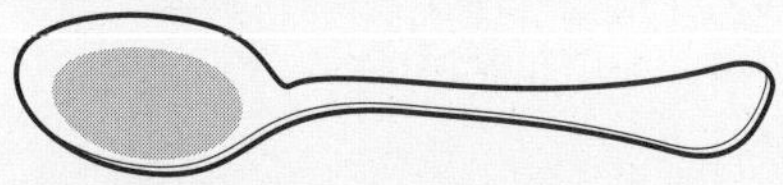

1 teaspoon = 5 milliliters

A liter is slightly larger than a quart. Many beverages are sold in 1-liter and 2-liter bottles.

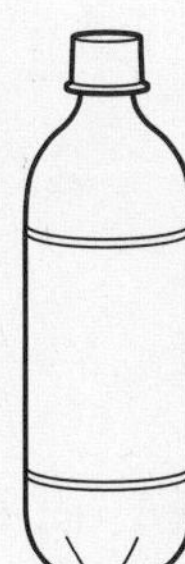

Choose the better estimate for each.

1. 

350 mL or 35 L

____

2. 

100 mL or 10 L

____

3. 

30 mL or 3 L

____

4. small milk carton

250 mL or 25 L

____

5. soup can

500 mL or 5 L

____

6. sports cooler

4 L or 40 L

____

7. Reasonableness Which is the better unit to use to measure the capacity of a bathtub: milliliters or liters? Explain your choice.

____

____

____

Name ________________________

Practice
15-3

Metric Units of Capacity

Choose the better estimate for each.

1. 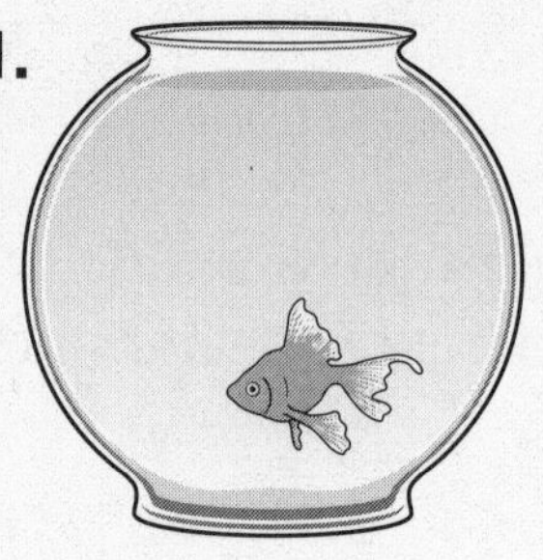

2 mL or 2 L

____

2. 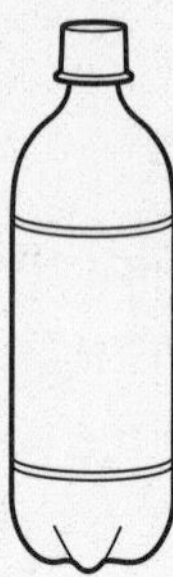

2 mL or 2 L

____

3. 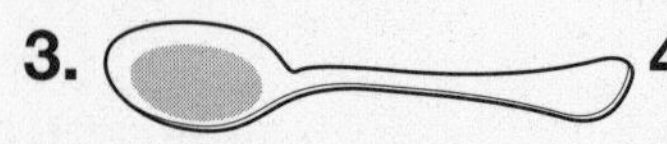

5 mL or 5 L

____

4. 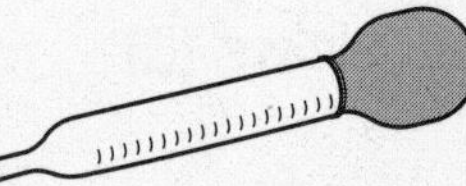

1 mL or 1 L

____

5. kitchen sink
2 L or 20 L

____

6. coffee cup
250 mL or 25 L

____

7. thermos
2 L or 20 L

____

8. pitcher
40 mL or 4 L

____

Choose the better unit to measure the capacity of each.

9. tea cup
mL or L

____

10. bath tub
mL or L

____

11. glass of juice
mL or L

____

12. washing machine
mL or L

____

Practice 15-3

13. Reasoning A liter is equal to 100 centiliters. Is a centiliter a greater measure than a milliliter? Explain.

____

____

____

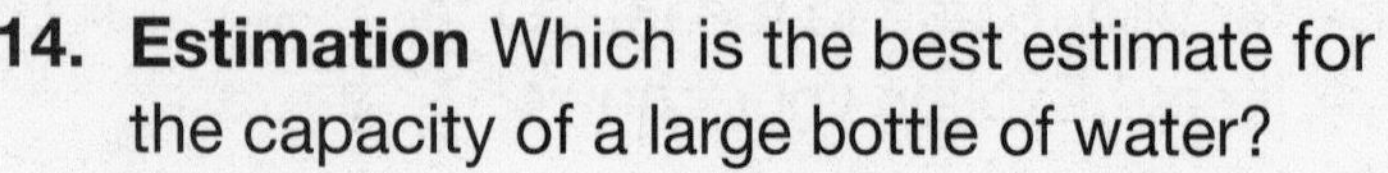

14. Estimation Which is the best estimate for the capacity of a large bottle of water?

A 1 L **C** 4 L

B 400 mL **D** 40 mL

Name ______________________________

Units of Mass

Mass is the measure of how much matter is in an object. Units of mass include grams (g) and kilograms (kg).

1 kilogram = 1,000 grams

A paper clip has a mass of about 1 gram.

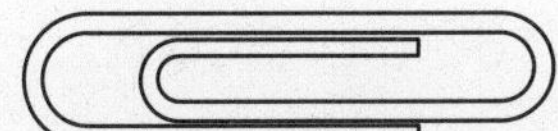

A large baseball bat has a mass of about 1 kilogram.

Choose the better estimate for each.

1. 

   150 g or 3 kg

   ____

2. 

   1 g or 100 g

   ____

3. 

   300 g or 3 kg

   ____

4. soccer ball
   10 g or 1 kg

   ____

5. tiger
   30 kg or 300 kg

   ____

6. dime
   2 g or 2 kg

   ____

7. **Number Sense** Julie has a box of paper clips that have a mass of 1 gram each. The entire box has a mass of 1 kilogram. How many paper clips are in the box? Explain your answer.

   ____

   ____

   ____

Name ______________________

Units of Mass

Choose the better estimate for each.

1. 

3 g or 3 kg

____

2. 
40 g or 40 kg

____

3. 
250 g or 25 kg

____

4. 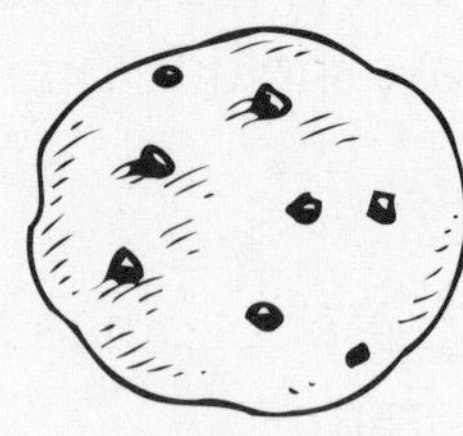
30 g or 300 g

____

5. crayon
20 g or 200 g

____

6. large dog
5 kg or 50 kg

____

7. quarter
5 g or 500 g

____

8. adult male
7 kg or 70 kg

____

Choose the best tool to measure each.

9. the mass of a phone ______

10. the length of a crayon ______

11. the temperature ______

12. the time for dinner ______

13. the capacity of a bowl ______

a. 

b. 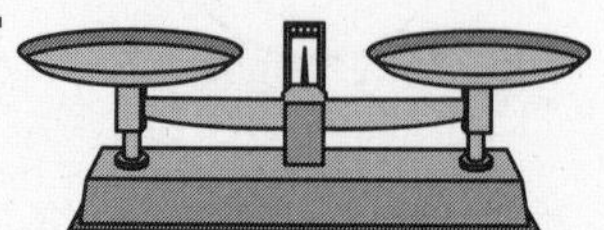

c. 

d. 

e. 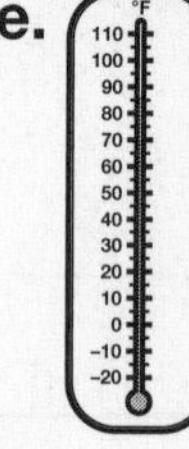

14. **Writing to Explain** Would you use grams or kilograms to find the mass of a letter? Explain.

____

____

____

15. **Estimation** Which is the best estimate for the mass of a pair of sneakers?

A 1 kg **B** 1 g **C** 10 kg **D** 10 g

Name ______________________________

Problem Solving: Make a Table and Look for a Pattern

Sharon has started a walking program with her puppy Fido. How many meters will they walk on Day 4? Day 5?

The table shows how many meters Sharon and Fido have walked each day. Look for a pattern.

Day	1	2	3	4	5
Distance Walked (m)	200	400	600		

Each day they walked 200 meters longer than the day before. Use the pattern to find how many meters they will walk on Day 4 and Day 5.

Day 4
600 m + 200 m = 800 m

Day 5
800 m + 200 m = 1,000 m

Complete the table. Explain the pattern. Solve.

1. Eddie has a board that is 80 centimeters long. He is cutting the board into pieces that are each 10 centimeters long. What is the length of the board after Eddie has made 3 cuts? 4 cuts?

Number of Cuts	0	1	2	3	4
Length of Board Left	80 cm	70 cm	60 cm		

____

____

____

____

2. Chuck is putting a border in his room. Each piece of border is 2 meters long. What is the length of 4 pieces of border? 5 pieces of border?

Number of Pieces	1	2	3	4	5
Total Length	2 m	4 m	6 m		

____

____

____

____

Name ____________________

Practice
15-5

Problem Solving: Make a Table and Look for a Pattern

Complete the table. Explain the pattern.

1. Fred is putting tables together to make one long table. Each table is shaped like a square and is 3 meters long. What is the length of 4 tables? 5 tables?

Number of Tables	1	2	3	4	5
Total Length	3 m	6 m	9 m		

____

____

____

____

2. Sheila is cutting a board that is 72 centimeters long. She is cutting the board into pieces that are each 9 centimeters long. What is the length of the board after Sheila has made 3 cuts? 4 cuts?

Number of Pieces	0	1	2	3	4
Length of Board Left	72 cm	63 cm	54 cm		

____

____

____

____

3. Cindy is linking toy train cars together. What is the total length of the train with 4 cars? 5 cars?

Number of Train Cars	1	2	3	4	5
Total Length	20 cm	40 cm	60 cm		

____

____

____

____

4. Dennis is stacking boxes on top of each other. Each box is 8 centimeters high. What is the height of 4 boxes? 5 boxes?

Number of Boxes	1	2	3	4	5
Total Height	8 cm	16 cm	24 cm		

____

____

____

____

Name ______________________________

Understanding Perimeter

The **perimeter** of a figure is the distance around it.

The perimeter is found by adding the lengths of the sides.

4 in. + 6 in. + 7 in. + 5 in. + 11 in. + 11 in. = 44 in.

The perimeter of the figure is 44 inches.

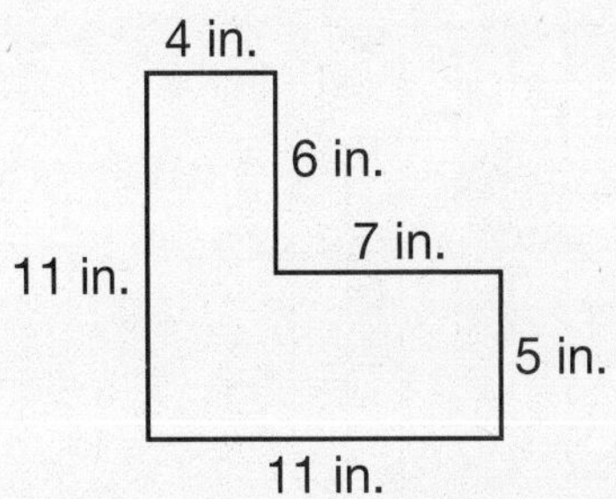

1. 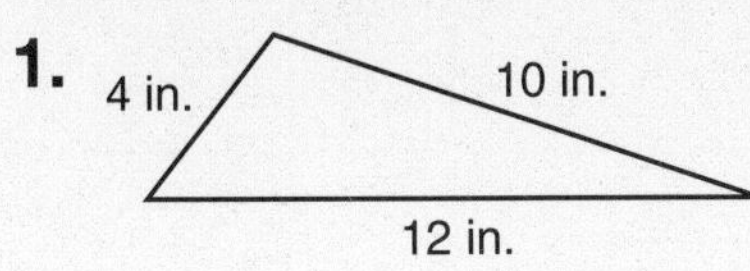

2. 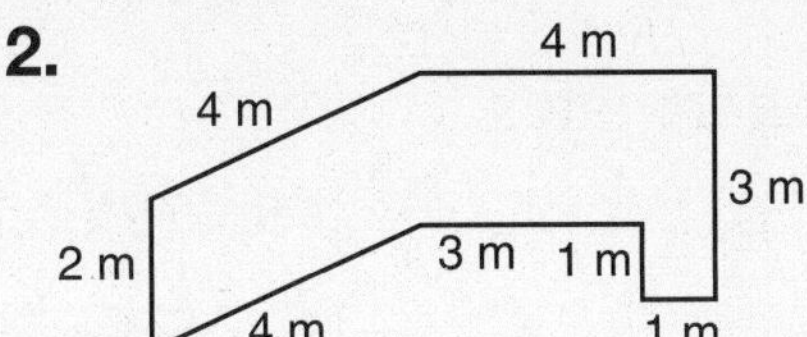

3. 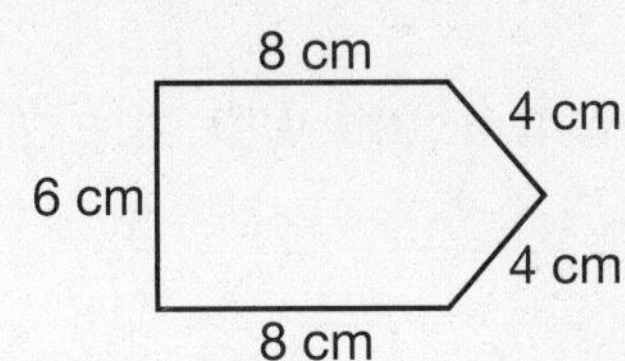

______________ ______________ ______________

Draw a figure with the given perimeter.

4. 6 units

5. 10 units

6. 10 units

7. **Number Sense** A rectangle has a length of 5 yards and a width of 3 yards. What is its perimeter? Explain your answer.

____

____

Name ______________________

Understanding Perimeter

Find the perimeter of each polygon.

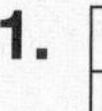

1. 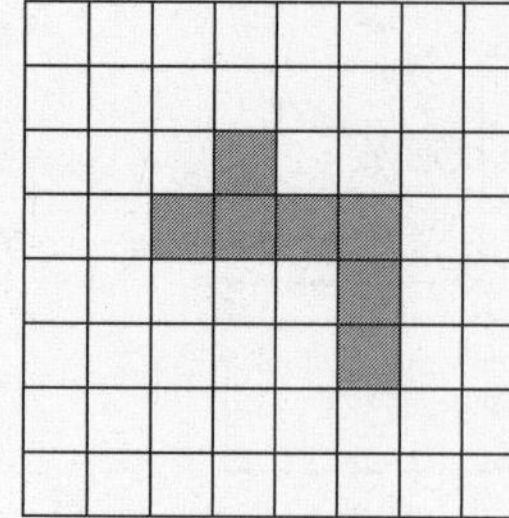

____

2. 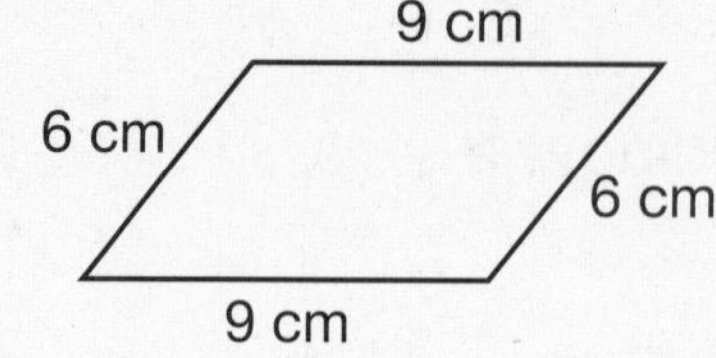

____

3. 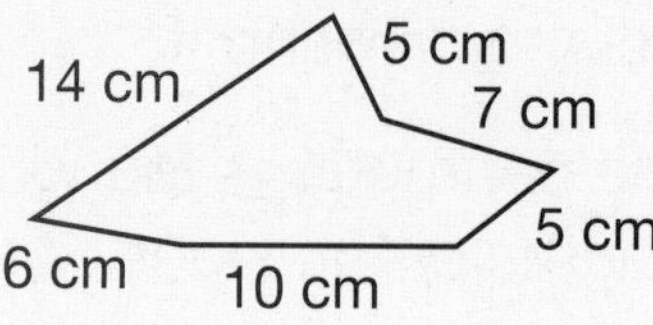

____

Draw a figure with the given perimeter.

4. 10 units

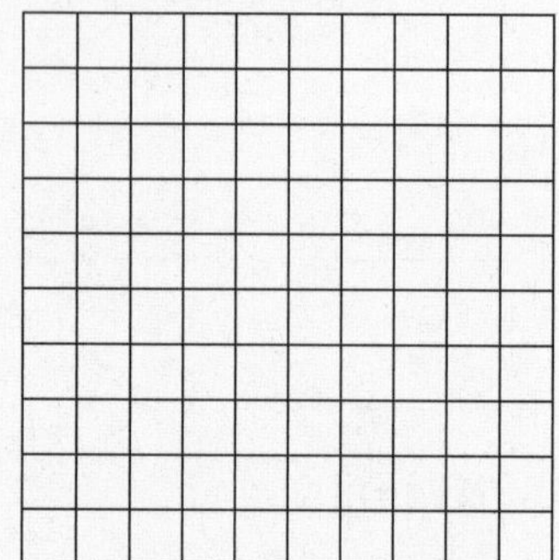

5. 22 units

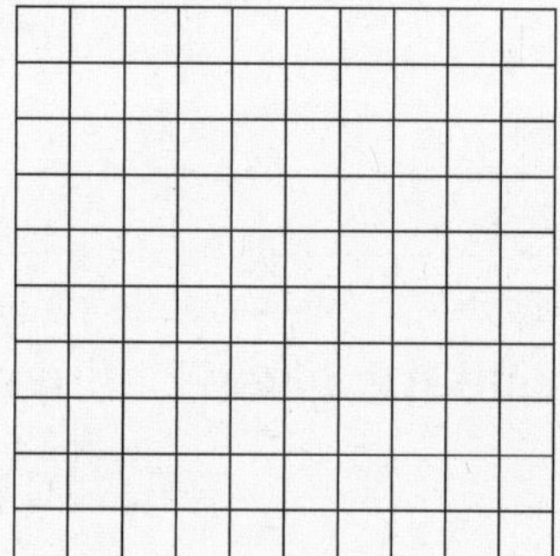

6. A park has the shape of a trapezoid. Two of the sides are 25 meters long. The other two sides are 40 meters and 20 meters long. What is the perimeter of the park?

____

7. Mr. Anders wants to put a fence around his backyard. His backyard is rectangular. The lengths of the sides are 75 yards, 45 yards, 75 yards, and 45 yards. How much fencing will Mr. Anders need?

____

8. **Explain It** When finding the perimeter of a figure on a grid, why do you not count the spaces inside the grid?

____

____

9. Which rectangle has a perimeter of 16 units?

A Length 5 units, width 3 units

B Length 10 units, width 6 units

C Length 8 units, width 1 unit

D Length 6 units, width 3 units

Name ______________________

Perimeter of Common Shapes

Use the properties of these common shapes to determine the missing side lengths. Then find the perimeter.

Rectangle	Square	Equilateral Triangle
Two pairs of sides have the same length.	All 4 sides have the same length.	All 3 sides have the same length.

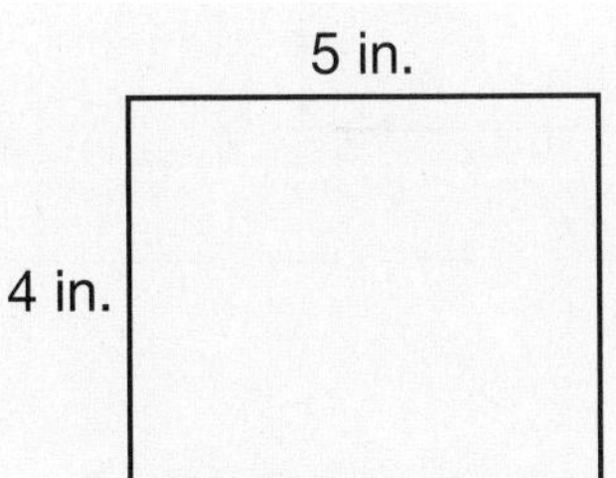

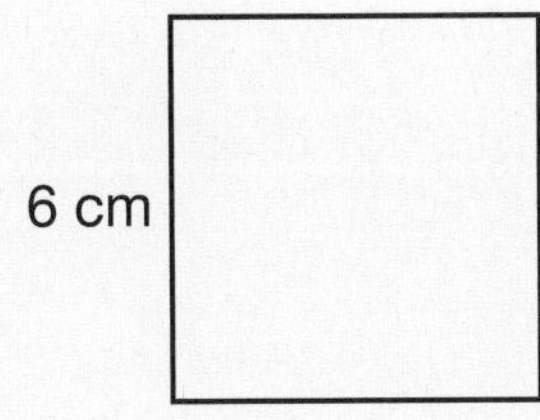

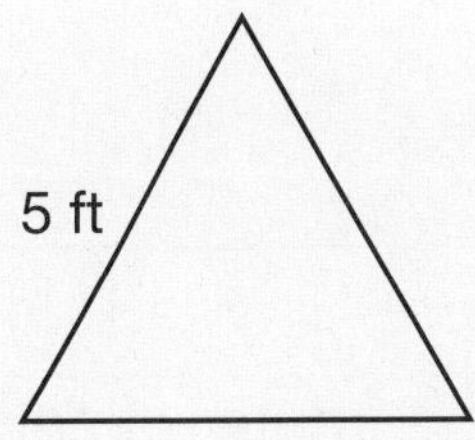

4 in. + 5 in. + 4 in. + 5 in. = 18 in.

6 cm + 6 cm + 6 cm + 6 cm = 24 cm

5 ft + 5 ft + 5 ft = 15 ft

Find the perimeter of each polygon.

1.

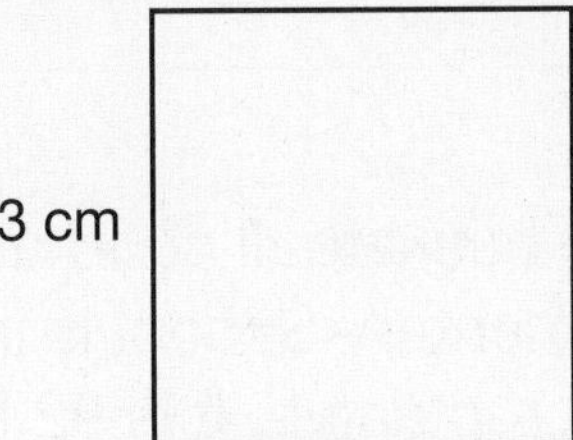

____

2.

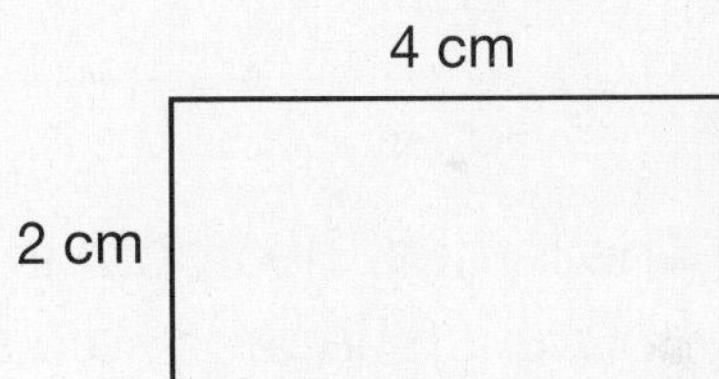

____

3.

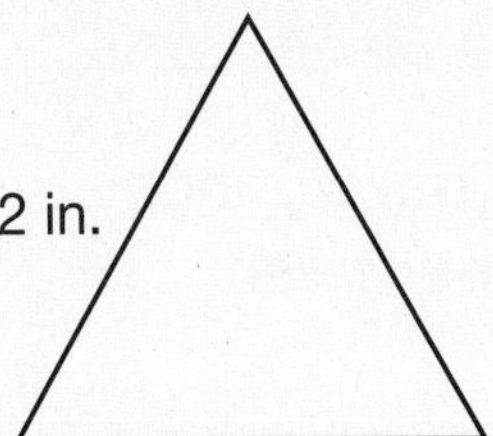

____

4.

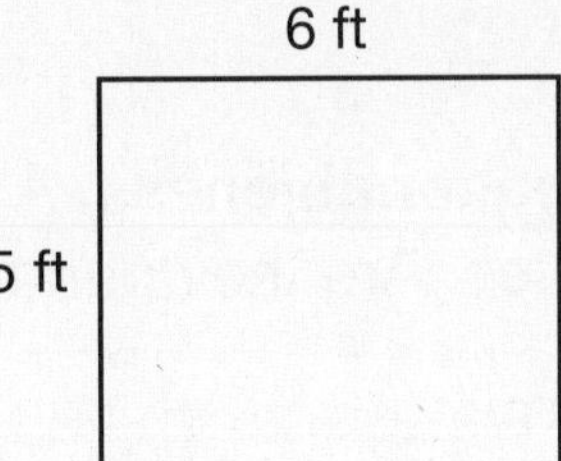

____

5. Reasonableness Can two different size squares have the same perimeter? Explain.

____

____

Name ___________________________

Practice 16-2

Perimeter of Common Shapes

Use a centimeter ruler to measure the length of the sides of each polygon. Find each perimeter.

1. 

____

2. 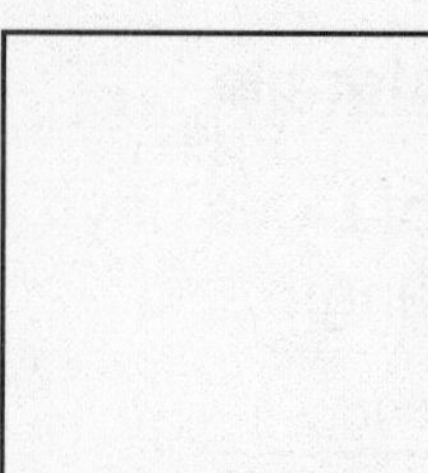

____

Find the perimeter of each figure.

3. 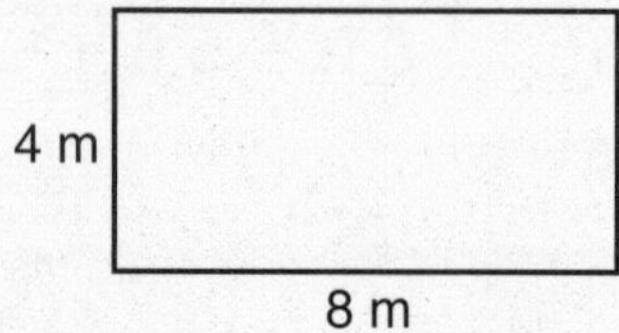

____

4. 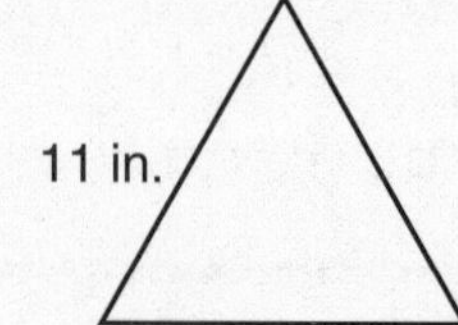

____

5. The largest bedroom in Lauren's house is shaped like a square with sides of 6 yards. What is the perimeter of that bedroom?

____

6. The basketball court at Johnson Elementary School is in the shape of a rectangle. It is 92 feet long and 46 feet wide. What is the perimeter of the basketball court?

____

7. Reasonableness A square and a pentagon each have 9-inch sides. Are their perimeters the same? Explain your answer.

____

____

8. What is the perimeter of a hexagon that has sides of 12 inches?

A 60 inches **B** 66 inches **C** 72 inches **D** 84 inches

Name ___________________________________

Different Shapes with the Same Perimeter

Different shapes can have the same perimeter.

These shapes have the same perimeter.

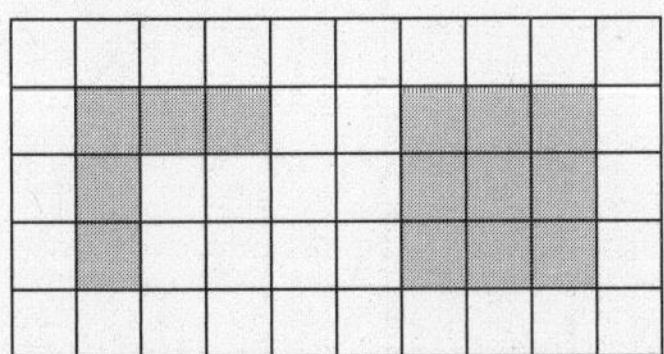

Both of these shapes have perimeters of 12 units.

Rectangles with different shapes can also have the same perimeter.

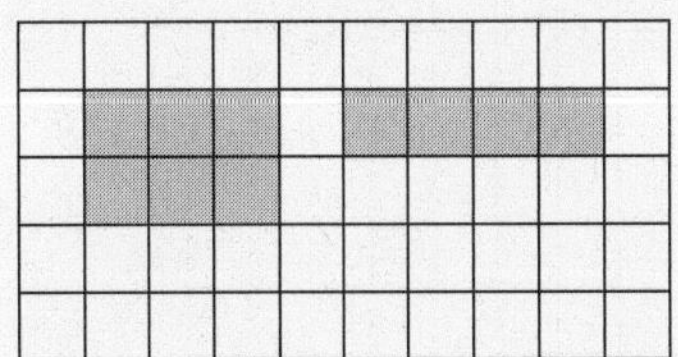

Both of these rectangles have perimeters of 10 units.

Draw a figure with each perimeter.

1. 8 units

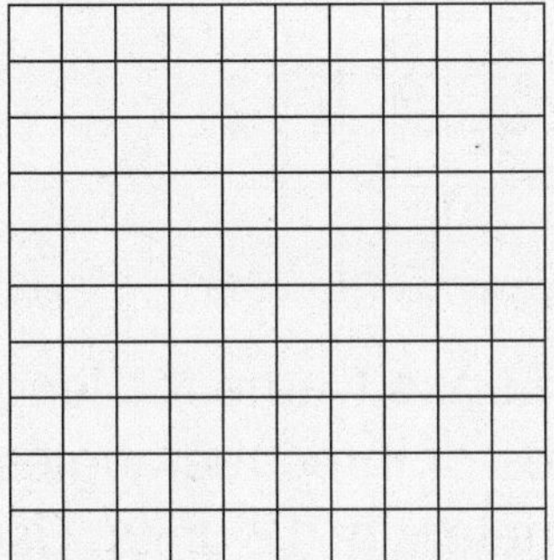

2. 12 units

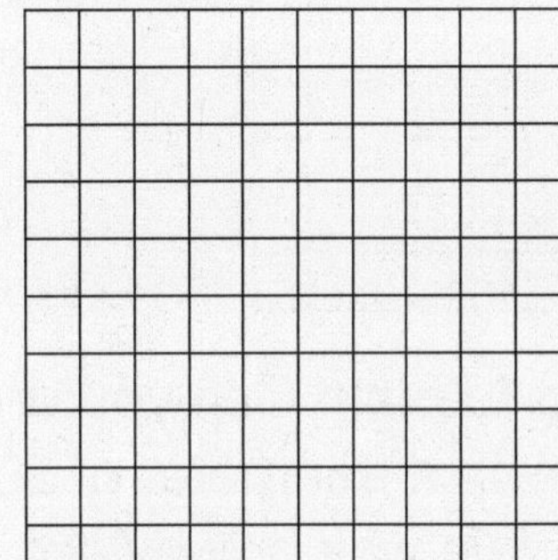

3. 10 units

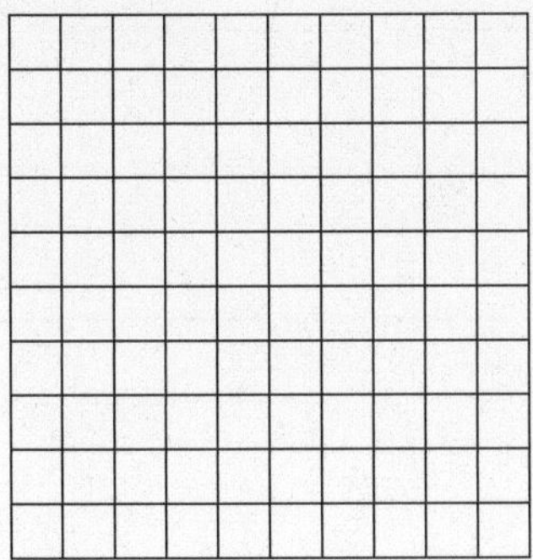

4. 14 units

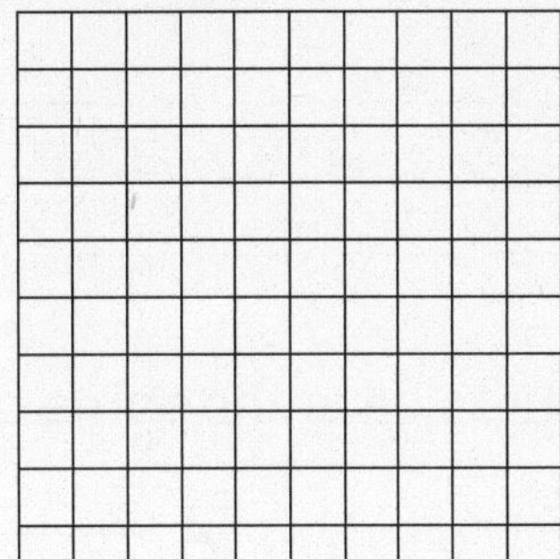

5. Name the lengths of the sides of three rectangles that have perimeters of 14 units. Use only whole numbers.

____

Name ________________________________

Practice
16-3

Different Shapes with the Same Perimeter

Draw a figure with the given perimeter on the grid paper.

1. 10 units

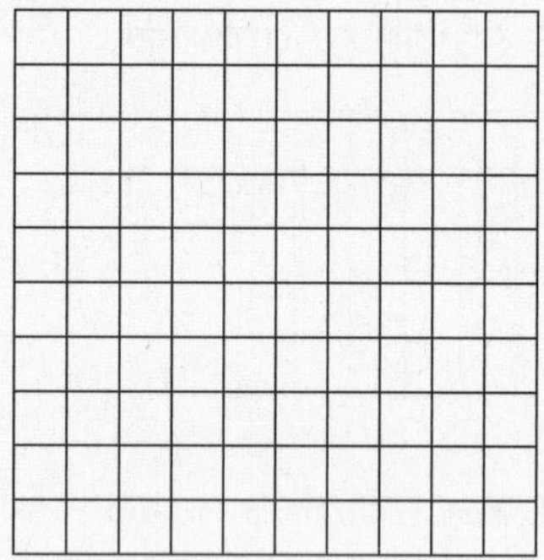

2. 16 units

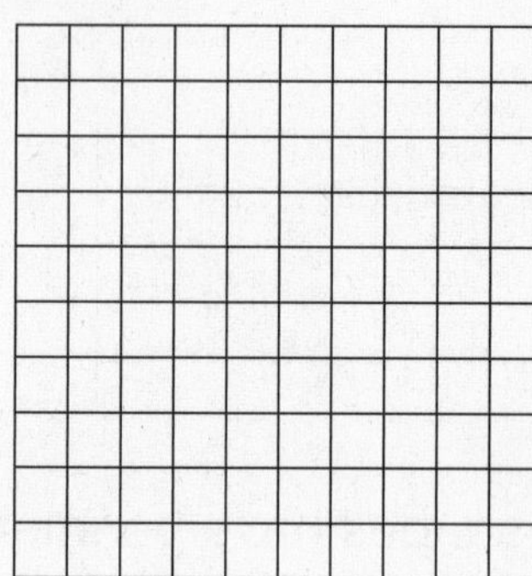

3. 14 units

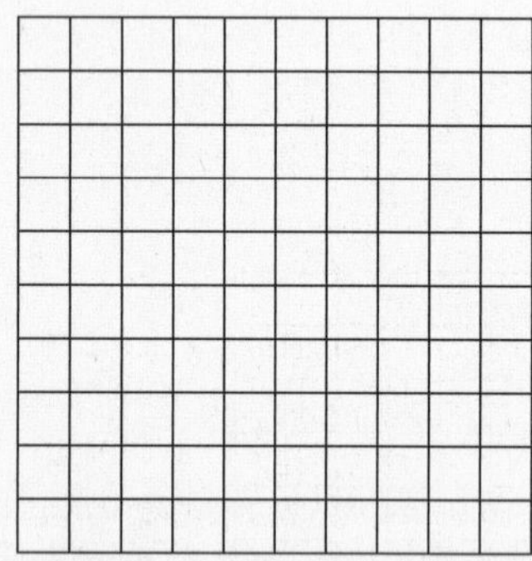

4. 18 units

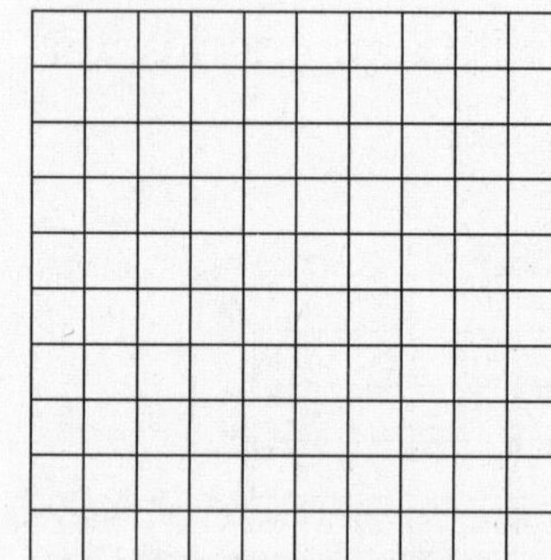

5. Writing to Explain Can you draw a square with a perimeter of 20 units? Explain why or why not.

____

____

____

6. Number Sense Name the lengths of the sides of three rectangles with perimeters of 12 units. Use only whole numbers.

____

____

____

7. Which figures have the same perimeter?

A 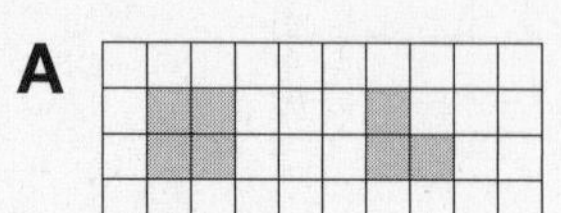

C 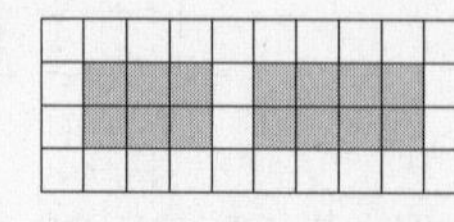

B 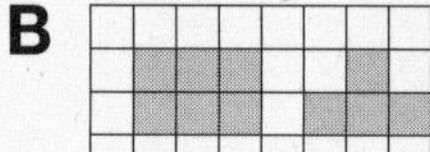

D 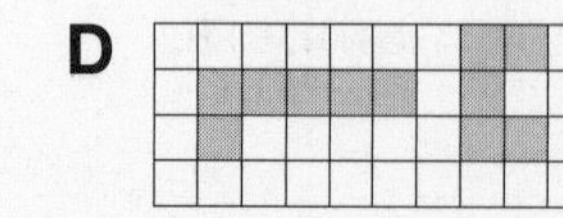

Practice 16-3

Name ______________________________

Problem Solving: Try, Check, and Revise

Bryce, Julie, and Katie saved a total of $50 to buy a birthday present for their mother. Julie and Katie saved the same amount of money. Bryce saved $5 more. How much money did Bryce save?

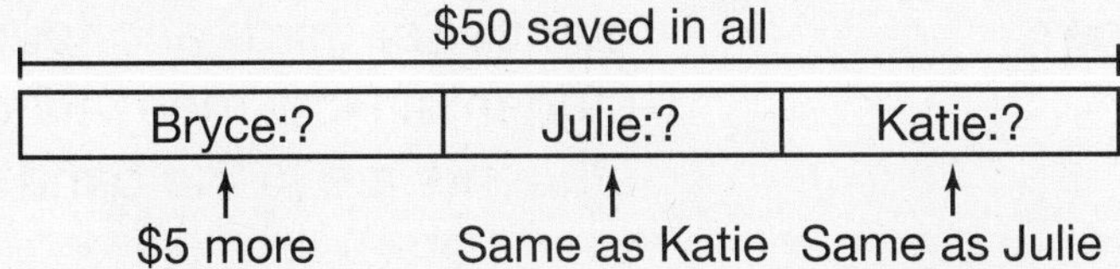

Try three numbers that add to 50. Julie and Katie saved the same amount, so their numbers are equal. Bryce's amount is $5 more.

Try #1

Try: $15 + $10 + $10 = $35

Check: $35 is too low.

You need $15 more.

Try #2

Revise by adding $5 more for each person.

Try: $20 + $15 + $15 = $50

Check: This is correct.

Bryce saved $20 for the present.

1. Ben and Cole have 36 airplane models all together. Ben has 8 more than Cole. How many airplane models does Ben have?

   ____

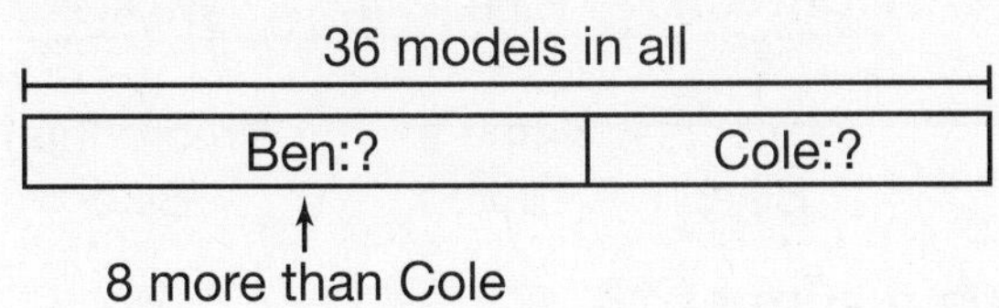

2. Jan, Mya, and Sara ran a total of 64 miles last week. Jan and Mya ran the same number of miles. Sara ran 8 less miles than Mya. How many miles did Sara run?

   ____

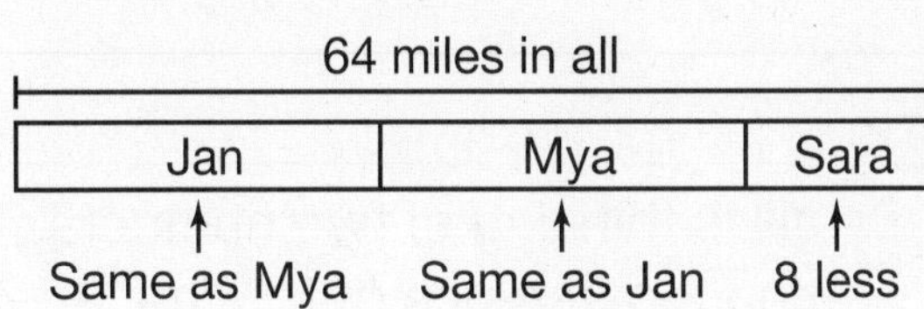

Name ______________________________

Practice
16-4

Problem Solving: Try, Check, and Revise

1. Carly and Rob combined their DVD collections. Now they have 42 DVDs all together. Carly had 4 more DVDs than Rob. How many DVDs did Carly have?

____

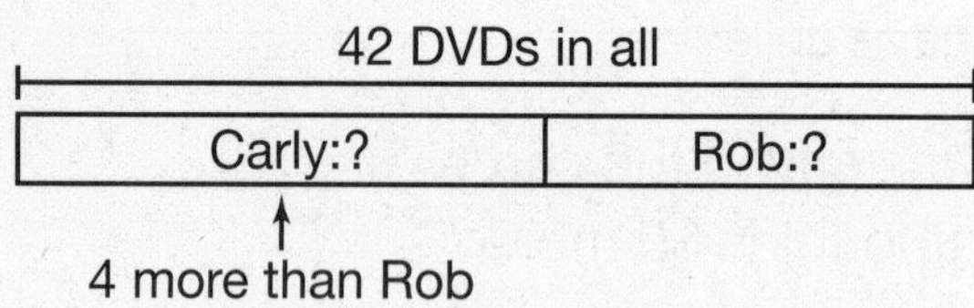

2. There are 33 students in the band. There are 6 more fifth-grade students than third-grade students. There is an equal number of third- and fourth-grade students. How many third-grade students are in the band?

____

33 students in all
3rd:?
4th:?
5th:?
Same as Grade 4
Same as Grade 3
6 more than Grade 3

3. Dave delivered 52 newspapers all together on Saturday and Sunday. He delivered 8 more newspapers on Sunday than on Saturday. How many newspapers did Dave deliver on Sunday?

____

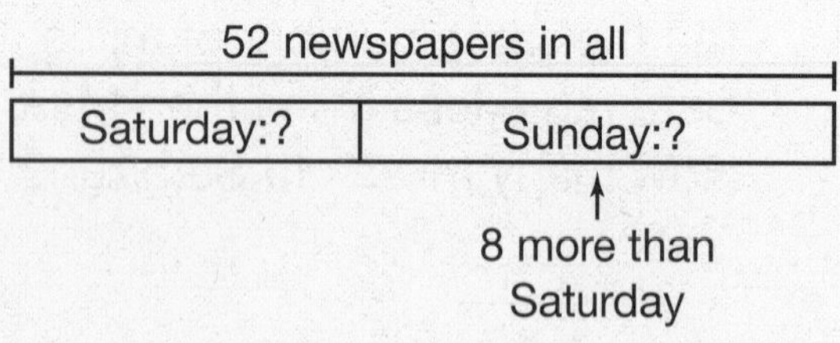

4. There are 24 students in Ms. Messing's class. Six more students walk to school than ride their bikes. The number of students that ride their bikes is the same as the number of students that are driven to school. How many students walk to school?

____

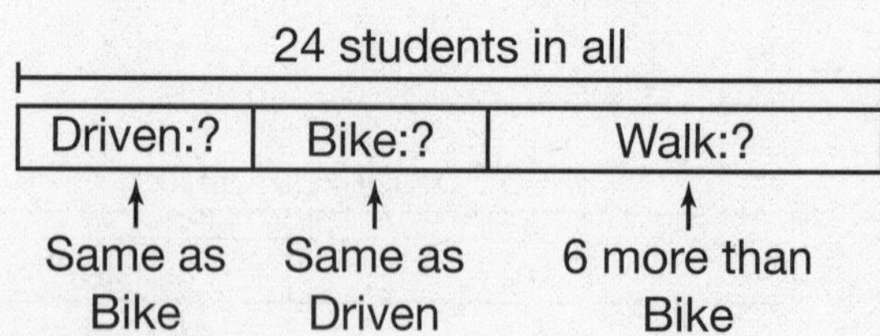

5. Jill is thinking of two numbers. They have a sum of 16 and a difference of 6. What are the two numbers?

A 16 and 6 **B** 13 and 3 **C** 12 and 4 **D** 11 and 5

Name ______________________

Reteaching
16-5

Understanding Area

The **area** of a figure can be found in two ways.

A **square unit** is a square with sides that are each 1 unit long.

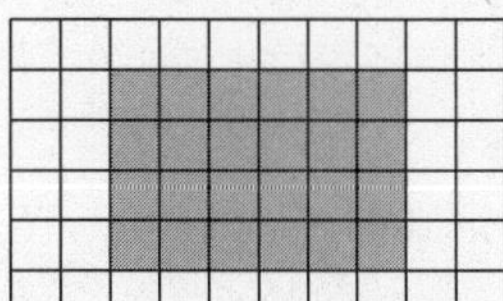

□ = 1 square inch

Count the square units in the shaded rectangle. There are 24 squares shaded. So, the area of the rectangle is 24 square inches.

You can think of the grid squares as an array.

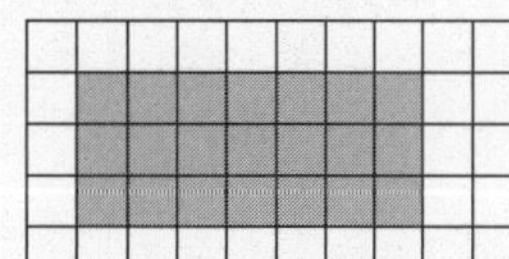

□ = 1 square centimeter

Each row has 7 squares. There are 3 rows, so multiply $3 \times 7 = 21$. The area of the rectangle is 21 square centimeters.

Find the area of each figure.

1.

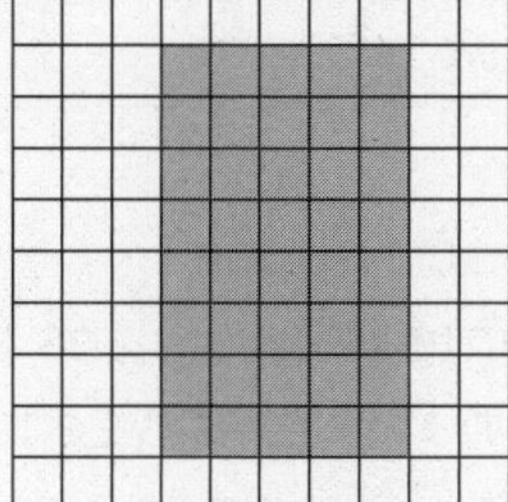

□ = 1 square inch

____

2.

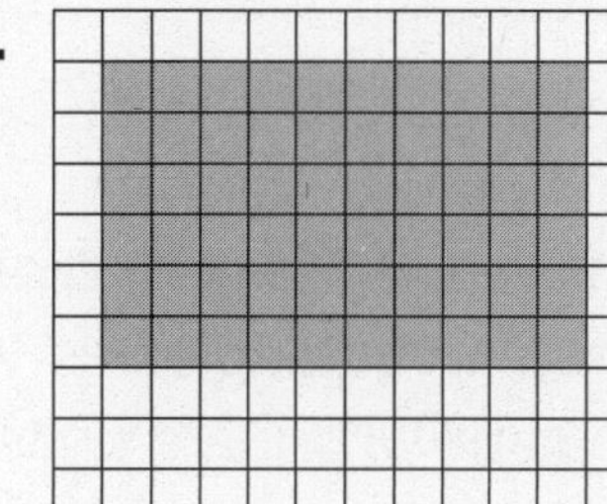

□ = 1 square meter

____

3.

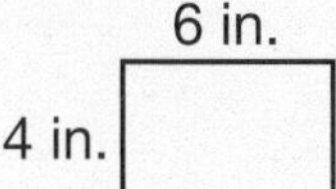

____

4. 5 cm

____

5. Reasonableness Can two different size rectangles have the same area? Explain.

____

____

Reteaching **16-5**

Name ________________________________

Practice
16-5

Understanding Area

Find the area of each figure.

1. 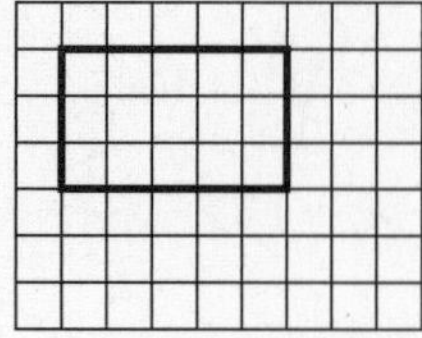

☐ = 1 square cm

____

2. 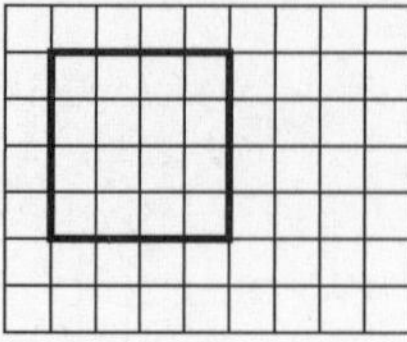

☐ = 1 square in.

____

3. 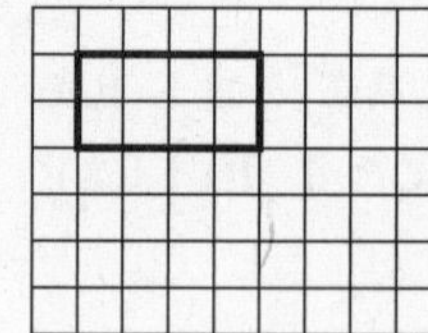

☐ = 1 square m

____

4. 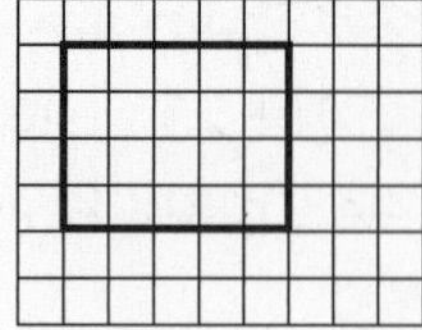

☐ = 1 square ft

____

5. 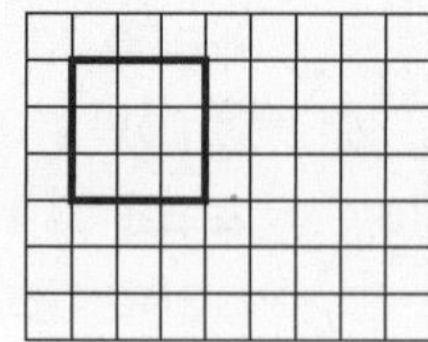

☐ = 1 square cm

____

6. 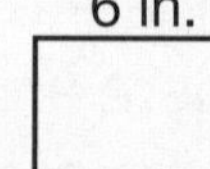

____

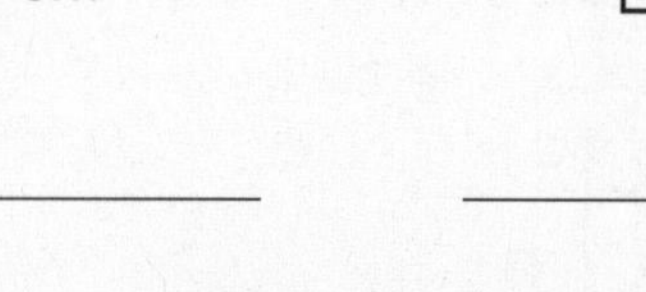

7. Draw a Picture On the grid, draw as many different rectangles as you can with areas of 12 square units.

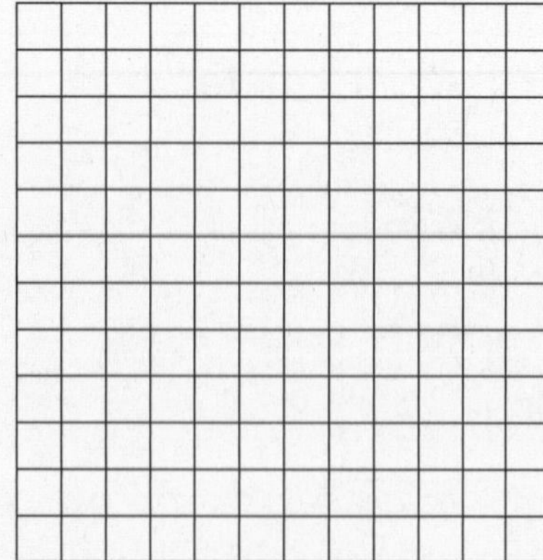

8. Reasoning Rectangular doghouses come in two sizes at the Super Z. The smaller size is 2 feet by 1 feet. The larger size is 4 feet by 2 feet. How many square feet greater is the larger doghouse?

____

9. What is the area of a square with sides of 5 inches?

A 10 square inches

B 20 square inches

C 25 square inches

D 50 square inches

Practice 16-5

Name ____________________

Estimating and Measuring Area

Two types of irregular figures can be placed on a grid.

If the shape completely fills the squares, count the squares.

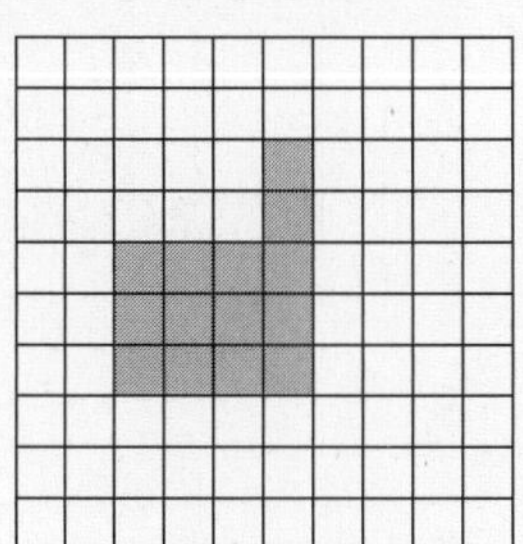

□ = 1 square inch

Count the squares by column or row. Let's add the columns from left to right.

3 + 3 + 3 + 5 = 14

The area is 14 square inches.

If the shape does not completely fill the squares, estimate the number of whole squares.

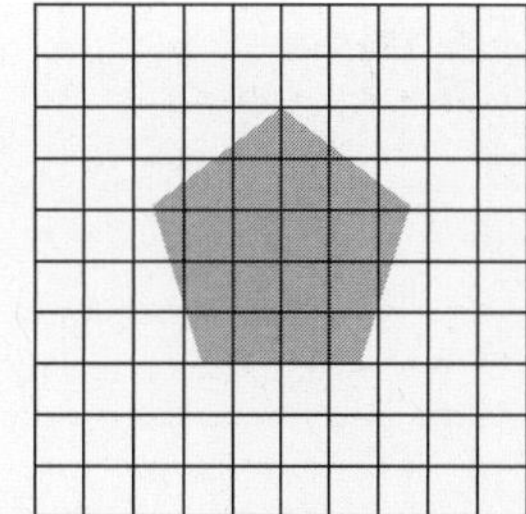

□ = 1 square inch

Count the whole squares that are filled. There are 12 whole squares.

Estimate the number of whole squares made from the partial squares. About 5 whole squares could be made.

12 + 5 = 17
The area is about 17 square inches.

Find the area.

1.

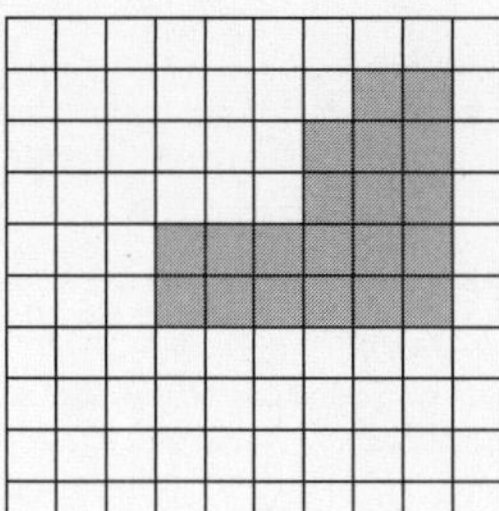

□ = 1 square foot

____

Estimate the area.

2.

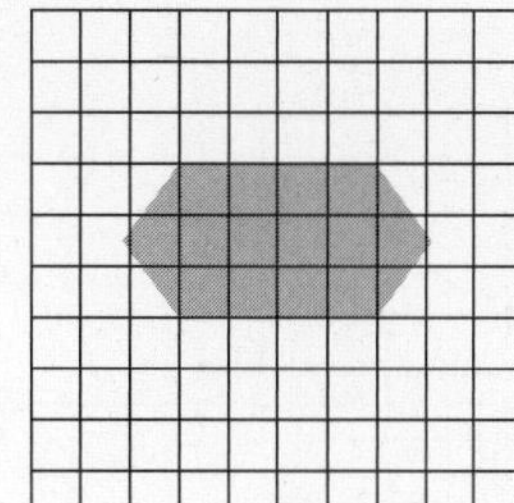

□ = 1 square centimeter

____

3. Writing to Explain How can you estimate the area of a circle on a grid?

____

____

Name ________________________

Practice
16-6

Estimating and Measuring Area

Find the area of each figure in square units.

1. 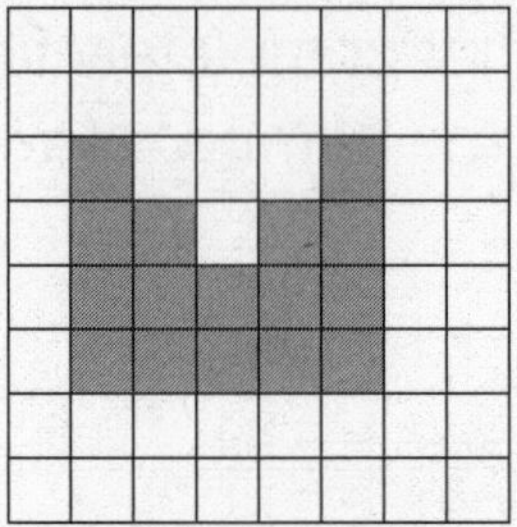

2. 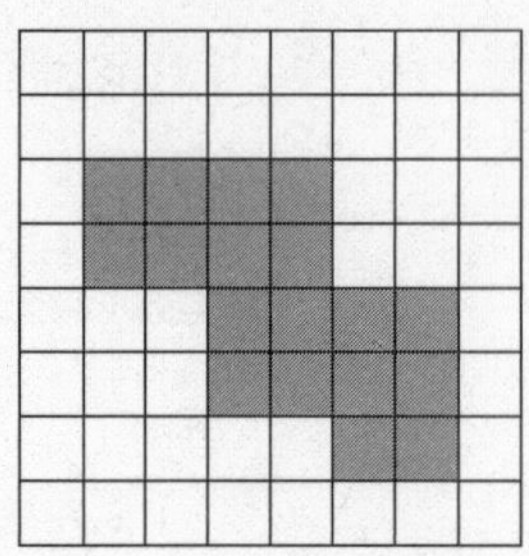

3. 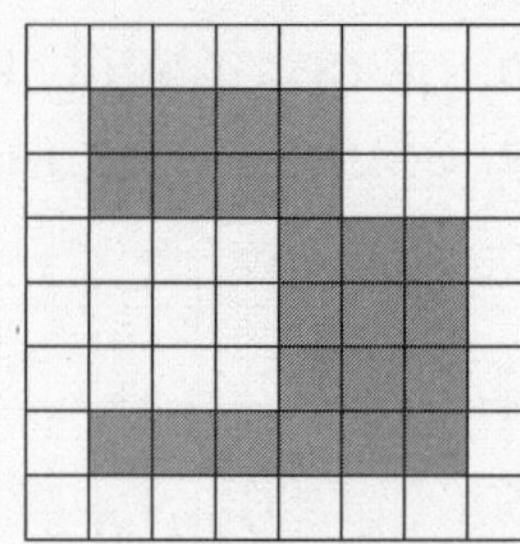

4. 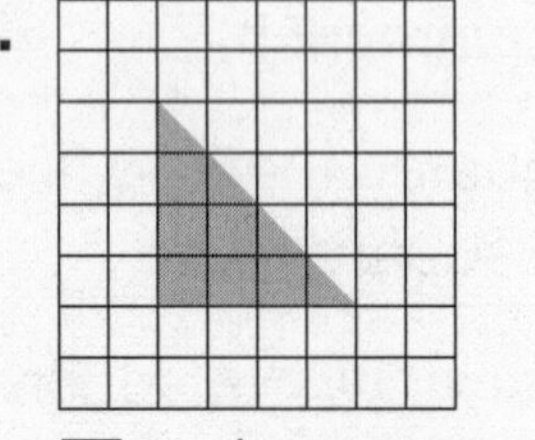

□ = 1 square cm

5. 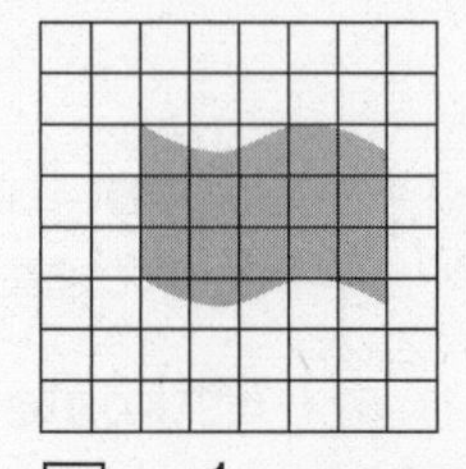

□ = 1 square foot

6. 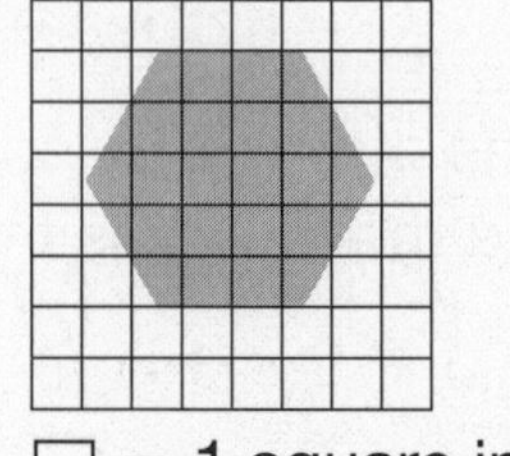

□ = 1 square inch

Practice **16-6**

7. Reasoning Use the grid. Draw two different figures that each have a perimeter of 14 units. Then find the area of each.

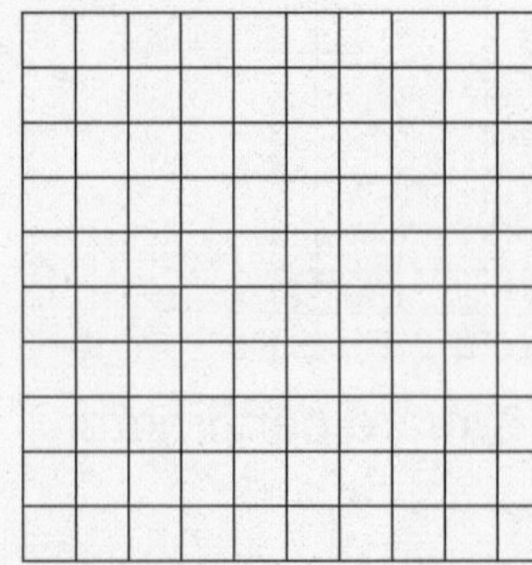

8. Explain It What is the difference between the perimeter and the area of a polygon?

9. What is the area of the figure to the right?

A 24 square units

B 25 square units

C 26 square units

D 27 square units

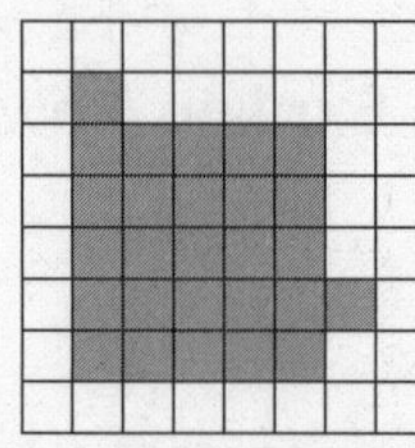

Name ______________________

Reteaching
16-7

Volume

Volume is the measure of the inside of a solid figure. Volume is measured in **cubic units**. A cubic unit is a cube with edges that are each 1 unit long.

To find the volume of a rectangular prism, follow these steps:

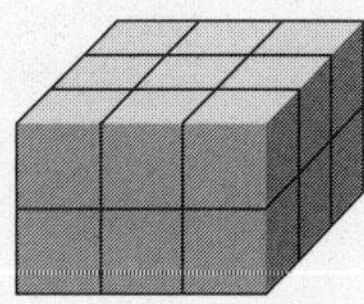

1. Count the number of cubes in each layer. — There are 9 cubes in each layer.
2. Multiply the number of cubes in each layer by the number of layers. — There are 2 layers. $2 \times 9 = 18$

The volume of the rectangular prism is 18 cubic units.

Find the volume of each figure in cubic units.

1. 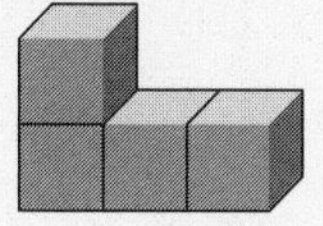 ______

2. 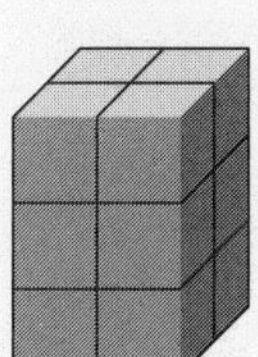 ______

3. 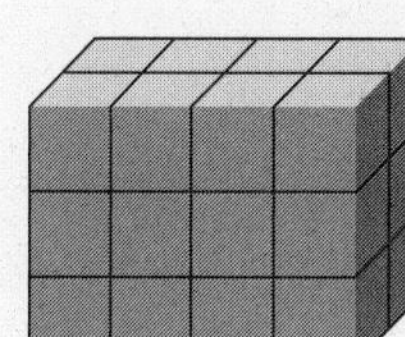 ______

4. 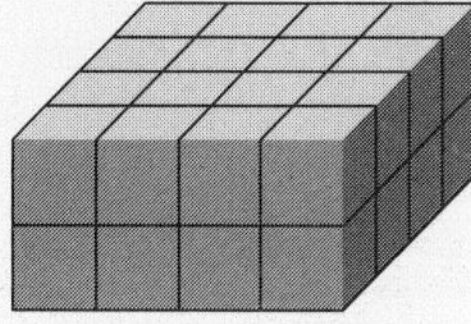 ______

5. 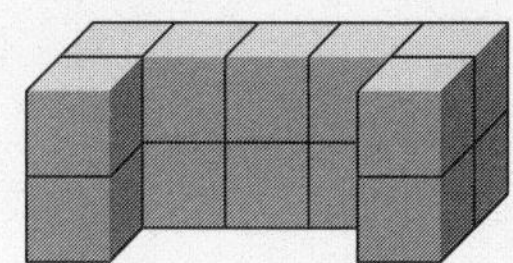 ______

6. 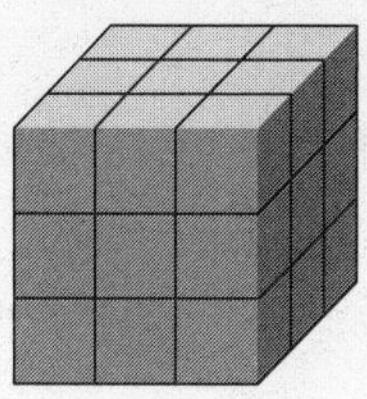 ______

7. **Explain It** How did you find the volume of the figure in Exercise 6?

____

____

____

Reteaching **16-7**

Name ______________________

Volume

Find the volume of each figure in cubic units.

1. 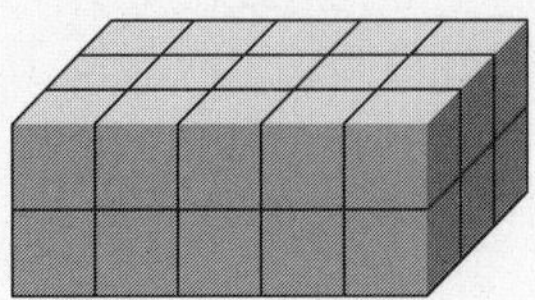

____

2. 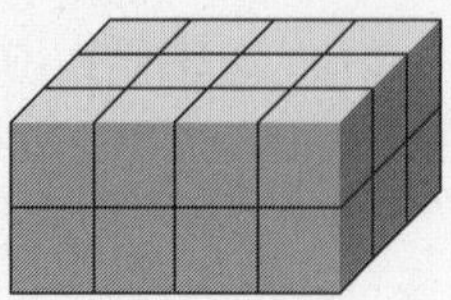

____

3. 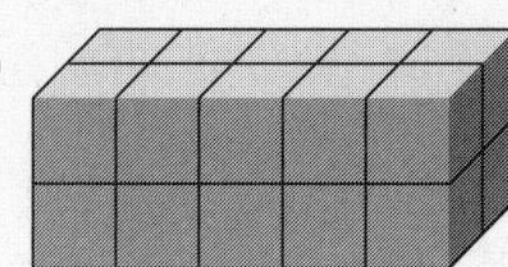

____

4. 

____

5. 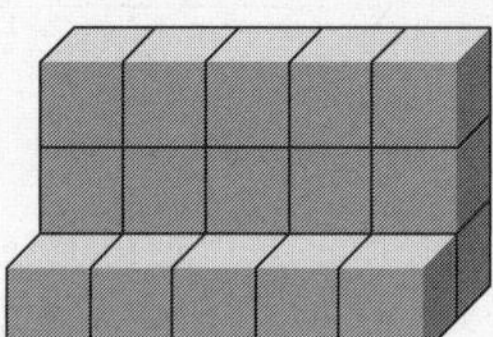

____

6. 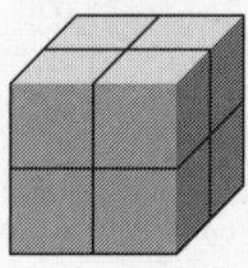

____

7. **Estimation** Use the cubes shown at the right to estimate the volume of the rectangular prism.

____

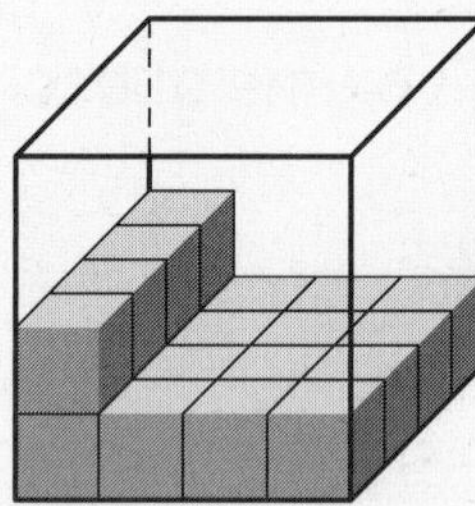

8. Kevin made a rectangular prism with 8 cubes in each layer. The prism has 4 layers. What is the volume of the rectangular prism?

____

9. **Explain It** How is finding volume different from finding area?

____

____

____

10. What is the volume of the figure at the right?

A 12 cubic units **C** 27 cubic units

B 24 cubic units **D** 36 cubic units

Name ______________________

Problem Solving: Solve a Simpler Problem

How can you find the area of the shaded figure to the right?

Think of it as 3 separate smaller figures.

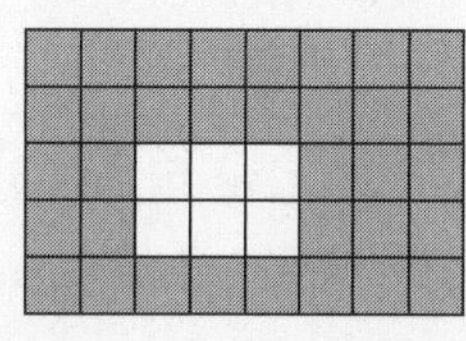

▩ = 1 square inch

Find the area of the 2 top rows.	2×8 sq in. $= 16$ sq in.
Find the area of the bottom row.	1×8 sq in. $= 8$ sq in.
Find the area of the two middle rows.	2×5 sq in. $= 10$ sq in.
Add the areas.	$16 + 8 + 10 = 34$

The area of the shaded figure is 34 square inches.

Solve. Use simpler problems.

1. Tyler High School has a T painted on the football field. The shaded part of the figure is the part that needs to be painted. What is the area of the painted part?

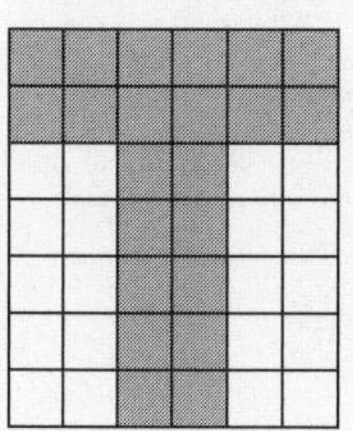

▩ = 1 square meter

____

2. Maria is tiling one of the walls in her kitchen. The shaded part of the figure is the part that needs to be tiled. What is the area of the part that needs tiling?

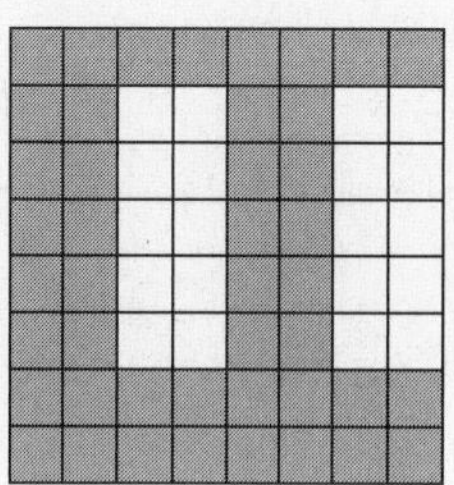

▩ = 1 square yard

____

3. Explain It Explain how you found your answer for Exercise 2.

____

____

Name ______________________

Practice
16-8

Problem Solving: Solve a Simpler Problem

Solve. Use simpler problems.

1. Ms. Finn is going to tile her kitchen floor. The shaded part of the figure is the part that needs to be tiled. What is the area of the shaded part?

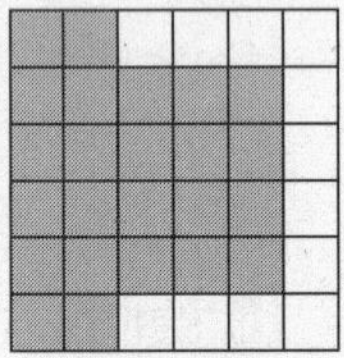

□ = 1 square yard

____

2. Alice is going to paint one of the walls in her bedroom. The shaded part of the figure is the part that needs to be painted. What is the area of the shaded part?

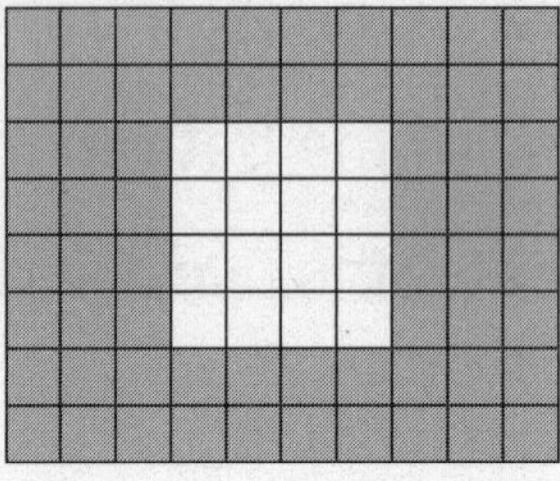

□ = 1 square foot

____

3. Harrison High School has an H painted on the football field. The shaded part of the figure is the part that needs to be painted. What is the area of the shaded part?

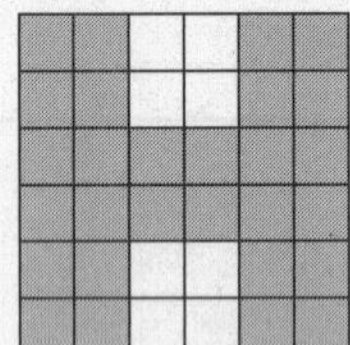

□ = 1 square meter

____

4. Mr. Rosen is going to repair the tiles in a shower. The shaded part of the figure is the part that needs to be tiled. What is the area of the shaded part?

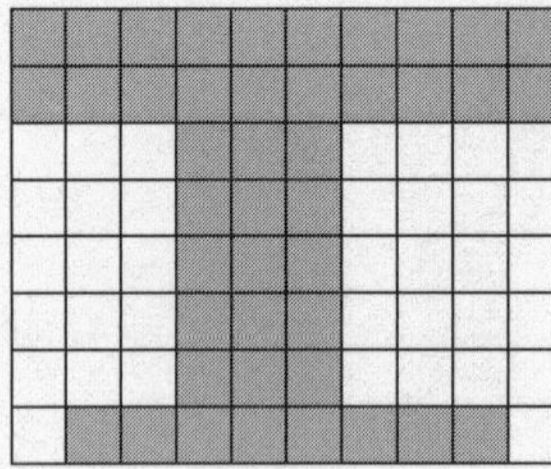

□ = 1 square foot

____

5. Luann is going to paint an L on her fence. The shaded part of the figure is the part that needs to be painted. What is the area of the shaded part?

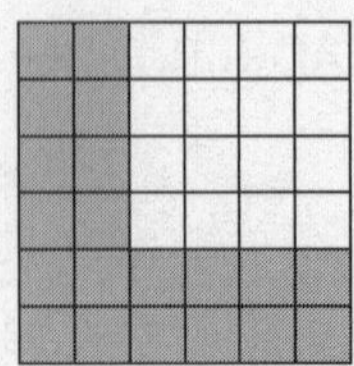

□ = 1 square inch

____

Name ______________________________

Time to the Half Hour and Quarter Hour

An hour is 60 minutes long. A half hour is 30 minutes long. A quarter hour is 15 minutes long.

The A.M. hours are the hours from 12 midnight to 12 noon. The P.M. hours are the hours from 12 noon to 12 midnight.

The clocks show three different times.

9:30
nine thirty
half past nine

12:15
twelve fifteen
15 minutes after 12
quarter after 12

1:45
one forty-five
45 minutes after 1
15 minutes to 2
quarter to 2

Write the time shown on each clock in two ways.

1.

____

____

2.

____

____

3.

____

____

4. Number Sense How many minutes are there in three quarters of an hour? Explain your answer.

____

____

____

Name ______________________

Time to the Half Hour and Quarter Hour

Write the time shown on each clock in two ways.

1. 

____

____

2. 

____

____

3. 

____

____

4. 

____

____

5. 

____

____

6. 

____

____

7. **Reasoning** The school bus stops at Randy's stop at 8:15 A.M. Randy arrived at the bus stop at quarter after 8. Did he miss the bus? Explain.

____

____

____

8. Which does **NOT** describe the time shown on the clock?

A five forty-five

B five fifteen

C quarter after five

D fifteen minutes after five

Name ______________________

Time to the Minute

You can skip count by fives and then count on to tell time when the minute hand is between numbers.

The minute hand is between 7 and 8.

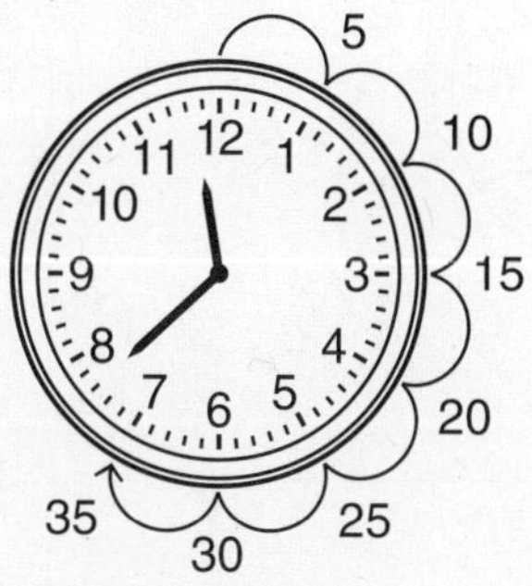

Count by 5s from 12 to 7. That is 35 minutes.

Count 3 more minutes. There are 38 minutes.

The hour hand is between 11 and 12. The time is 11:38, or 22 minutes to 12.

Write the time shown on each clock two ways.

1. 

____

____

2. 

____

____

3. 

____

____

Name ______________________

Practice
17-2

Time to the Minute

Write the time shown on each clock in two ways.

1. 

____

____

2. 

____

____

3. 

____

____

4. 

____

____

5. 

____

____

6. 

____

____

Practice 17-2

7. **Geometry** What type of angle is formed by a clock's hands when it is 3:00? ______________

8. The movie Mike watched lasted 1 hour 26 minutes. How many minutes did the movie last? ______________

9. Jan's alarm clock sounded at the time shown on the clock below. At what time did the alarm clock sound?

A six ten

B six twenty-two

C six thirty-eight

D seven twenty-two

Name ____________________

Units of Time

There are 60 minutes (min) in an hour (h).
There are 24 hours in a day (d).
There are 7 days in a week (wk).

To change from a larger unit to a smaller unit, multiply.

To find the number of hours in 2 days, add: 24 + 24 = 48.
So, there are 48 hours in 2 days.

Complete to change the units.

1. 6 weeks = ■■ days

____

2. 3 days = ■■ hours

____

3. How many days are there in 7 weeks?

____

4. How many minutes are there in 9 hours?

____

5. How many days are there in 3 weeks, 4 days?

____

6. How many minutes are there in 4 hours, 30 minutes?

____

7. **Writing to Explain** Nikki's school day lasts 7 hours, 20 minutes. How many minutes does Nikki's school day last? Explain how you found your answer.

____

____

____

____

Name ______________________________

Practice 17-3

Units of Time

Change the units. Complete.

1. 5 hours = ■■■ minutes
____

2. 3 weeks = ■■ days
____

3. 8 weeks = ■■ days
____

4. 6 hours = ■■■ minutes
____

5. How many minutes are in 3 hours, 30 minutes?
____

6. How many days are there in 4 weeks, 3 days?
____

7. Kendra watched two movies. The first lasted 100 minutes. The second lasted 1 hour, 55 minutes. Which movie was longer? By how many minutes?
____
____
____

8. **Writing to Explain** How many hours are there in a week? Explain how you found your answer.
____
____
____
____

9. The Wilson family is going on a 5-week vacation through Australia and New Zealand this summer. How many days will the Wilson's be on vacation?
____

10. Lacy slept 8 hours last night. How many minutes did Lacy sleep?

A 400 **C** 640

B 480 **D** 800

Practice 17-3

Name ______________________

Elapsed Time

A children's museum is open from 1:00 P.M. to 6:35 P.M. every day.
How long is the museum open?

Step 1

Start at the starting time.

Step 2

Count the hours.

There are 5 hours.

Step 3

Count the minutes.

There are 35 minutes.

The museum is open 5 hours, 35 minutes.

Find the elapsed time.

1. Start Time: 3:30 P.M.
End Time: 7:00 P.M.

____

2. Start Time: 8:10 A.M.
End Time: 10:55 A.M.

____

3. Start Time: 1:20 P.M.
End Time: 2:00 P.M.

____

4. Start Time: 8:00 A.M.
End Time: 1:15 P.M.

____

5. **Write a Problem** Write the start time and the ending time of an activity that you did during the weekend. Then find the elapsed time. Write your answer in hours and minutes.

____

____

____

Name ______________________

Practice **17-4**

Elapsed Time

Find the elapsed time.

1. Start Time: 6:00 P.M.
   End Time: 7:15 P.M.

   ____

2. Start Time: 9:30 A.M.
   End Time: 1:45 P.M.

   ____

3. Start Time: 3:10 P.M.
   End Time: 4:00 P.M.

   ____

4. Start Time: 11:30 A.M.
   End Time: 5:30 P.M.

   ____

5. Start Time: 7:30 A.M.
   End Time: 10:50 A.M.

   ____

6. Start Time: 9:00 P.M.
   End Time: 4:30 A.M.

   ____

7. Edie is 1 year old. She naps from 12:45 P.M. to 2:30 P.M. each day. How long is Edie's nap?

   ____

8. Mr. Wellborn arrives at work at 8:40 A.M. He leaves for work 50 minutes before he arrives. At what times does Mr. Wellborn leave for work?

   ____

9. **Writing to Explain** How long is your school day? Explain how you found your answer.

   ____

   ____

   ____

   ____

10. Gary's father dropped him off at soccer practice at 2:45 P.M. His mother picked him up at 5:00 P.M. How long did soccer practice last?

    A 2 hours, 15 minutes

    B 2 hours, 25 minutes

    C 3 hours, 15 minutes

    D 3 hours, 25 minutes

Name ______________________

Reteaching **17-5**

Temperature

Temperature can be measured in degrees Fahrenheit (°F) and degrees Celsius (°C).

Water freezes at 32°F and boils at 212°F.
Water freezes at 0°C and boils at 100°C.

To read a thermometer, find where the bar ends. Each mark represents 2° on each scale.

The temperature is three marks above 80°F, or 86°F.
The temperature is 30°C.

Write each temperature in °F and °C.

1.

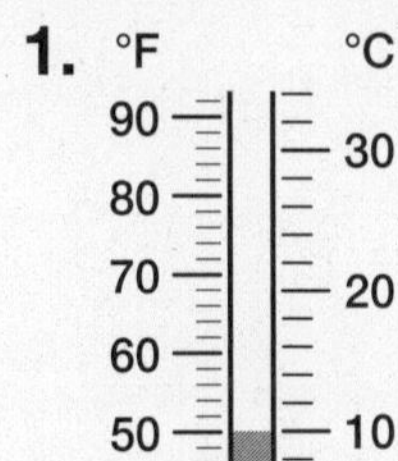

____

____

2.

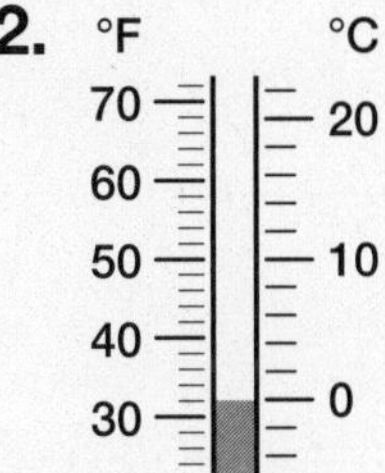

____

____

3.

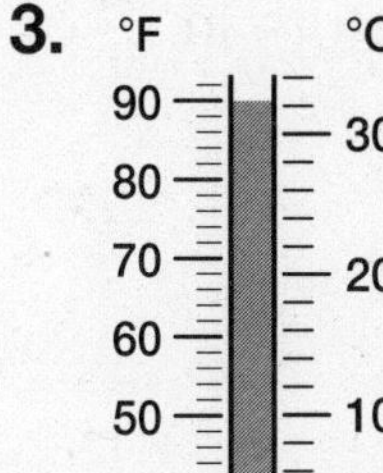

____

____

Estimation Choose the better temperature for each activity.

4. jogging

20°C or 40°C

____

5. sledding

20°F or 60°F

____

6. swimming

40°F or 80°F

____

Reteaching **17-5**

Name ______________________

Practice **17-5**

Temperature

Write each temperature in °F and °C.

1. 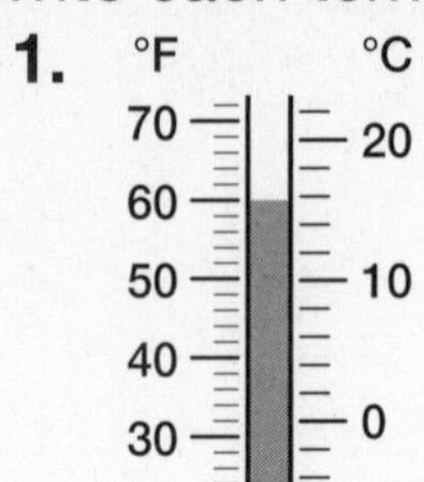

2. 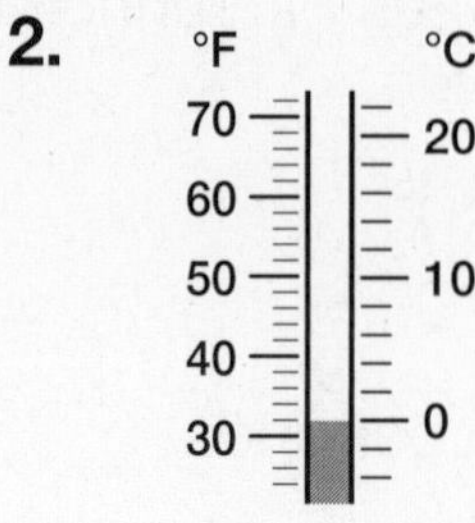

3. 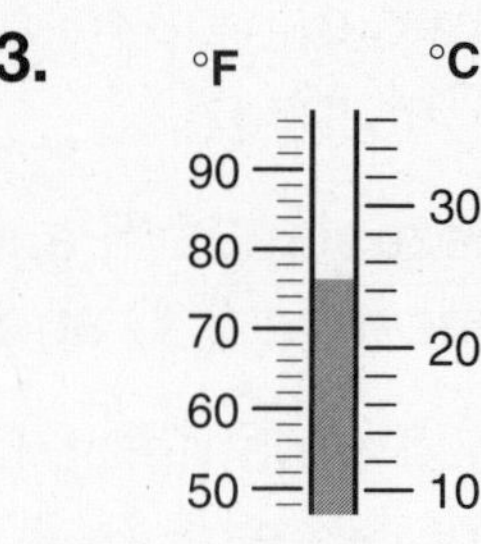

______________ ______________ ______________

______________ ______________ ______________

4. Reasonableness At 30°, Edgardo said the temperature was warm enough to go swimming. Did he mean to give the temperature in °F or °C? Explain.

____

____

____

5. The thermometer shows the high temperature in Helen's town Friday.

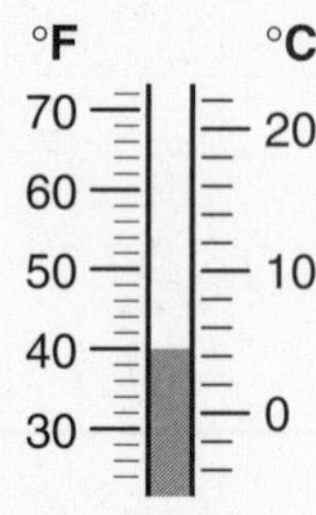

What was the high temperature in °F?

____

6. The normal high temperature in Dallas in January is 54°F. Which thermometer shows that temperature?

A 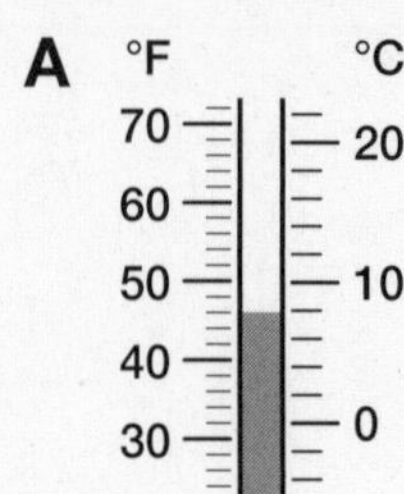

B 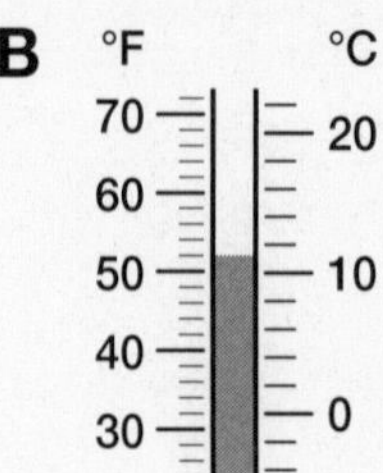

C 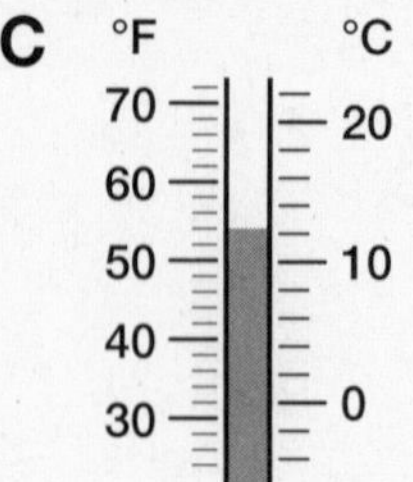

D 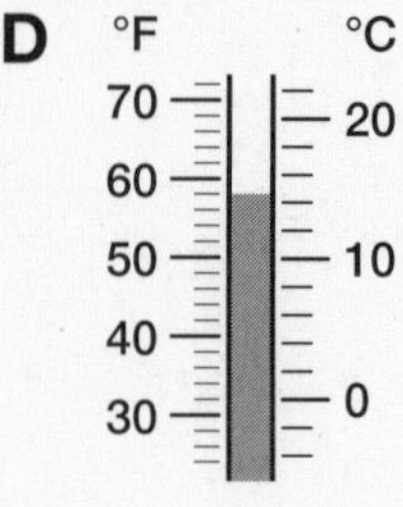

Name ______________________________

Problem Solving: Work Backward

Natalie finished listening to music at 4:30 P.M. She had listened to a CD that lasted 40 minutes. She spent 15 minutes listening to radio music after the CD finished. Then she listened to another CD for 45 minutes. At what time did Natalie start listening to music?

You can work backward to solve problems. Use each piece of information to find the starting time.

Natalie finished listening to music at 4:30 P.M.

She listened to the second CD for 45 minutes.	45 minutes before 4:30 P.M. is 3:45 P.M.	
She spent 15 minutes listening to radio music.	15 minutes from 3:45 P.M. is 3:30 P.M.	
She listened to the first CD for 40 minutes.	40 minutes before 3:30 P.M. is 2:50 P.M.	

Natalie started listening to music at 2:50 P.M.

Solve the problem by drawing a picture and working backward.

1. The temperature at 6 P.M. was 72°F. This temperature was 8°F less than at 4 P.M. The temperature at 10 A.M. was 5°F greater than the 4 P.M. temperature. What was the temperature at 10 A.M.?

____

Name ____________________

Practice
17-6

Problem Solving: Work Backward

Solve the problem by drawing a picture and working backward.

1. Will arrived at his mother's office at 3 P.M. It took him 30 minutes to walk from his home to the mall. He was in the mall for 45 minutes. It then took him 15 minutes to walk to his mother's office. At what time did Will leave home?

____

2. At 12 noon, Leslie recorded the temperature as 56°F. The temperature had increased by 8°F from 10 A.M. The temperature at 8 A.M. was 2°F warmer than it was at 10 A.M. What was the temperature at 8 A.M.?

____

3. The test that Keyshawn's class took finished at 10:30 A.M. The first part of the test took 30 minutes. There was a 15-minute break. The second part of the test also took 30 minutes. At what time did the test start?

____

4. The temperature was 16°C when Becky returned home at 6 P.M. The temperature was 4°C warmer at 3 P.M. than it was at 6 P.M. It was 3°C warmer at 12 noon than it was at 3 P.M. What was the temperature at 12 noon?

____

Practice 17-6

5. Elliot finished studying at 4:45 P.M. He spent 30 minutes reading a social studies chapter. He spent 45 minutes on his math homework. In between reading and math, Elliot took a 20-minute break. At what time did Elliot begin studying?

   A 3:00 P.M. **B** 3:10 P.M. **C** 3:30 P.M. **D** 6:20 P.M.

Name ______________________

Using Mental Math to Multiply

You can use multiplication patterns to help multiply multiples of 10, 100, and 1,000.

When one of the factors ends in zeros, multiply the nonzero digits. Then write the extra zeros.

9 × 100

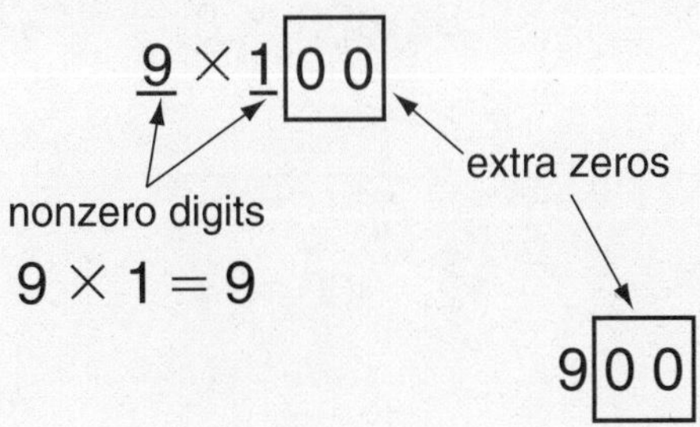

9 × 100 = 900

12 × 2,000

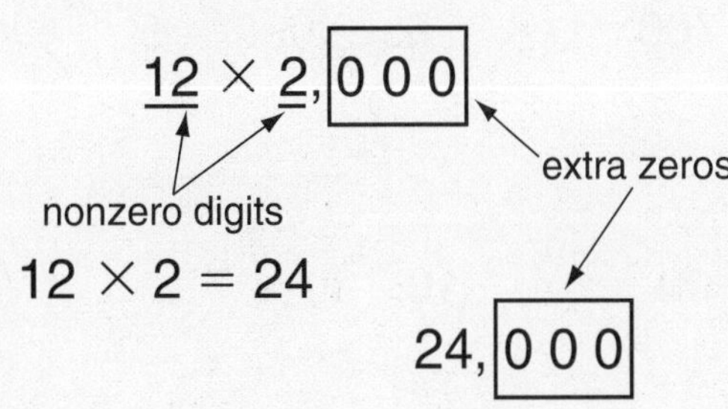

12 × 2,000 = 24,000

Use mental math to find each product.

1. 8 × 10 = ______ **2.** 7 × 100 = ______

3. 4 × 1,000 = ______ **4.** 3 × 50 = ______

5. 600 × 3 = ______ **6.** 4,000 × 7 = ______

Find the missing number in each number sentence.

7. ☐ × 100 = 600 **8.** 40 × ☐ = 360

9. **Number Sense** Karen says, "When I have a factor with exactly 2 zeros at the end, my answer will always have exactly 2 zeros at the end." Do you agree? Explain.

____

____

____

____

Name ______________________

Practice
18-1

Using Mental Math to Multiply

Find each product.

1. 3 × 10 ______

2. 6 × 100 ______

3. 9 × 1,000 ______

4. 80 × 3 ______

5. 4 × 700 ______

6. 2,000 × 5 ______

7. 6 × 400 ______

8. 800 × 8 ______

9. 6 × 900 ______

10. 90 × 7 ______

11. 3,000 × 4 ______

12. 500 × 4 ______

13. Ms. Armstrong works 40 hours each week. How many hours does she work in 4 weeks?

______

14. There are 2,000 pounds in one ton. How many pounds are there in 6 tons?

______

15. **Number Sense** A century is 100 years. How many years are there in 8 centuries?

______

16. One metric ton equals 1,000 kilograms. How many kilograms are there in 7 metric tons?

______

17. **Explain It** How can you use mental math to multiply 800 × 5?

______

______

______

18. Each time you pass "Start" on a board game you receive 300 points. How many points will you receive if you pass "Start" 6 times?

A 180 **B** 1,800 **C** 18,000 **D** 180,000

Practice **18-1**

Name ___________________________

Reteaching
18-2

Estimating Products

You can use rounding to estimate products. Remember, look at the digit to the right of the place that you are rounding. If the digit is 5 or more, round up. If the digit is less than 5, leave the digit in the rounding place alone.

Estimate 6×22.

Round 22 to the nearest ten.

22 rounds to 20.

$6 \times 20 = 120$

So, 6×22 is about 120.

Estimate 8×37.

Round 37 to the nearest ten.

37 rounds to 40.

$8 \times 40 = 320$

So, 8×37 is about 320.

Estimate each product.

1. 8×91 ________

2. 4×69 ________

3. 3×53 ________

4. 2×23 ________

5. 7×67 ________

6. 9×63 ________

7. 8×78 ________

8. 5×36 ________

9. 8×52 ________

10. 9×27 ________

11. 6×31 ________

12. 7×88 ________

13. 8×39 ________

14. 5×43 ________

15. 6×64 ________

16. **Number Sense** Is 4×87 less than 360? How do you know?

____

____

____

Name ______________________________

Practice
18-2

Estimating Products

Estimate each product.

1. 5×53 ______ **2.** 7×48 ______ **3.** 6×58 ______ **4.** 8×22 ______ **5.** 3×73 ______

6. 9×42 ______ **7.** 4×93 ______ **8.** 8×57 ______ **9.** 6×52 ______ **10.** 7×63 ______

11. 8×54 ______ **12.** 2×97 ______ **13.** 6×78 ______ **14.** 5×37 ______ **15.** 7×58 ______

16. Reasoning Marcia said that if she estimates 73×7, the product will be less than the exact answer. Is she correct? Explain.

____

____

____

17. Audrey delivers 38 newspapers each day of the week except Sunday. About how many newspapers does she deliver in a week? ______

18. Explain It Each video game at an arcade requires 55 tokens. Tom has 100 tokens. He said he can play 2 games. Is he correct? Explain.

____

____

____

19. A basketball player scores an average of 32 points per game. About how many points will he score in 8 games? ______

20. Which is the best estimate for 67×9?

A 540 **B** 630 **C** 670 **D** 700

Practice 18-2

Name ______________________

Multiplication and Arrays

You can draw a picture of an array to show multiplication.

Multiply 3×17.

What You Show

What You Think

3 rows of 1 ten = 3 tens

3 rows of 7 ones = 21 ones

$30 + 21 = 51$

To find the product, count the tens and the ones.
Then add them together.

There are 3 tens and 21 ones. Add $30 + 21 = 51$.

So, $3 \times 17 = 51$.

Use place-value blocks or draw an array to find each product.

1. 4×14 ______ **2.** 2×37 ______ **3.** 5×21 ______ **4.** 3×43 ______ **5.** 6×18 ______

6. 3×46 ______ **7.** 7×13 ______ **8.** 2×19 ______ **9.** 9×14 ______ **10.** 3×34 ______

11. Strategy Practice Explain how you can multiply 3×24 by using arrays. Then give the product.

____

____

____

Name ______________________

Practice
18-3

Multiplication and Arrays

Find each product. You may use place-value blocks or draw a picture to help.

1. 3 × 17

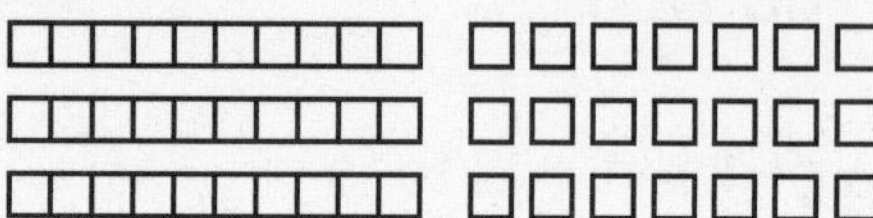

______

2. 2 × 22

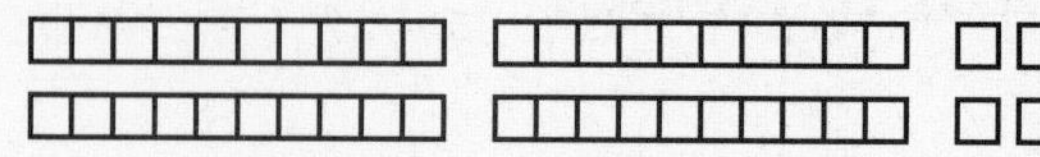

______

3. 5 × 34 ______

4. 4 × 13 ______

5. 3 × 57 ______

6. 2 × 34 ______

7. 6 × 22 ______

8. 3 × 43 ______

9. 5 × 26 ______

10. 6 × 18 ______

11. 4 × 24 ______

12. 5 × 29 ______

For **13** through **15**, use the table at the right.

Days Worked in April

Employee	Days Worked
Bob	19
Josh	25
Marvin	13

13. Bob works 7 hours each day. How many hours did he work in April all together?

______

14. Josh works 8 hours each day. How many hours did he work in April all together?

______

15. Marvin works 9 hours each day. How many more hours did Bob work than Marvin in April?

______

16. **Explain It** How can you use an array to find 4 × 13?

____

____

17. What is the product of 27 × 4?

A 36 **B** 88 **C** 108 **D** 127

Practice **18-3**

Name ______________________________

Reteaching **18-4**

Breaking Apart to Multiply

You can make multiplication easier by breaking greater numbers apart by place value.

Find 3×35.

Break apart 35 as $30 + 5$.

First multiply the ones, then multiply the tens.

$3 \times 5 = 15$ $3 \times 30 = 90$

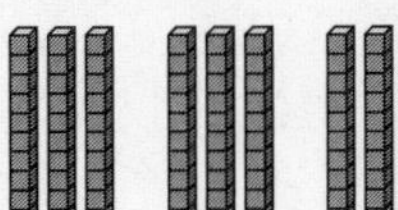

Add the partial products: $15 + 90 = 105$

So, $3 \times 35 = 105$.

Complete.

1. 5×23

5×2 tens = ☐ tens or 100

5×3 ones = 15 ones or ☐

☐ + ☐ = ☐

2. 4×46

$4 \times 40 =$ ☐

$4 \times 6 =$ ☐

☐ + ☐ = ☐

Find each product. You may use place-value blocks or drawings to help.

3. 6×21 ______ **4.** 5×43 ______ **5.** 3×16 ______ **6.** 5×22 ______ **7.** 4×29 ______

8. 3×52 ______ **9.** 7×26 ______ **10.** 4×34 ______ **11.** 6×17 ______ **12.** 2×47 ______

13. Number Sense Tim said, "To find 6×33, I can add $18 + 18$." Do you agree with him? Why or why not?

____

____

Name ______________________

Practice
18-4

Breaking Apart to Multiply

Find each product. You may use place-value blocks or draw a picture to help.

1. 4 × 43 ______ **2.** 7 × 18 ______ **3.** 5 × 13 ______ **4.** 2 × 88 ______ **5.** 4 × 34 ______

6. 3 × 49 ______ **7.** 6 × 42 ______ **8.** 4 × 56 ______ **9.** 3 × 25 ______ **10.** 5 × 24 ______

11. 2 × 54 ______ **12.** 4 × 37 ______ **13.** 7 × 22 ______ **14.** 6 × 16 ______ **15.** 6 × 37 ______

16. A carpenter makes chairs with slats that run across the back of the chairs as shown. Each chair uses 7 slats. He needs to make 24 chairs. How many slats must he make?

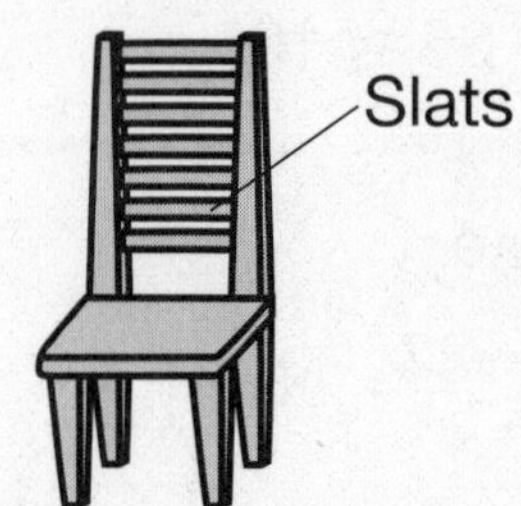

____

17. Each piece of wood trim is 6 feet long. Exactly 19 pieces are needed to go around a room. How many feet of wood trim are needed?

____

18. Writing to Explain How can you multiply 42 × 8 by breaking apart numbers?

____

19. A runner runs 34 miles each week. How many miles does the runner run in 5 weeks?

____

20. Which is equal to 5 × 25?

A 25 + 10 **B** 100 + 5 **C** 115 **D** 100 + 25

Practice **18-4**

Name ____________________

Reteaching
18-5

Using an Expanded Algorithm

You can multiply 2-digit numbers by finding partial products.

Find 3 × 27.
First multiply the ones. Next, multiply the tens.
Then, add the partial products.

What You Show

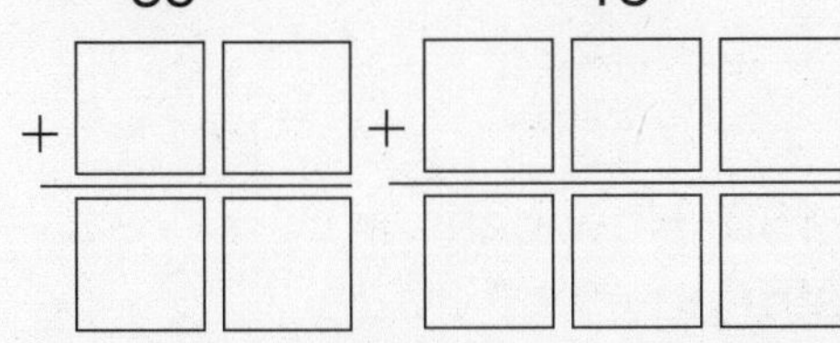

What You Write

```
  27
×  3
  21 ——→ 3 × 7
+ 60 ——→ 3 × 20
  81
```

So, 3 × 27 = 81.

For **1** and **2** complete. For **3** through **5**, find the product.
Use place-value blocks or drawings to help.

1. 17 × 5 = 35 + ☐☐ = ☐☐

2. 23 × 6 = 18 + ☐☐☐ = ☐☐☐

3. 43 × 4

4. 56 × 3

5. 14 × 8

6. Number Sense Mindy's backyard is 38 yards wide.
There are 3 feet in a yard. How many feet are in 38 yards?

____

Reteaching **18-5**

Name ______________________

Practice
18-5

Using an Expanded Algorithm

In **1** and **2,** complete. In **3** through **5**, find each product. You may use place-value blocks or drawings to help.

1. $\begin{array}{r} 27 \\ \times\ 3 \\ \hline 21 \\ +\ \square\square \\ \hline \square\square \end{array}$

2. $\begin{array}{r} 43 \\ \times\ 5 \\ \hline 15 \\ +\ \square\square\square \\ \hline \square\square\square \end{array}$

3. $\begin{array}{r} 19 \\ \times\ 4 \\ \hline \end{array}$

4. $\begin{array}{r} 36 \\ \times\ 5 \\ \hline \end{array}$

5. 6×45 ______

Find each product. You may use place-value blocks or drawings to help.

6. $\begin{array}{r} 96 \\ \times\ 3 \\ \hline \end{array}$

7. $\begin{array}{r} 27 \\ \times\ 5 \\ \hline \end{array}$

8. $\begin{array}{r} 57 \\ \times\ 4 \\ \hline \end{array}$

9. $\begin{array}{r} 44 \\ \times\ 3 \\ \hline \end{array}$

10. 6×27 ______

11. An area in Norway gets sunlight all day for 14 weeks straight during the summer. How many days is 14 weeks?

______

12. There are 19 tables end-to-end in a line at a flea market. Each table is 6 feet long. How many feet long is the line of tables?

______

Practice 18-5

13. Reasoning Suppose you know that $9 \times 20 = 180$. How can you use this fact to find 9×24? Explain your strategy.

______

______

______

______

14. A pound is equal to 16 ounces. How many ounces are there in 6 pounds?

A 66 **B** 86 **C** 96 **D** 106

Name ______________________________

Multiplying 2- and 3-Digit by 1-Digit Numbers

You can multiply a 2-digit or a 3-digit number by a 1-digit number without finding partial products.

Find 6×48.
Estimate $6 \times 50 = 300$.

Step 1

Multiply the ones.
Regroup if needed.

$6 \times 8 = 48$ ones
Regroup 48 ones as 4 tens and 8 ones.

$$\begin{array}{r} {}^{4} \\ 48 \\ \times\ 6 \\ \hline 8 \end{array}$$

Step 2

Multiply the tens.
Add the regrouped tens.

$6 \times 4 = 24$ tens
24 tens + 4 tens = 28 tens

$$\begin{array}{r} {}^{4} \\ 48 \\ \times\ 6 \\ \hline 288 \end{array}$$

Is the answer reasonable?
Yes. 288 is close to the estimate of 300.
So, $6 \times 48 = 288$.

For **1** and **2**, complete. For **3** through **10**, find the product. Use place-value blocks or drawings to help.

1. $\begin{array}{r} \square \\ 14 \\ \times\ 7 \\ \hline \square 8 \end{array}$

2. $\begin{array}{r} \square \\ 26 \\ \times\ 9 \\ \hline \square\square 4 \end{array}$

3. $\begin{array}{r} 36 \\ \times\ 4 \\ \hline \end{array}$

4. $\begin{array}{r} 73 \\ \times\ 6 \\ \hline \end{array}$

5. $\begin{array}{r} 47 \\ \times\ 5 \\ \hline \end{array}$

6. $\begin{array}{r} 36 \\ \times\ 7 \\ \hline \end{array}$

7. $\begin{array}{r} 54 \\ \times\ 3 \\ \hline \end{array}$

8. $\begin{array}{r} 289 \\ \times\ 7 \\ \hline \end{array}$

9. $\begin{array}{r} 647 \\ \times\ 8 \\ \hline \end{array}$

10. $\begin{array}{r} 862 \\ \times\ 2 \\ \hline \end{array}$

11. Reasonableness Rick multiplied 53×7 and got a product of 351. Is Rick correct? Explain why or why not.

____

____

____

Name ______________________

Practice
18-6

Multiplying 2- and 3-Digit by 1-Digit Numbers

Estimate and then find each product. You may use drawings to help.

1. 48×4 **2.** 52×7 **3.** 36×3 **4.** 67×5 **5.** 4×33

Find each product.

6. 53×4 **7.** 61×3 **8.** 74×4 **9.** 96×2 **10.** 5×57

11. 3×487 **12.** 632×4 **13.** 8×275 **14.** 396×5

15. Bruce reads 35 pages of a book each day. It will take him 9 days to finish the book. How many pages are in the book?

16. **Estimation** Jose drinks 64 fluid ounces of water each day. About how many fluid ounces of water does he drink each week?

17. **Reasonableness** Celeste multiplied $44 \times 5 = 202$. Is her product reasonable? Explain why or why not?

18. Each bus in the Turtle System can seat 48 passengers. How many passengers can be seated on 6 Turtle System buses?

A 248 **B** 252 **C** 268 **D** 288

Practice 18-6

Name ______________________

Reteaching
18-7

Problem Solving: Draw a Picture and Write a Number Sentence

Mr. Petty commutes 28 miles to and from work 4 days each week. How many miles does he commute to work each week?

You can use a diagram to show what you know.

_________ miles in all

28	28	28	28

Multiply.

$$\begin{array}{r} 28 \\ \times\ 4 \\ \hline \end{array}$$

Mr. Petty commutes 112 miles each week.

Estimate to check.

28 rounds to 30.

$30 \times 4 = 120$

Since 112 is close to 120, the answer is reasonable.

1. Joel rode his bicycle 14 miles each of the 6 days he cycled this week. How many miles did he cycle all together?

_________ miles in all

14	14	14	14	14	14

2. There are 24 hours in each day. There are 7 days in one week. How many hours are there in one week?

_________ hours in all

24	24	24	24	24	24	24

3. Ms. Till works 8 hours each day that she works. In February she worked 19 days. How many hours did she work in February?

_________ hours in all

19	19	19	19	19	19	19	19

4. Estimation It is suggested that you drink 8 cups of water each day. About how many cups of water will you drink in one month?

____

Tip: A month can have as few as 28 days or as many as 31 days.

Name ______________________________

Practice
18-7

Problem Solving: Draw a Picture and Write a Number Sentence

1. At dress rehearsal Wednesday, there were 66 people in the audience. On opening night Thursday, there were 3 times as many people. How many people were in the audience for opening night?

Dress Rehearsal | 66 |

Opening Night | 66 | 66 | 66 | **3 times as many**

__________ people in all

2. At Heather and Bob's wedding, there were 32 tables. Each table seats 8 people. All of the tables were full. How many people attended the wedding?

__________ people in all

| 32 | 32 | 32 | 32 | 32 | 32 | 32 | 32 |

The chart shows the number of calories in fats, proteins, and carbohydrates. Use the chart for **3** through **5**.

Nutritional Information

Ingredients	Calories Per Gram
Protein	4
Carbohydrate	4
Fat	9

3. The energy bar that Kyle is eating has 37 grams of carbohydrates. How many calories are from carbohydrates in the energy bar?

__________ calories in all

| 37 | 37 | 37 | 37 |

4. A serving of chicken has 27 grams of protein and 3 grams of fat. How many calories are in a serving of chicken?

____

5. A banana has 27 grams of carbohydrates. It has a total of 121 calories. How many of its calories come from sources other than carbohydrates?

____

6. Write a Problem Write a problem that can be solved by drawing a picture. Draw the picture and solve the problem.

Practice **18-7**

Name ______________________

Reteaching
19-1

Mental Math

You can use a pattern to divide multiples of 10, 100, and 1,000.

Find 180 ÷ 2.	Find 3,600 ÷ 4.	Find 6,000 ÷ 2.
Use a basic fact and then follow the pattern.	Use a basic fact and then follow the pattern.	Use a basic fact and then follow the pattern.
18 ÷ 2 = 9	36 ÷ 4 = 9	6 ÷ 2 = 3
180 ÷ 2 = 90	360 ÷ 4 = 90	60 ÷ 2 = 30
	3,600 ÷ 4 = 900	600 ÷ 2 = 300
		6,000 ÷ 2 = 3,000
The dividend is 10 times greater, so the quotient is 10 times greater.	The dividend is 100 times greater, so the quotient is 100 times greater.	The dividend is 1,000 times greater, so the quotient is 1,000 times greater.

To find the quotient, start with a basic fact. Then write the number of 0s that are left in the dividend.

Use patterns and mental math to find each quotient.

1. 16 ÷ 8 ________

160 ÷ 8 ________

1,600 ÷ 8 ________

2. 54 ÷ 6 ________

540 ÷ 6 ________

5,400 ÷ 6 ________

3. 35 ÷ 5 ________

350 ÷ 5 ________

3,500 ÷ 5 ________

4. Reasonableness Andy said that 2,000 ÷ 4 = 5,000 because 20 ÷ 4 = 5 and the dividend has 3 zeros. Is Andy correct? Explain why or why not.

____

____

____

Name ______________________

Practice
19-1

Mental Math

Use patterns to find each quotient.

1. 24 ÷ 4 ________
240 ÷ 4 ________
2,400 ÷ 4 ________

2. 42 ÷ 6 ________
420 ÷ 6 ________
4,200 ÷ 6 ________

3. 12 ÷ 3 ________
120 ÷ 3 ________
1,200 ÷ 3 ________

4. 25 ÷ 5 ________
250 ÷ 5 ________
2,500 ÷ 5 ________

5. 63 ÷ 7 ________
630 ÷ 7 ________
6,300 ÷ 7 ________

6. 64 ÷ 8 ________
640 ÷ 8 ________
6,400 ÷ 8 ________

Use mental math to find each quotient.

7. 240 ÷ 3 ________

8. 5,600 ÷ 8 ________

9. 1,000 ÷ 5 ________

10. 490 ÷ 7 ________

11. 1,500 ÷ 3 ________

12. A race is 1,600 yards long. The runners have to run 4 laps around the track. How many yards is each lap?

____

13. There were 80 people at a banquet. They were seated at 4 tables. Each table had the same number of people. How many people were at each table?

____

14. **Writing to Explain** How can you use a pattern to find 2,100 ÷ 3? What is the quotient?

____

____

15. On a cross-country trip, the Smiths drove 2,700 miles in 9 days. They drove the same number of miles each day. How many miles did they drive each day?

A 3
B 30
C 300
D 3,000

16. **Number Sense** How many $5 bills are there in $2,000?

____

Practice 19-1

Name ______________________

Reteaching
19-2

Estimating Quotients

To estimate quotients, you can use a number that is close to the dividend.

Pedro has 357 CDs on 5 shelves. Each shelf has about the same number of CDs. About how many CDs are on each shelf?

Use a number that is close to 357 and is easy to divide by 5.

You know that $35 \div 5 = 7$ and $350 \div 5 = 70$.

So, $357 \div 5$ is about 70, so Pedro has about 70 CDs on each shelf.

Estimate each quotient.

1. $78 \div 4$ ________ **2.** $306 \div 8$ ________ **3.** $437 \div 5$ ________ **4.** $348 \div 6$ ________ **5.** $2{,}957 \div 9$ ________

6. $732 \div 9$ ________ **7.** $4{,}729 \div 7$ ________ **8.** $524 \div 6$ ________ **9.** $393 \div 4$ ________ **10.** $2{,}035 \div 4$ ________

11. The Klein family drove 422 miles in 8 hours. What number would you use to estimate the number of miles the Klein family drove in all? About how many miles did they drive each hour?

____

12. Writing to Explain Mrs. O'Neill has 6 monthly payments left on her car. She still owes $1,932. About how much money does she have to pay each month? Explain how you found your answer.

____

____

Name ______________________

Practice
19-2

Estimating Quotients

Estimate each quotient.

1. 78 ÷ 8 ________ **2.** 221 ÷ 3 ________ **3.** 620 ÷ 9 ________ **4.** 225 ÷ 6 ________ **5.** 5,341 ÷ 8 ________

6. 537 ÷ 6 ________ **7.** 2,512 ÷ 4 ________ **8.** 348 ÷ 7 ________ **9.** 427 ÷ 7 ________ **10.** 1,925 ÷ 6 ________

11. 812 ÷ 9 ________ **12.** 1,253 ÷ 4 ________ **13.** 3,173 ÷ 8 ________ **14.** 2,833 ÷ 6 ________ **15.** 4,173 ÷ 5 ________

16. There are 365 days in a year. Elroy has piano practice once every 5 days. About how many times does Elroy have piano practice in a year?

____

17. A restaurant offers a buffet dinner for $9. The restaurant earned $5,517 in buffet dinner receipts last week. About how many dinners were served?

____

18. **Number Sense** Will the estimate of 537 ÷ 8 be less than or greater than the actual quotient? Explain your answer.

____

____

____

19. There are 225 students that signed up to play in a basketball league. Each team will have 8 players. About how many teams will there be?

A 2

B 20

C 3

D 30

Practice **19-2**

Name ___________________

Connecting Models and Symbols

Find 45 ÷ 3.

Step 1

Use place-value blocks to show 45. Draw 3 circles to show how many equal groups you will make.

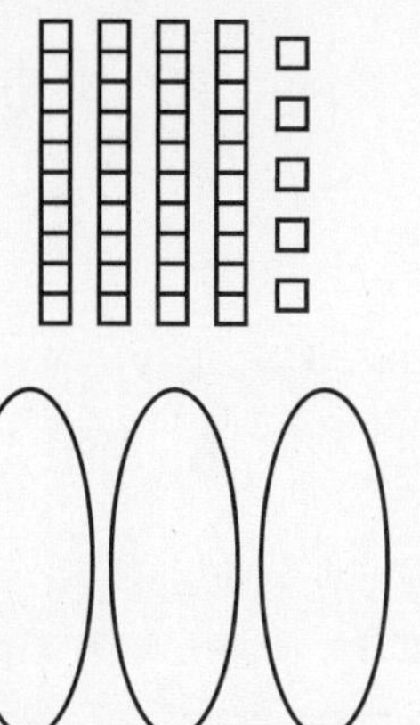

Step 2

Divide the tens. Put an equal number of tens in each circle. There will be 1 ten left over.

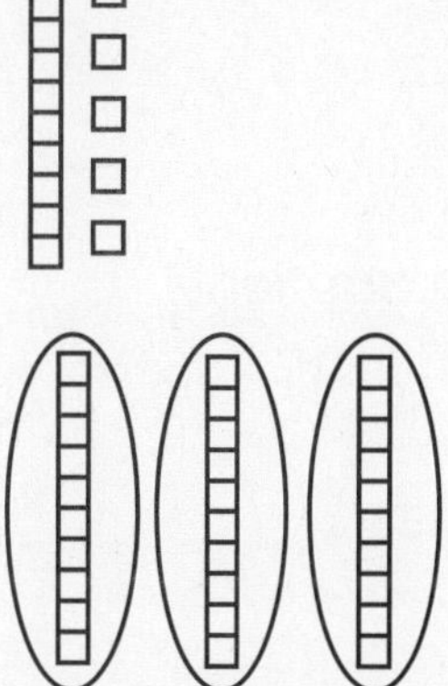

Step 3

Regroup the leftover ten as ones. Combine them with the ones that were already there. Place an equal number of ones in each circle.

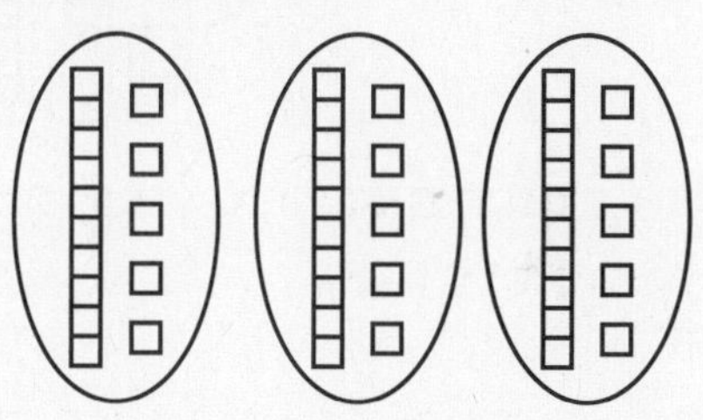

There are 1 ten and 5 ones in each group or 15.
So, 45 ÷ 3 = 15

Complete. Find the quotient.

1. 52 ÷ 4

$4\overline{)52}$

$4\overline{)52}$
− 40
____

$4\overline{)52}$
− 40
____
−
____
0

Use pictures to help you find each quotient.

2. 64 ÷ 4 ______

3. 54 ÷ 2 ______

4. 65 ÷ 5 ______

5. 84 ÷ 4 ______

6. 75 ÷ 3 ______

Name ____________________

Practice **19-3**

Connecting Models and Symbols

Use pictures or place-value blocks to help you find each quotient.

1. 42 ÷ 3

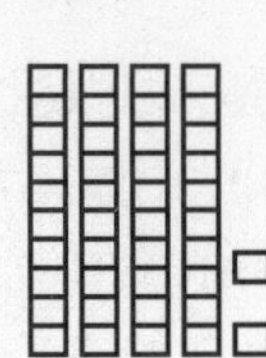

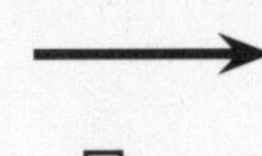

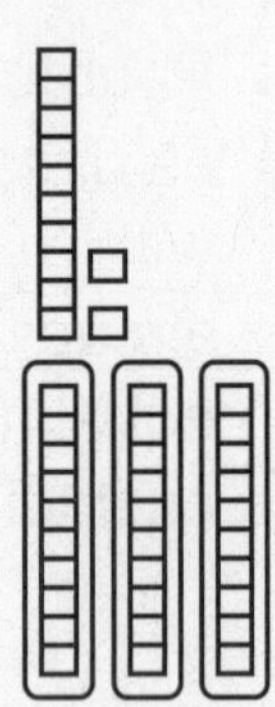

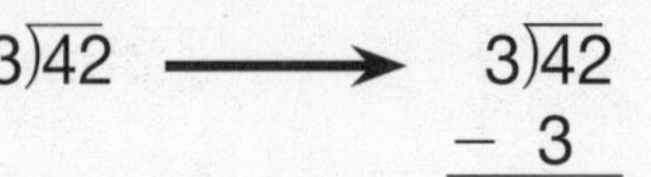

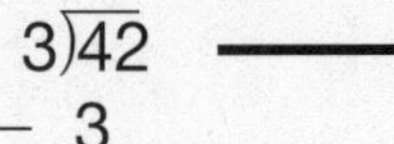

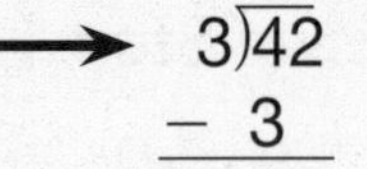

Use pictures to help you find each quotient.

2. 54 ÷ 3 ______ **3.** 76 ÷ 2 ______ **4.** 95 ÷ 5 ______ **5.** 68 ÷ 4 ______ **6.** 90 ÷ 6 ______

7. 52 ÷ 2 ______ **8.** 78 ÷ 6 ______ **9.** 98 ÷ 7 ______ **10.** 48 ÷ 3 ______ **11.** 38 ÷ 2 ______

12. Trisha collected 4 times as many bugs as Shirley. Trisha collected 60 bugs. How many did Shirley collect?

______

13. Max bought 6 CDs for $96. All of the CDs cost the same amount. How much money did each CD cost?

______

14. **Estimation** Will the quotient of 63 ÷ 3 be greater than or less than 20? Explain.

______

15. Mrs. Wong baked 72 cookies on 4 cookie sheets. Each cookie sheet had the same number of cookies. How many cookies were on each cookie sheet?

A 14

B 16

C 17

D 18

Practice **19-3**

Name ____________________

Reteaching
19-4

Dividing 2-Digit Numbers

Find 51 ÷ 3.

	What You Think	What You Write
Step 1	Divide the tens. 5 tens ÷ 3 = 1 ten with 2 tens left over.	1 ⟵ 1 ten in each group 3)51 − 3 ⟵ (3 × 1) tens used 2 ⟵ 2 tens left over
Step 2	Regroup the tens as ones. 2 tens = 20 ones. Combine with the 1 one already there.	1 3)51 − 3↓ 21 Bring down the 1 one. 21 ones in all
Step 3	Divide the ones.	17 ⟵ 17 ones in each group 3)51 − 3 21 − 21 ⟵ (7 × 3) ones used 0 ⟵ 0 ones left over

Complete. Check your answer.

1.

```
    1 □
4 | 6 8
  − 4 ↓
    □ 8
  − □ □
      □
```

2.

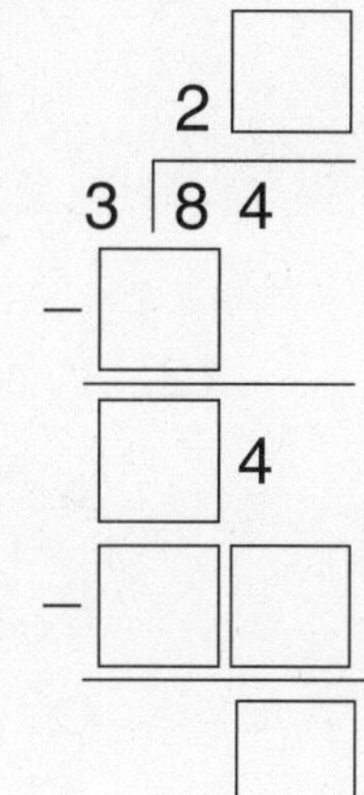

```
    2 □
3 | 8 4
  − □
    □ 4
  − □ □
      □
```

3.

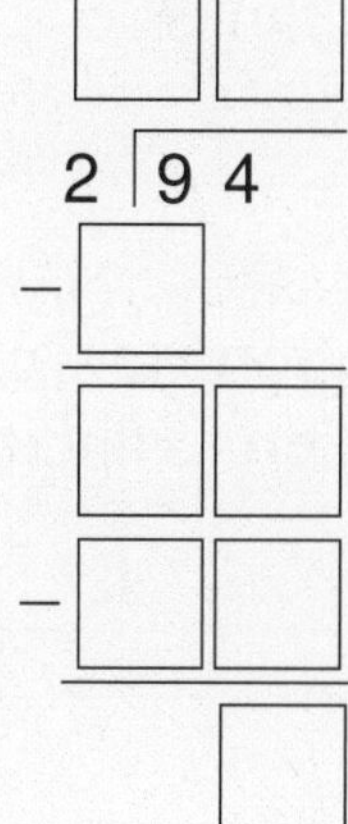

```
    □ □
2 | 9 4
  − □
    □ □
  − □ □
      □
```

Divide. Check your answers.

4. 72 ÷ 2 = ________ **5.** 63 ÷ 3 = ________ **6.** 96 ÷ 4 = ________

7. Number Sense How can you use multiplication to check if a quotient is correct?

____

____

Reteaching **19-4**

Name ______________________________

Dividing 2-Digit Numbers

Complete. Find each quotient. Check your answers.

1.
```
   3
 3)96
 - 9
   6
 -
   0
```

2.
```
 5)75
 -
  _5
 -
  __
```

3.
```
   1
 4)68
 - 4
  _8
 -
   0
```

4.
```
 2)98
 -
  _8
 -
  __
```

5.
```
 6)78
 - 6
  _8
 -
   0
```

6.
```
 3)69
 -
   9
 -
  __
```

7.
```
   1
 5)65
 -
  _5
 -
   0
```

8.
```
 4)56
 -
  _6
 -
  __
```

9. Jennifer has 57 fish. She wants to put them in 3 fish tanks. If she puts the same number of fish in each tank, how many fish will be in each tank?

____

10. There are 84 chairs in a restaurant. Each table in the restaurant has 6 chairs around it. How many tables does the restaurant have?

____

11. Estimation How can you use estimation to find the quotient of 57 ÷ 3?

____

____

____

____

12. Which has the greatest quotient?

A 75 ÷ 3

B 76 ÷ 4

C 72 ÷ 2

D 75 ÷ 5

Name ______________________________

Dividing with Remainders

Jim has 22 sports cards. Each plastic sleeve holds 6 cards. How many sleeves will be filled? Will there be any cards left over?

Find 22 ÷ 6.

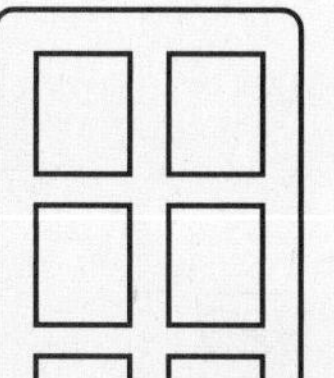

$$\begin{array}{r} 3\text{ R}4 \\ 6\overline{)22} \\ -\,18 \\ \hline 4 \end{array}$$

So, 3 sleeves are filled and there are 4 cards left over.

Divide. Check your answer.

1. $4\overline{)23}$ **2.** $7\overline{)32}$ **3.** $5\overline{)33}$

Use counters or draw a picture to find each quotient and remainder.

4. $8\overline{)45}$ **5.** $4\overline{)18}$ **6.** $9\overline{)51}$ **7.** $5\overline{)43}$

8. $6\overline{)27}$ **9.** $3\overline{)25}$ **10.** $8\overline{)57}$ **11.** $6\overline{)40}$

12. Reasoning Why must a remainder be less than the divisor?

____

____

Name ______________________________

Practice
19-5

Dividing with Remainders

Complete. Check your answers.

1. $\begin{array}{r} \text{R} \\ 5\overline{)36} \\ -\underline{\quad} \end{array}$

2. $\begin{array}{r} \text{R1} \\ 7\overline{)36} \\ -\underline{\quad} \end{array}$

3. $\begin{array}{r} \text{R} \\ 8\overline{)52} \\ -\underline{\quad} \end{array}$

Find each quotient. Check your answers.

4. $6\overline{)45}$
5. $8\overline{)37}$
6. $3\overline{)20}$
7. $9\overline{)80}$

8. $7\overline{)38}$
9. $5\overline{)42}$
10. $7\overline{)62}$
11. $8\overline{)20}$

12. **Number Sense** Regina is going to divide a number by 8. What is the greatest remainder that she can have?

 ____

13. There are 43 girls signed up for cheerleading. Each cheerleading squad will have exactly 8 girls. How many squads will there be? How many girls will not be on a cheerleading squad?

 ____

14. **Reasoning** Each costume that Ms. Wren makes uses 3 yards of yarn. She has 26 yards of yarn. How many complete costumes can Ms. Wren make?

 ____

15. The chorus has 21 students. For a concert, they are being driven in cars that can each hold 4 students. How many cars are needed?

 A 4

 B 5

 C 6

 D 7

Name ________________________________

Multiple-Step Problems

When solving a multiple-step problem, you may need to find the answer to a hidden question. A hidden question is a question that is not asked, but whose answer is needed to solve the problem.

A politician served 30 years in elected office in Washington, D.C. A term in the Senate is 6 years and a term in the House of Representatives is 2 years. She served 3 terms in the Senate. How many terms did she serve in the House of Representatives?

What do you know?

- She served 3 terms in the Senate.
- A term in the Senate is 6 years.
- A term in the House is 2 years.
- She served 30 years all together.

What do I need to find out?

- How many years did she serve in the Senate? (This is the hidden question).
- How many years did she serve in the House?
- How many terms did she serve in the House?

Find the number of years she served in the Senate:
3 terms × 6 years = 18 years.

Find the number of years she served in the House:
30 years − 18 years = 12 years.

Find the number of terms she served in the House:
12 years ÷ 2 = 6.

The politician served 6 terms in the House of Representatives.

Solve.

1. There are 8 players on a basketball team. All but 2 players scored 6 points each. The other two players scored the same number of points. The team scored 72 points. How many points did the other two players each score?

____

HINT: Hidden Question—How many points were scored altogether by the players who scored 6 points each?

Name ____________________

Practice **19-6**

Problem Solving: Multiple-Step Problems

Solve. Answer the hidden question first.

1. Marcus counted a total of 40 wheels from bicycles and tricycles while sitting on a park bench. Marcus counted 11 bicycles. How many tricycles did Marcus count?

   ____

   HINT: Hidden Question—How many wheels did the bicycles have?

2. Julie bought 15 baseballs and some softballs. The total cost of the balls is $90. Each ball costs $5. How many softballs did Julie buy?

   ____

   HINT: How much money did Julie spend on baseballs?

3. Bert bought 4 books for $7 each and a magazine for $5. He paid with a $50 bill. How much money did Bert receive back from the cashier?

   ____

   HINT: Hidden Question—How much money did Bert spend?

4. A community group bought 12 student tickets and 3 adult tickets to the movies. The total cost of the tickets was $96. Student tickets cost $6. How much money does an adult ticket cost?

   ____

   HINT: How much money did the group spend on student tickets?

5. There are 48 students in the band. The boys and girls are in separate rows. There are 6 students in each row. There are 3 rows of boys. How many rows of girls are there?

   ____

   HINT: Hidden Question—How many boys are there?

6. **Write a Problem** Write a real-world problem that can be solved by finding and answering a hidden question.

   ____

   ____

   ____

Name ______________________

Organizing Data

Students in Ms. Mayer's class were asked to name their favorite subject in school. The results are listed below.

Favorite Subject			
Reading	Math	Social Studies	Math
Math	Science	Math	Reading
Science	Math	Math	Math
Social Studies	Reading	Reading	Social Studies
Math	Reading	Science	Math

You can make a tally chart of the data. Each | represents 1 and each ~~||||~~ represents 5.

Favorite Subject

Subject	Tally	Number
Reading	~~||||~~	5
Math	~~||||~~ ||||	9
Science	|||	3
Social Studies	|||	3

For **1** and **2**, use the survey data above.

1. What is the most popular subject in the survey?

____

2. Use tally marks to show the total number of votes that reading and math received.

____

3. The favorite animals at a zoo are shown below. Use this data to make a tally chart.

Lion	Monkey	Lion	Tiger
Bear	Tiger	Bear	Lion
Bear	Lion	Tiger	Tiger
Tiger	Lion	Monkey	Bear

Name ____________________

Practice **20-1**

Organizing Data

For **1** through **6**, use the survey data at the right.

1. Make a tally chart for the data.

Favorite Type of Music		
Rock	Jazz	Country
Jazz	Rock	Rock
Rock	Country	Rap
Country	Rock	Rap
Country	Country	Country
Rap	Rap	Rock
Country	Rap	Jazz
Rap	Jazz	Country
Country	Rock	Rap

2. How many people were surveyed in all?

____

3. Which type of music was picked by the most people?

____

4. Which type of music was picked by the fewest people?

____

5. Which two types of music were picked by the same number of people?

____

6. **Writing to Explain** How does making a tally chart help you to organize data?

____

____

____

7. **Number Sense** Which number is represented by 𝍸 𝍸 𝍸 ||||?

A 16

B 17

C 19

D 20

Practice **20-1**

Name ______________________________

Reading Pictographs and Bar Graphs

Pictographs use pictures or parts of pictures to represent data.
Bar graphs use bars to represent data.

Pictographs

Gold Medals Won at 1998 Winter Olympics

Japan	
Italy	
Canada	
Korea	

Each = 1 gold medal.

Japan won 5 gold medals.

Canada won 6 gold medals.

Bar Graphs

2000 Summer Olympics

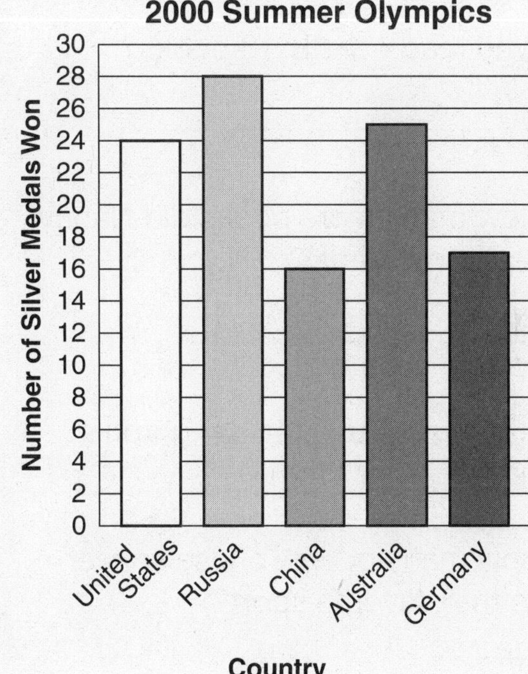

__________ won 28 silver medals in 2000.

Germany won __________ silver medals in 2000.

Use the pictograph to answer **1** and **2**.

1. How many houses were built in City B in 2002?

____

2. How many houses were built in City A in 2002?

____

Number of Houses Built in 2002

City	
City A	
City B	
City C	
City D	

Each = 10 houses.

Each = 5 houses.

Name ______________________

Reading Pictographs and Bar Graphs

For **1** through **4**, use the pictograph at the right.

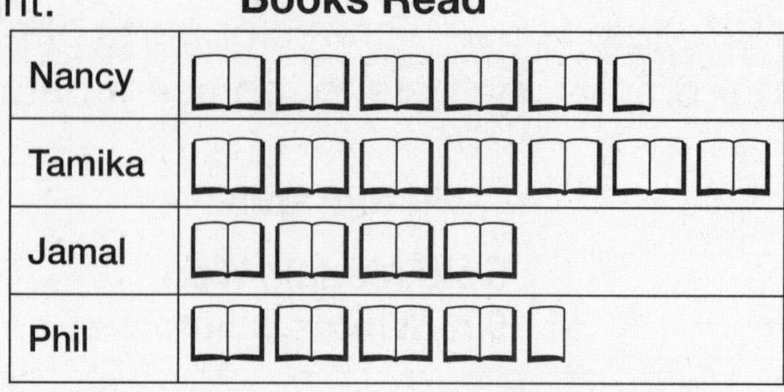

1. Who read the most books?

____

2. Who read exactly 18 books?

____

3. How many more books did Nancy read than Jamal?

____

4. Who read the fewest books?

____

For **5** through **8**, use the bar graph at the right.

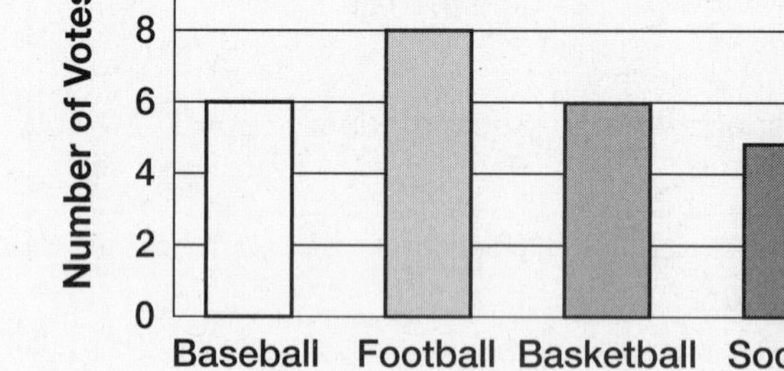

5. How many people chose soccer as their favorite sport?

____

6. Which sport was chosen as the favorite?

____

7. **Reasonableness** Casey said that 40 people were surveyed. Is his answer reasonable? Explain.

____

____

____

8. Which sentence is true?

A Baseball and basketball received the same number of votes.

B More people chose soccer than baseball.

C More people chose football than basketball and soccer combined.

D More people chose baseball than football.

Name ______________________________

Making Pictographs

Reteaching
20-3

The tally table shows food items that were ordered for lunch. Follow the steps below to make the pictograph.

Food	Tally	Number
Pasta	~~IIII~~ I	6
Salad	IIII	4
Casserole	~~IIII~~ ~~IIII~~	10
Fish	~~IIII~~ III	8

Items Ordered

Pasta	🍴🍴🍴
Salad	🍴🍴
Casserole	🍴🍴🍴🍴🍴
Fish	🍴🍴🍴🍴

Each 🍴 = 2 meals

Step 1

Write a title that explains what the pictograph shows.

Step 2

Choose a symbol. For this pictograph, use a fork. Decide how many meals each fork will represent.

Step 3

Draw the number of symbols that are needed for each food.

The tally table shows how Ms. Hashimoto's classed voted for their favorite types of movies to rent.

1. Complete the table.

Favorite Video	Tally	Number
Action	~~IIII~~ III	
Comedy	III	
Drama	~~IIII~~ I	
Animated	~~IIII~~ ~~IIII~~	

2. Complete the pictograph.

____

Action	
Comedy	
Drama	
Animated	

Each [videotape] = ___ votes.

3. Writing to Explain Why did you choose the number that each symbol represents?

____

____

Name ______________________________

Practice **20-3**

Making Pictographs

For **1** and **2**, use the chart.

1. Make a pictograph to show the data in the chart. Write a title. Choose the key.

Color of Cars

Color	Tally	Number
Red	𝍸 𝍸 𝍸 I	16
Green	𝍸 𝍸 𝍸 𝍸	20
Silver	𝍸 𝍸 𝍸 𝍸 IIII	24
Black	𝍸 𝍸 IIII	14

2. Reasonableness Why did you choose the number for each symbol that you chose?

____

____

____

3. Fred is going to make a pictograph showing the number of tomatoes that he picked each day. He picked 30 Monday, 25 Tuesday, 35 Wednesday, and 40 Thursday. Which would be the best number to use for each symbol?

A 1 **C** 5

B 2 **D** 20

4. Explain It Pamela made a pictograph showing students' favorite drinks. Pamela drew 3 glasses to represent the 6 students who chose chocolate milk. Is her pictograph correct? Explain.

Favorite Drinks

Drink	Number of Students
Chocolate milk	🥛🥛🥛
Fruit juice	🥛🥛🥛🥛

Key Each 🥛 = 2 students.

____

____

____

Name ______________________________

Making Bar Graphs

The table shows the number of birds that visited a bird feeder.

Day	Number of Birds
Monday	6
Tuesday	4
Wednesday	7
Thursday	5
Friday	3

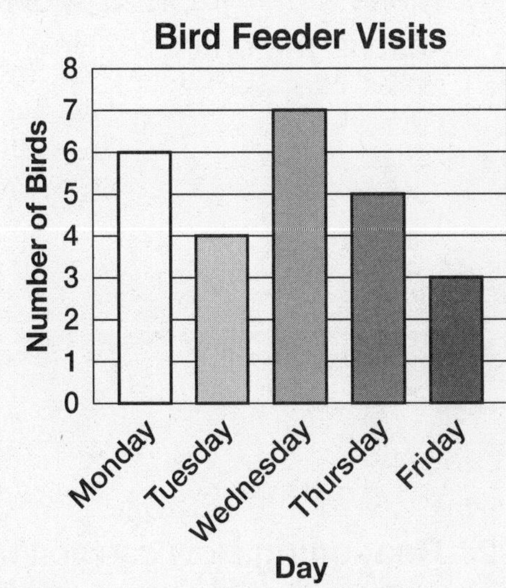

Follow the steps below to make the bar graph at the right.

Step 1

Write each of the days and label the bottom of the graph "Day."

Step 2

Number the scale. Label the scale "Number of Birds."

Step 3

Make the bars for each day.

Step 4

Give the graph a title.

Use the table below for **1** and **2**.

Field Day Results

Team	Points
Bulls	45
Colts	30
Pigs	25
Rams	40

1. Make a bar graph. Remember to label your graph and add a title.

2. **Writing to Explain** Why did you choose the scale you did?

____

____

Name ______________________

Practice 20-4

Making Bar Graphs

For **1** and **2**, use the chart at the right.

1. Make a bar graph to show the data in the chart.

Favorite States to Visit

State	Number of Votes
New York	25
Florida	35
California	30
Hawaii	20

2. Reasoning How can you use a bar graph to determine which state had the least number of votes?

____

____

3. Explain It Describe your process for determining the scale for a bar graph.

____

____

____

4. The table at the right shows the number of phone calls Mrs. Walker made during 5 days of fundraising. Which is the scale you would use to make a bar graph of the data?

A by 1s

B by 2s

C by 5s

D by 10s

Fundraising Calls

Day	Phone Calls
Saturday	26
Sunday	19
Monday	20
Tuesday	24
Wednesday	16

Practice 20-4

Name ______________________________

Ordered Pairs and Line Graphs

Ordered pairs are used in coordinate grids and in line graphs. The first number in an ordered pair gives the distance to the right of 0. The second number gives the distance above 0. So, the ordered pair (3, 2) is located 3 units to the right of 0 and 2 units above 0.

Ordered pairs

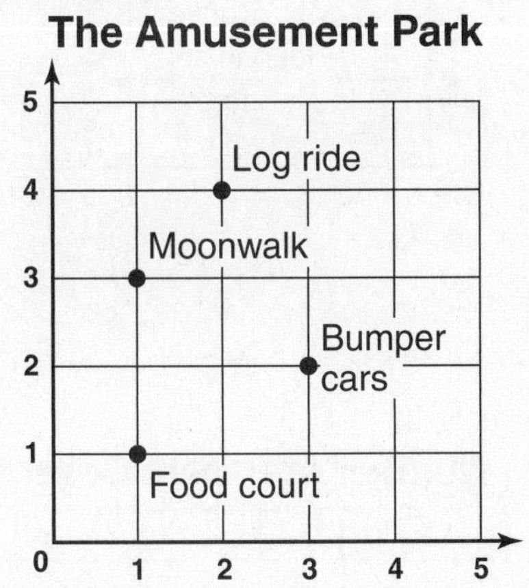

Which ride is located at (1, 3)?
Start at (0, 0)
Count 1 unit to the right of 0.
Count 3 units above that point.

The Moonwalk is located at (1, 3).

Line graphs

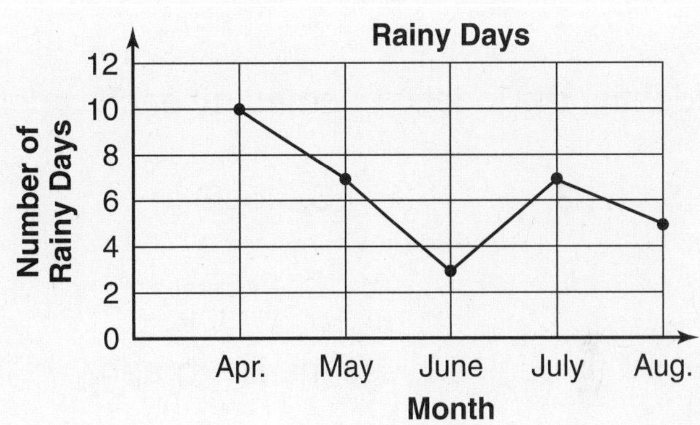

How many rainy days were there in May?
Find May on the horizontal axis.
Find the point above May.
It is located between the 6 and 8.

Since 7 is between 6 and 8, there were 7 rainy days in May.

Write the ordered pair that describes the location of each point.

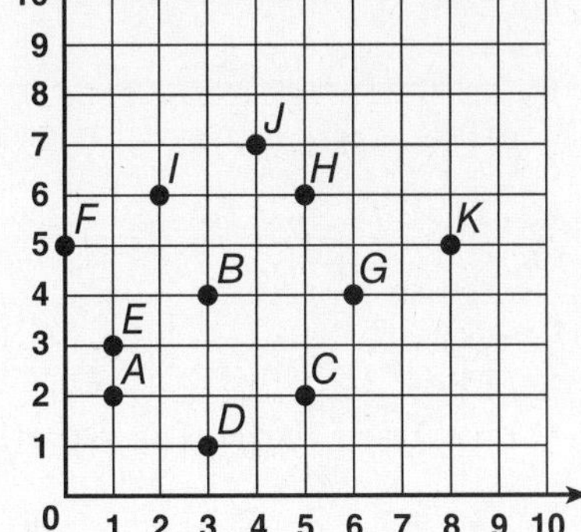

1. *A* ____________ **2.** *K* ____________

Give the letter of the point named by each ordered pair.

3. (0, 5) ____________ **4.** (6, 4) ____________

5. Writing to Explain Describe the difference between locating a point at (2, 4) and a point at (4, 2).

____

Name ___________________________________

Practice
20-5

Ordered Pairs and Line Graphs

Write the ordered pair for each point on the grid.

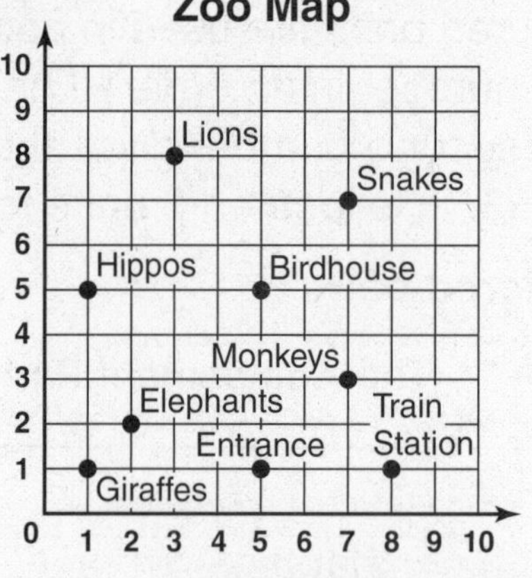

1. Elephants ___________ **2.** Train Station ___________

3. Hippos ___________ **4.** Snakes ___________

Identify the location named by each ordered pair.

5. (7, 3) ___________ **6.** (5, 5) ___________ **7.** (5, 1) ___________ **8.** (3, 8) ___________

For **9** through **12**, use the line graph.

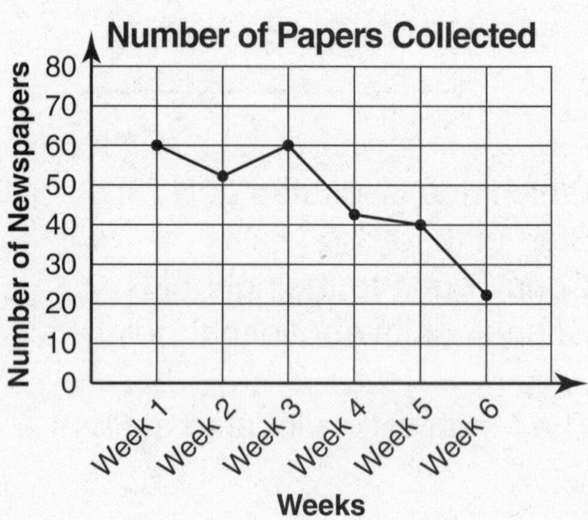

9. How many newspapers were collected in Week 1? ___________

10. How many more newspapers were collected in Week 3 than Week 5?

____

11. Explain It What happened to the number of newspapers collected each week after Week 3?

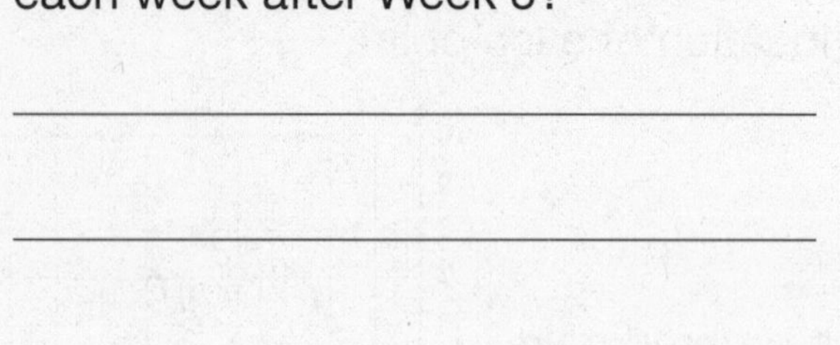

____

____

____

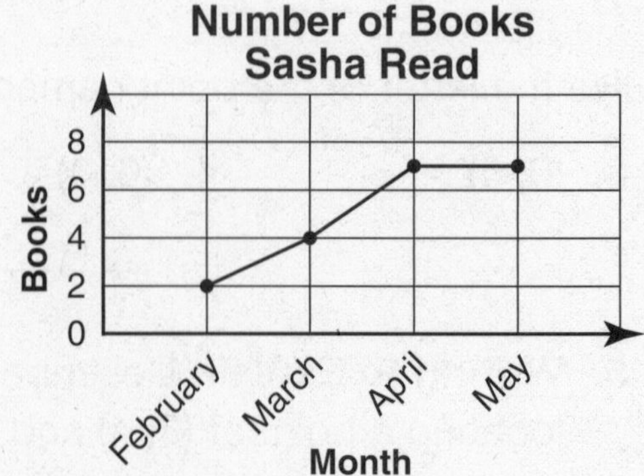

12 How many more books did Sasha read in April than February?

A 2 **C** 5

B 4 **D** 7

Practice **20-5**

Name ______________________

How Likely?

You can describe the chance of something happening by using the words **certain, likely, unlikely,** or **impossible.**

Look at this spinner.

It is **certain** that the spinner will land on 1, 2, 3, or on a line.

It is **impossible** that the spinner will land on 4.

It is **likely** that the spinner will land on 1.

It is **unlikely** that the spinner will land on 2.

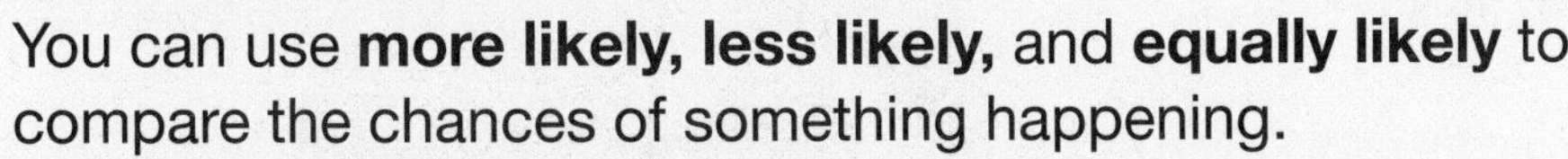

You can use **more likely, less likely,** and **equally likely** to compare the chances of something happening.

It is **more likely** that the spinner will land on 1 than 2.

It is **less likely** that the spinner will land on a line than on 1.

It is **equal likely** that the spinner will land on 2 or 3.

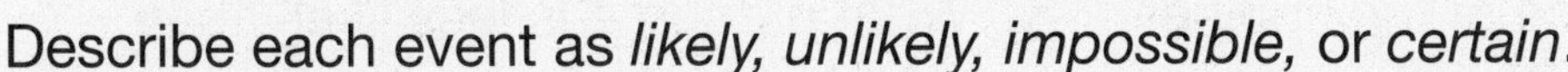

Describe each event as *likely, unlikely, impossible,* or *certain*.

1. Next week will have 7 days.

____

2. Janet's dog has 4 legs.

____

Suppose you pick a card from the hat without looking.
Describe each pick as *likely, unlikely, impossible,* or *certain.*

3. Picking a shaded card

____

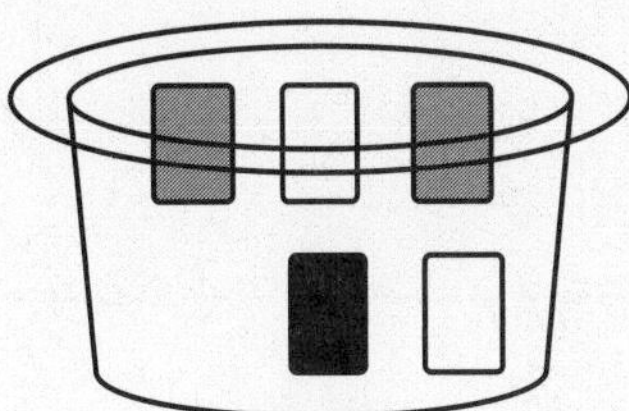

4. Picking a round card

____

5. Picking a black card

____

Name ______________________

Practice **20-6**

How Likely?

Gene is an adult with a dog named Bob. Describe each event as likely, unlikely, impossible, or certain.

1. Bob will sleep tonight.

____

2. Bob will weigh more than Gene.

____

3. Bob will eat.

____

4. Bob will read a book.

____

For **5** through **8,** use the spinner at the right.

4 1 1 3 1 3 2 2

5. What outcome is more likely than 2?

____

6. What outcomes are equally likely?

____

7. Describe the chance of the spinner landing on 5.

____

8. What outcome is less likely than a 3?

____

9. Explain It What is the difference between a likely event and an unlikely event?

____

____

____

____

10. Dana and Rose are playing a card game. Dana has cards with 3 circles, 4 squares, 2 triangles, and 1 rectangle. If Rose picks one card from Dana's hand without looking, which card will she most likely pick?

A circle **B** square **C** triangle **D** rectangle

Name ______________________

Reteaching
20-7

Outcomes and Experiments

An experiment is used to test a theory. You can predict what will happen with an experiment. The prediction should be based on what might happen, although it may not.

Suppose you were going to spin the spinner to the right 30 times. How many times do you predict each letter will be spun?

Step 1

Use what you know about the spinner. There are 6 sections in all.

W = 1 section
X = 3 sections
Y = 1 section
Z = 1 section

Step 2

Make a table to predict what will happen in 30 spins.

W	1	2	3	4	5
X	3	6	9	12	15
Y	1	2	3	4	5
Z	1	2	3	4	5
Total Spins	6	12	18	24	30

So, the prediction is that the spinner will land 5 times on W, Y, and Z and 15 times on X.

In **1** through **3**, use the spinner and the table below.

1. Complete the table.

A	2	4		8	10	
B	1	2	3		5	10
C	1	2	3		5	10
Total Spins	4	8	12	16	20	

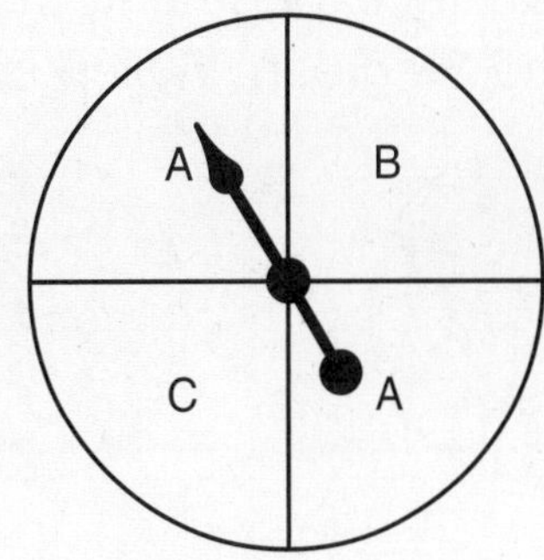

2. Reasoning If you spin the spinner 100 times, will it land on B more times than on A? Explain.

____

____

3. If you spin the spinner 100 times, what is the best estimate of how many times you'll spin the letter A? __________

Name ______________________

Outcomes and Experiments

For **1** through **3**, use the spinner to the right and the table below.

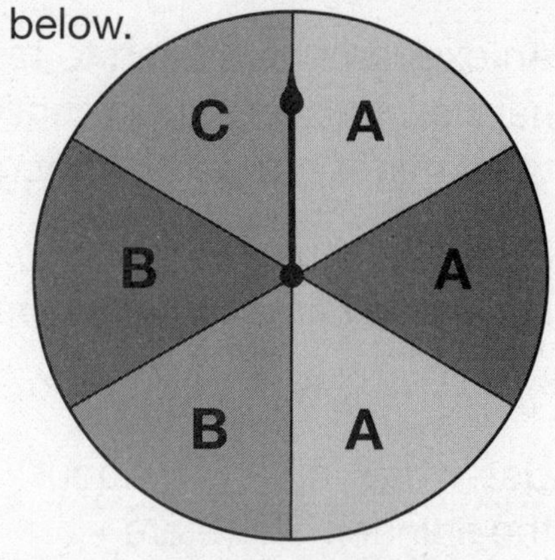

1. Complete the table.

A	3	6		12	15		45
B	2	4	6	8		20	30
C	1	2	3	4	5	10	
Total Spins	6	12	18		30	60	

2. Reasoning Predict what is likely to happen in 120 spins.

____

____

____

3. Do the experiment using a number cube. Let 1, 2, and 3 represent A; 4 and 5 represent B; and 6 represent C. Toss the number cube 30 times. See if it matches your prediction above. What happened?

____

____

____

4. In a probability experiment, the spinner results were 10 blue, 10 red, and 30 green. Which spinner most likely gave these results?

A

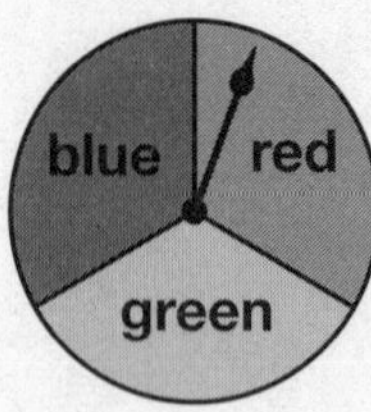

B

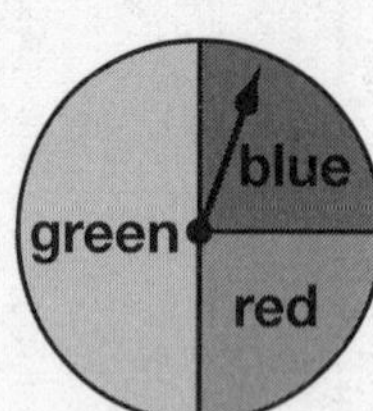

C

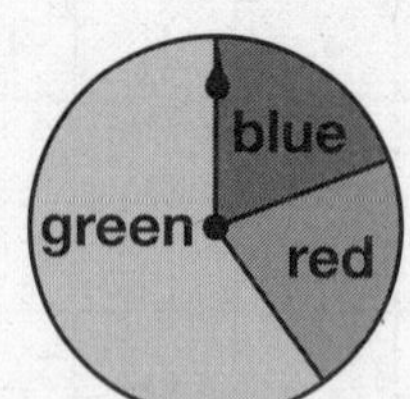

D

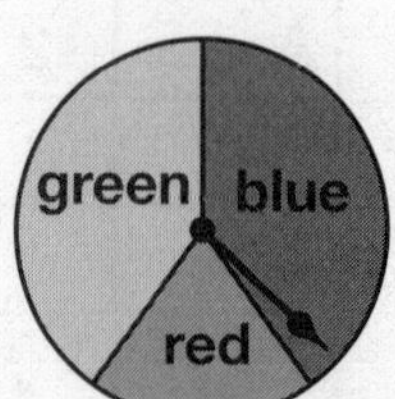

Name ______________________________

Line Plots and Probability

A line plot is used in the same way as a tally chart. It is used to show numerical data. A line plot uses an X to show an outcome.

The data show the numbers spun in 30 spins.

1	2	4	3	6	5	1	7	4	3
2	6	3	5	4	7	1	2	6	1
1	3	6	2	5	1	4	2	7	3

The line plot at the right can be used to show the data.

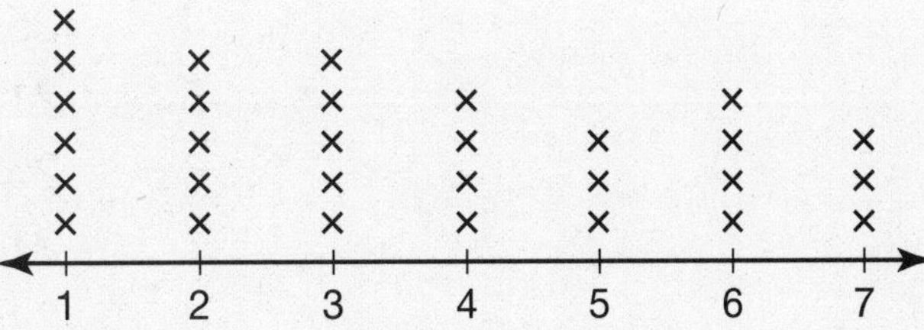

Mark played a game with two number cubes. He found the sum of the number cubes. The results are shown in the table.

1. Make a line plot to show the data.

Number Cube Tosses

Toss	Sum	Toss	Sum	Toss	Sum
1	7	11	6	21	7
2	4	12	9	22	10
3	6	13	9	23	9
4	8	14	10	24	7
5	5	15	10	25	5
6	5	16	5	26	12
7	6	17	8	27	7
8	2	18	5	28	9
9	10	19	3	29	8
10	8	20	8	30	12

2. How many Xs do you show for 8?

____

3. Which sum from 2–12 did Mark not toss at all?

____

Name ______________________

Practice
20-8

Line Plots and Probability

For **1** through **4**, use the data at the right.

1. Make a line plot to show the data.

Number of Points Katie Scored

Game	Pts	Game	Pts	Game	Pts
1	23	11	25	21	24
2	25	12	30	22	26
3	30	13	27	23	25
4	25	14	22	24	28
5	21	15	26	25	27
6	26	16	21	26	26
7	21	17	29	27	29
8	24	18	25	28	30
9	28	19	21	29	22
10	20	20	23	30	24

2. How many Xs do you show for 24 points?

____

3. Which number of points did Katie only score once?

____

4. Which number of points did Katie score the most?

____

5. Which two point totals did Katie score exactly four times each?

____

For **6** and **7**, use the line plot at the right.

6. How many fewer students read 5 books than 8 books?

____

7. How many students read less than 7 books?

A 11 **C** 17

B 14 **D** 22

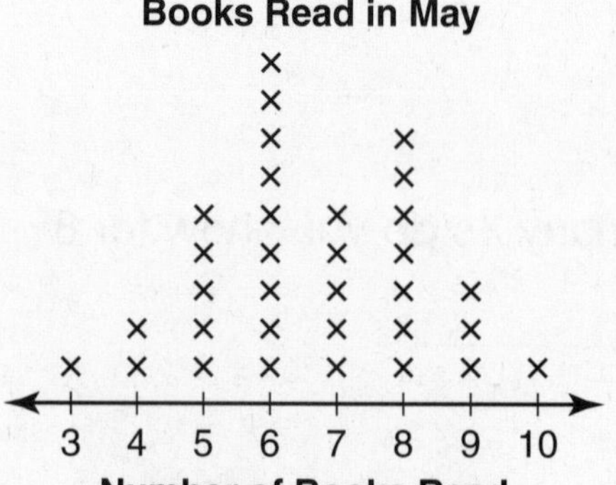

Practice 20-8

Name ______________________

Problem Solving: Use Tables and Graphs to Draw Conclusions

Students were asked to name their favorite type of dog.
The pictograph shows the results of the survey.

Students' Favorite Dogs

Dog	Number Counted
Beagle	
Collie	
Shepherd	
Poodle	
Dalmatian	

Each = 2 votes.

Which dog was chosen by *exactly* 5 students? Shepherd

Which dog was chosen by 2 more students than a Dalmatian? Beagle

For **1** through **3**, use the chart below.

Quarter	Points Scored
1st	7
2nd	3
3rd	10
4th	6

1. The chart shows how many points a football team scored. How many points were scored altogether?

____

2. **Write a Problem** Write a word problem that is different from Exercise 1 that can be solved by reading the chart.

____

____

3. Make a graph to represent the data in the chart. Choose a bar graph or a pictograph.

Reteaching 20-9

Name ______________________

Practice **20-9**

Problem Solving: Use Tables and Graphs to Draw Conclusions

Use the pictographs for **1** through **4**.

Girls Shoes Sold at Just Shoes

Sneakers	
Sandals	
Pumps	
Boots	

Girls Shoes Sold at All Shoes

Sneakers	
Sandals	
Pumps	
Boots	

Each = 10 shoes. Each = 5 shoes.

1. Which type of shoe was sold the most at Just Shoes?

______

2. Which two types of shoes were sold equally at All Shoes?

______

3. Which store sold the most pumps?

______

4. How many sneakers were sold in all?

______

For **5** and **6**, use the bar graph at the right.

5. How many cars were washed altogether?

______

Cars Washed by Grade

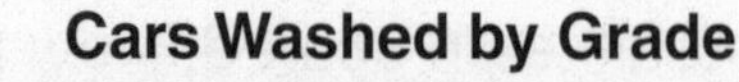

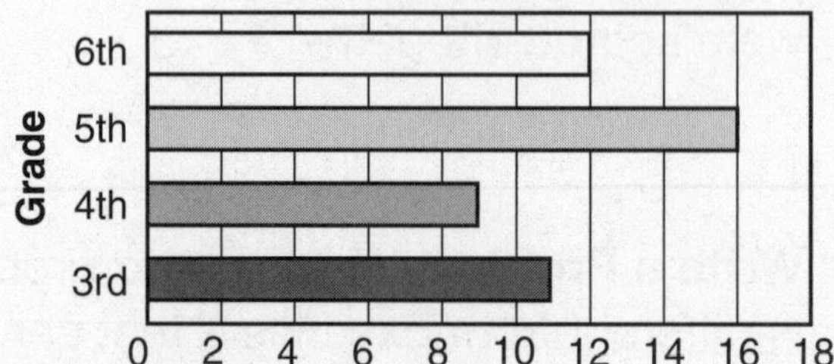

6. **Write a Problem** Write a word problem different from Exercise 5 that can be solved by reading the graph.

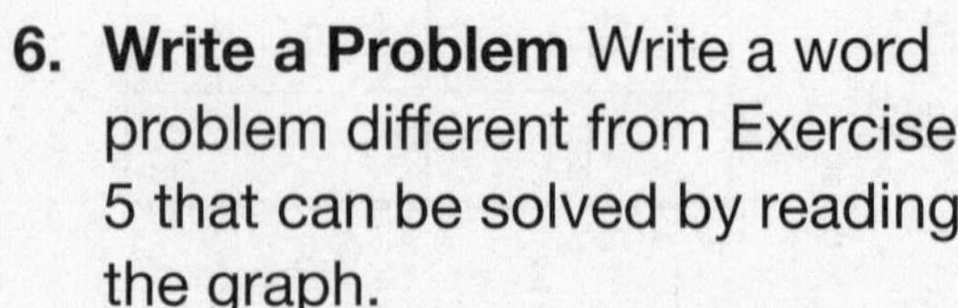

______

______

Students Receiving an A or a B

Test	Tally
1	卌 卌 ||
2	卌 卌 卌 |
3	卌 卌 卌
4	卌 |||

7. According to the tally chart, how many more students received an A or a B in Test 2 than in Test 4?

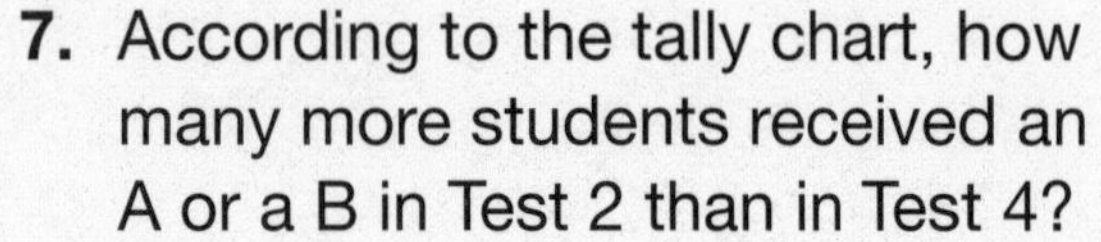

______

Practice 20-9